The Clinician's Handbook

SECOND EDITION

The Clinician's Handbook

—— Essential Knowledge for Mental Health Professionals ——

Sheri Bauman and Chadwick W. Royal

cognella®
SAN DIEGO

Bassim Hamadeh, CEO and Publisher
Amy Smith, Senior Project Editor
Jeanine Rees, Production Editor
Emely Villavicencio , Senior Graphic Designer
Kylie Bartolome, Licensing Specialist
Natalie Piccotti, Director of Marketing
Kassie Graves, Senior Vice President, Editorial

3970 Sorrento Valley Blvd., Ste. 500, San Diego, CA 92121

Brief Contents

Detailed Contents

Preface

Since the publication of the first edition of this book in 2007, there have been dramatic events that impacted all aspects of life around the world. We have endured the recession from December 2007 to June 2009 (Rich, 2013), the COVID-19 pandemic and associated disruptions (beginning March 11, 2020), natural disasters, increased violence and shootings, the war in Ukraine, the Israel-Hamas war, and the stark and hostile political divisions that have become pervasive in the country. These conditions contribute to increased numbers of Americans with mental health disorders and symptoms. Mental health professionals are under considerable pressure in their work, not only because they are the recipients of clients' suffering, but also because the need for clinicians greatly exceeds available providers (Reinert et al., 2021). On the other hand, we now have a national hotline (988) for crisis intervention and support and a text-based free crisis counseling service (Text HOME to 741741). Telemental health was widely used during the pandemic and continues to be a treatment option (likely not to go away); artificial intelligence (AI) mobile apps and chatbots are commonly sought for assistance. These innovations, while useful, cannot replace professional mental health care.

In the course of professional training, as a counselor or psychologist, students take courses prescribed by their programs and accreditation bodies (Council for Accreditation of Counseling and Related Educational Programs [CACREP], American Psychological Association [APA]) to prepare for these careers. These courses and experiences provide a firm foundation of knowledge and solid basic skills. Upon completion of their programs, most have identified a theoretical orientation to guide their clinical approach. What is lacking is knowledge about specific issues or common client problems. It is often not until field experiences in practicum and internships that students directly confront some of the issues that they may face as a clinician, and many become acutely aware of their ignorance. Even after graduation and licensure, professionals often still harbor doubts about their competence as they anticipate the range of issues and clients they may encounter (i.e., imposter syndrome). Mental health professionals soon learn that the "presenting issue" is often not the only issue; indeed, it may not even be the primary issue. Clients may have a situational problem, for example, that temporarily impedes their functioning, so they seek counseling or therapy. As the treatment unfolds and a strong therapeutic alliance develops, the client may feel safe enough to reveal and explore deeper issues. Ethically, the clinician cannot abandon the client; even if it is necessary to refer to a specialist, the counselor must work with the client until the transition is successfully accomplished.

Although there are many announcements for workshops and webinars that offer training on important topics and innovations in treatment, time and financial constraints limit the number one can attend. There is always another one that looks exciting and useful. In addition, there are a number of books available on any given topic, and it is impossible to read them all. And how is the counselor to know which of the many books available would provide the overview they need? What is needed is an overview of many important topics rather than in-depth information about a few. We wished for single volume to consult for a basic orientation to the many topics about a counselor may encounter. The seeds of this book had been planted.

As a beginning practitioner, one of the ethical standards admonishes counselors to "practice in a nondiscriminatory manner within the boundaries of professional and personal competence; they also have a responsibility to abide by the ACA [American Counseling Association] Code of Ethics" (ACA, 2014, p. 7); that can be daunting. The ethical standards also say, "Counselors practice in specialty areas new to them only after appropriate education, training, and supervised experience. While developing skills in new specialty areas, counselors take steps to ensure the competence of their work and protect others from possible harm" (p. 8). How are neophyte counselors to become competent in the wide range of issues they might encounter, particularly when their education and training have not covered a particular client type or concern?

Many models of training for helping professionals are based on the triad of awareness, knowledge, and skills. This book addresses the first two prongs of the triad. The reader will gain awareness of these important issues and will acquire basic information, knowledge of treatment approaches, case study examples, and additional resources. There are volumes of material available on each of the topics in the book, and our intent is to distill essential information so that the reader will have a solid foundation from which to develop competencies and skills (the last prong of the triad).

As counselor-educators, we strive to provide students with the best possible preparation. However, at a master's level, there are only so many courses a student is able to take. Program requirements are to some extent dictated by professional standards for preparation, and this limits the number of electives that a student is free to choose. CACREP training standards do not require specific training in any of the topics discussed in this book. In some programs, a few of these topics are briefly touched on in more general courses, such as a crisis intervention course. More often than not, limited resources (both financial and personnel) restrict the number of specific courses that can be offered and taken.

One of the refrains we often hear from students is "What will I do if I get a client who [fill in the problem]?" Even more urgent are the anxious questions when the student does meet such a client in a field experience! Taking a course in each topic would keep students in school for years! Most helping professionals receive training as a generalist; some choose to specialize and obtain additional training and certification post-degree. Neophyte and early career clinicians are ready to apply basic skills but may be uncertain of the best approach to use when an issue emerges during treatment.

Although some professionals choose to specialize in certain kinds of clients, or age groups, or issues, and thus may believe they will never have to work with individuals who [fill in the problem again], the reality is that most clinicians are generalists to some extent. Those who practice in rural areas may be the only professional available and find themselves serving a wide range of client issues. Even clinicians in more populated areas may not always be able to find a specialist in a particular problem. All good clinicians need to have a working familiarity with many issues so they can, at a minimum, make appropriate referrals (and do so effectively), work with a client in a crisis situation, and consult intelligently with other professionals.

Acknowledgments

We would like to thank Kassie Graves, Amy Smith, and the editorial team at Cognella for their support and guidance. We would also like to thank the following students from the counseling program at North Carolina Central University for their assistance: Tessa Miller, Eliana Peters, Maggie Schnur, Helen Svoboda-Barber, and Trent Stamer.

SB: There are many individuals I wish to thank for their roles in creating this book. I think it is appropriate to begin by thanking all my clients, who have taught me so much over the years, and who inspired me to keep learning. For putting their trust in me, and sharing their struggles and triumphs, I sincerely thank each one. In addition, the individuals who shared their personal journeys and allowed me to include them in the book as case studies made an enormous contribution to this work, which I deeply appreciate. I also must thank my students, whose challenging questions and quest for learning have kept me on my figurative toes. To my former clinical supervisor and now valued friend, Greg Kopp, whose clinical skills are a model for me, and whose encouragement has been unwavering, I extend my heartfelt thanks. Most of all, I am deeply grateful for the constant support and patience of my husband, Bob, who never doubted that I could write this book, and who did so many things to allow me the time to devote to this project. His understanding and nurturance made this book possible.

CR: I thank Sheri Bauman, whose text I have been using in one of my courses since it was first published. From the very first moment I read it, I could tell that this was an author who had spent a great deal of time as a clinician and was sharing things that she had learned "in the trenches." I am grateful for the need that she saw and fulfilled by writing a text such as this. In addition, I am thankful that she replied to my inquiry when I asked if she was planning on updating her text. As a bonus, she graciously allowed me to assist with this update. The more that I have gotten to know her, the more in awe I have been by her breadth of knowledge and experience, her seemingly perpetual curiosity, and her productivity as a scholar. It has become clear to me why I have always had a fondness and appreciation for her text.

PART I

CONTEXT

CHAPTER 1

Introduction

In 2021, 41.7% American adults received treatment for a mental health disorder, the highest rate since 2002 (Elflein, 2023). Nevertheless, less than 50% of those in need received services (Lattie et al., 2022), highlighting the discrepancy between demand and availability. An international study of children and adolescents concluded that increased mental health symptoms were evident in this age group compared to estimates from before the pandemic (Samji et al., 2022), and researchers emphasized the need for practitioners to respond to this need (Carroll & Hayes, 2023), which is particularly acute for persons of color (Thomeer et al., 2023). The current status quo implies that there is and will continue to be a need for qualified mental health professionals to close the gap. Thus, we want to contribute to the preparation and support of mental health providers to ensure they are equipped to manage the varied and challenging issues they may encounter in their important work.

This book provides a working familiarity with a range of topics that clinicians in schools, private practice, community agencies, and other mental health settings are likely to confront at some point in their careers. As clinicians and educators, we wanted a book that offered this kind of material concisely in one volume. Since we could not find such a book, we wrote one! We hope readers will feel more knowledgeable about the many issues their clients may bring. Our intent is to provide an awareness of essential topics that will enhance professional competence and confidence, offer information about various treatment approaches, and include recommendations for additional resources to consult for more information. This book is *not* intended to provide complete training to become a specialist in any of these topics. Some readers will find particular topics of sufficient interest to seek further in-depth reading and training to become experts, but they will nevertheless feel sufficiently prepared to respond professionally to any issue they may face.

We chose topics based on our own clinical experiences as a school counselor, a counselor in a university counseling center, a community mental health counselor, as counselor-educators, and as a psychologist and counselor in private practice. We also listen to the questions our students ask and pay attention to their anxiety. The topics were selected because they are rarely covered in depth in a graduate training program but are issues that counselors will likely encounter in their work with clients. In the first edition of this book, a chapter on substance abuse was included; since many programs do have a course in addictions or substance abuse, we chose to remove that chapter from this edition and to devote space to issues less likely to receive focused attention in a dedicated course.

It many ways, the separate issues overlap. For example, chronic sexual abuse is a trauma, and some survivors develop posttraumatic stress disorder (PTSD) and other symptoms. Others may develop eating disorders, engage in self-harm, or have problems with substance abuse. Suicide is covered in a separate chapter but is clearly related to all the other topics in the book. A clinician will find that it is difficult to treat any of these issues without touching on others. This is to say that each of the chapters can stand alone in terms of information, but in reality, they are all linked and interrelated.

We want to emphasize that mental health professionals are people first, and they are subject to many of the same challenges and uncertainties their clients are facing. It is critical that counselors seek therapy as needed in order to ensure their own experiences are not clouding their clinical judgment. In addition, we stress ongoing self-care as an essential practice. Taking care of one's overall health and well-being keeps the counselor balanced. Practices such as exercise, healthy eating, setting boundaries, meditation and yoga, getting enough sleep, enjoying nature, and so forth are activities counselors often recommend to clients; they need to heed their own advice. Doing so helps avoid becoming impaired or experiencing burnout (Posluns & Gall, 2020).

How This Book Is Organized

We have organized all chapters using a similar format to facilitate using the book as a reference as well as a text. That is, each chapter is designed to stand alone, and while the order appears logical to us, reading the chapters in any order should not present a problem. Each chapter begins with a brief introduction, followed by an authentic case study, which illustrates the topic of that chapter and provides a context for the rest of the chapter. Then most chapters follow a consistent format:

- An initial section including a definition and description of the problem offers a foundation and vocabulary for understanding the chapter.
- A section on prevalence provides information on the relative frequency of the problem in various populations.
- The Developmental Influences section discusses what is known about how the problem unfolds over the life span and highlights particular events that may increase the risk for the problem and examine how problems may impact people differently at different points in their lives.
- Digital media offer tools for clinicians and clients, with positive and negative influences. We discuss these in each chapter.
- A section on assessment outlines the current state of knowledge in that critical area.
- The Treatment Options and Considerations section reviews the available treatments and factors that influence the effectiveness of treatment.
- Issues of diversity impact the way counselors work with clients; these variables deserve special attention with many topics. In some cases, multicultural factors are not yet understood, but the reader is alerted to potential concerns. Clients with disabilities will be discussed in this section.
- The section on counselor issues is a very important one, as it raises readers' sensitivity to factors that may influence their ability to work with clients with a given issue. We have included a note to school counselors in this section, as their role is different from that of other mental health professionals.
- Finally, the Ethical Concerns section addresses particular ethical dilemmas associated with the topic.

A summary concludes each chapter, followed by a section recommending resources—print, digital, film and television, and in the community—that interested readers may wish to consult to increase their understanding of the topic. Although we include important reference books for clinicians, we also include novels and self-help books when applicable. We believe that one can deepen their understanding of an issue by relating to the characters in a well-written novel and believe that literature is a valuable resource for psychology. Novels can also be useful as bibliotherapy for some clients, and it is important for clinicians to know which books are appropriate for which clients.

Finally, we include in each chapter a number of exercises or activities that can be used in classes to deepen students' understanding and engage them more personally with the material. Instructors might wish to assign some or all of these to students or groups and use them as the basis for expanded discussions of the chapter.

A Word About Language

We use the terms *counselor*, *mental health professional*, *clinician*, and *therapist* interchangeably and consider them synonymous. We use the term *counseling* in a generic sense of providing support, guidance, information, and understanding to others in order to help them overcome obstacles and barriers to optimal functioning. Certainly, counselors do this, but so do counseling and clinical psychologists, social workers, marriage and family therapists, and nurses. The book is for helping professionals in a variety of settings and from a variety of disciplines, although those settings often determine professional titles.

At times, we use terms that may not be familiar to all readers. We provide a definition in a box close to the first use of the term. The reader will also note references to the DSM-5-TR throughout the text. This refers to the *Diagnostic and Statistical Manual of Mental Disorders*, fifth edition, text revision, which is used by practitioners from all disciplines to arrive at a diagnosis of any mental disorder. In the DSM, criteria for a diagnosis of each disorder are specified, including time markers (how long symptoms have to be present), criteria for ruling out the diagnosis, and subtypes. Many students will study the current version of the DSM in their course in diagnosis and treatment planning.

We use the gender-neutral term *they* instead of *he or she* and *him or her* as it is now considered grammatically acceptable and is less awkward (Lattie et al., 2022)

Who Will Use This Book?

This book can be a basic text for a graduate or upper-division undergraduate seminar on topics for helping professionals in programs for counselors, psychologists, social workers, and nurses but will also be useful to students in practicum and internship courses. Instructors may wish to use the book to introduce future clinicians to all of these topics or use it as a resource when students confront these issues in their field experiences. Note that there are 10 chapters. In our experience, covering a new chapter every week of a 15-week semester, particularly when each one is dense with information, leads to rushed and sometimes superficial treatment of the material. We hope that having fewer chapters will allow for more in-depth coverage, provide time to utilize some of the recommended media, and an opportunity to do some of the exercises to enhance students' learning.

Although we would like the book to be useful for all helping professionals, some may find a particular chapter of special interest and may wish to pursue this topic more in depth. For such readers, this book can be a springboard for further study and training. We hope that students will find this book a useful resource that will become part of their professional libraries and be consulted often during their careers as helping professionals. This is the book we have always wanted on our shelves!

CHAPTER 2

COVID-19

Impact on Mental Health

Disclaimer: Given the sociopolitical climate in the United States, we need to acknowledge our assumptions that underlie this chapter. COVID-19 is real; vaccines are safe and offer protection against infection; masks are helpful in reducing the transmission of the disease; and the medical community, the Centers for Disease Control and Prevention (CDC), and the World Health Organization (WHO) are expert, professional, and trustworthy, continually updating their knowledge and recommendations as more research is conducted.

Introduction

The COVID-19 pandemic has been "the single deadliest acute public health crisis in American history" (Treglia et al., 2022). Virtually everyone on the planet has been affected in some way by the COVID-19 pandemic that appeared in numerous countries in 2020. As of March 2023, there had been more than 760,000,000 cases around the world and almost 7 million deaths (WHO, 2023). The mental health impacts of infection and deaths directly affected patients and their families. Indirect effects of restrictions, lockdowns, and social distancing, enacted to prevent transmission, contributed to increased mental health symptoms in society at large (Silver, 2020).

Unlike other catastrophes (hurricanes, fires, violent events, hate crimes), the pandemic is not a single incident with predictable duration. It also affects the entire population, so there are few unaffected people who could help with recovery (Osofsky et al., 2020). At present, there is no cure, although treatments have been developed to mitigate the severity of an infection, and a series of vaccines that are widely available greatly reduces the risk of getting COVID. Although the public health emergency expired on May 11, 2023, many COVID-inspired changes in our lives will persist going forward. It is important to recognize that the pandemic was not shielded from other tragic events; there were also hurricanes and other weather-related crises, political unrest, and disturbing news about violence and police responses (Silver et al., 2021) that compounded the stress. These multiple stressors contributed to an increase in domestic violence and sexual abuse (Taylor, 2020). Not only is this the only pandemic we have experienced in our lifetime, it happened in an era when digital communications were available and widely used by much of the population, providing instantaneous information, with both positive and negative effects.

Terminology

We begin with definitions to ensure a common vocabulary:

- **COVID-19 (coronavirus disease)** is an infectious disease that is caused by a specific virus (SARS-CoV-2) that has developed several variants since its origin. Most people who are infected recover without needing intensive medical intervention, but it is lethal to others. Because people can become ill or die at any age, the impact covers the entire life span. Because COVID-19 infected people from all over the globe, it is called a **pandemic.** The WHO declared COVID-19 a pandemic on March 11, 2020.
- **Long COVID** is a constellation of symptoms that persist (or appear) after recovery from an infection. The duration and severity of symptoms of the condition vary widely, and there are no cures; treatment involves attempts to reduce the intensity of symptoms and attendant life disruption.
- An **epidemic** is a sudden increase in the prevalence of a disease in a specific area or population (e.g., Ebola in western Africa).
- A disease that is **endemic** is a disease that is constantly present with an area or population, such as malaria in certain regions of the world (and polio in the United States at one time).

CASE STUDIES

The responses to the pandemic created conditions that exacerbated existing mental health disorders or precipitated symptoms in previously well-functioning persons. One of the many unique challenges is the rapid spread of infection, putting great strain on medical facilities and health care workers. The rapid decline in the condition of some patients caught families unaware. Social support was less available given travel restrictions and social distancing, sometimes isolating families from sources of comfort and stability. Protective policies in hospitals prohibited family members from visiting their suffering loved ones and greatly limited the implementation of funeral or other cultural practices and rituals that help survivors begin the healing process. The restrictions against visiting also increased patient insecurity and reduced compliance with treatment and elevated anxiety. For nurses, negative impacts on mental health include stressful communication with family members, usually by phone, and planning for care following discharge (Correia et al., 2022). It is not surprising that among other mental health issues (anxiety, depression, PTSD, suicidality), prolonged grief is likely to affect many people who lost a loved one. COVID has exacted an enormous toll around the globe, and no one case study could illustrate the many ways mental health has been affected. We include several examples from the media to raise awareness of the myriad mental health challenges created by this pandemic.

Medical workers were on the frontlines of efforts to manage the disease. The case of Dr. Steve Kassapidis, an ICU doctor interviewed in April 2020, exemplifies the multiple stressors for medical workers (Bunkall, 2020). He described his strong emotional involvement when treating coworkers or coworker's family members; professional detachment was impossible to maintain. In addition, as a frontline medical worker, Dr. Kassapidis feared for his own health and that of his family. When a long-time patient of his died alone because family were not allowed to visit, Dr. Kassapidis struggled emotionally. He also noticed that overburdened and stressed medical personnel were not always prompt in notifying family members of a death; he worried about the heartbreak when a family learns their loved one died several days earlier. He describes his inability to sleep, persistent nightmares, and the pressure he feels not to slow down or take care of himself.

A devastating loss was that of Kristen Mc Mullen, 30 years old and healthy. She developed symptoms of COVID, then developed coronavirus pneumonia, sought treatment, and was initially given medication and sent home. Symptoms rapidly worsened, and she had to be hospitalized. She was treated and placed on a ventilator but did not improve. She gave birth to her daughter on July 27 via emergency c-section. Hospital staff took two photos of mom and baby before rushing Kristen to the ICU, where her condition continued to decline until she died on August 6, 2021 (Neale, 2021). A Facebook page posted by FOX13News reported the story and elicited thousands of comments. One said, "These stories are truly sad, but this world can use some recovery stories as well. There are more of them than sad ones. The media sure does a great job of pouring nothing but fear on everyone. Also a sad story." Some other comments were contentious, while others described their own losses. In today's world, social media can provide support and information, but also hateful and disturbing comments.

Then there is the Macias family, all of whom contracted COVID (Mark, 2021). The children recovered quickly. Not so for mom Davy Macias, a nurse, who had an emergency c-section as she was dying from COVID. She never saw her newborn child. Her husband, Daniel, a teacher, died of COVID 2 weeks later, having seen only photos of his new daughter taken by nurses. The couple left behind the newborn and four other children (ages 7, 5, 3, and 2). It is hard to comprehend the toll this tragedy took on the children and extended family. Numerous other stories about families who experienced multiple COVID deaths in a short period of time were covered in various news media, and there were surely many more that were not reported.

Sometimes it was family members of patients who experienced difficulties. Paul Stewart, 55, was living with his parents when he experienced symptoms that we now recognize as COVID related. Although he was ill for a few days, he recovered and never tested for COVID. However, Paul's 86-year-old father contracted COVID and spent a week in the hospital before dying on April 9, 2020. Paul struggles with nagging guilt, believing he killed his father (Schuppe, 2020). A similar story, albeit with a more positive outcome, is that of Teresa Xie (Xie, 2021), who believed she had followed all precautionary measures at her college, including frequent testing and social distancing, but at Thanksgiving, she decided to fly home for the remainder of the semester since all her classes were now online. Crowded airports and planes are breeding grounds for the virus, as Teresa later realized. After being home for a week, Teresa exhibited some symptoms and promptly tested positive for COVID. Her symptoms were mild, and she quarantined in her room. Ten days later, her father began showing signs of COVID. His tests were negative, but his breathing became increasingly difficult. He got a chest scan; COVID pneumonia was the diagnosis. Although it took almost 2 months, he recovered, but the guilt Teresa felt lingered.

One of the many challenges experienced by survivors is managing the anger that arises when someone dies, especially if the survivor believes the death was preventable. In some cases, the deceased had refused to be vaccinated; when they died, survivors were angry at the individual while grieving the loss at the same time. The daughter of Mark Anthony Urquiza, a 65-year-old healthy Arizona man who died of COVID after a 3-week-long illness (Ortiz, 2020), wrote a scathing critique of state and federal response to the pandemic in her father's obituary, stating that his death was the result of their inaction and unclear leadership. She is taking action to protect others from the nightmare her family endured. Among other things, she has created a Facebook group "marked by COVID" to provide support and community to others who had similar losses.

Digital Media Influences on Mental Health During/After COVID

The influence of digital media on the mental health of the population is captured in this quotation from Depoux et al. (2020): "We need to combat the pandemic of social media panic" (p. 1). Because the virus first appeared in China, racist behavior toward Asian-appearing people increased regardless of whether the individual actually came from China. Depoux et al. (2020) quote the director of the WHO, who said that "misinformation on the coronavirus might be the most contagious thing about it (para. 2)." In an effort to combat the faulty information, WHO (2022) created a website called Mythbusters that provides accurate and current information.

Although COVID-19 is the only pandemic most Americans have experienced in our lifetime, historical pandemics (the Black Death in the 14th century, the Spanish flu in 1918 [during World War I]) could be instructive. However, the contemporary context is so different from those eras that it is difficult to extract lessons learned. COVID arrived in a time when digital communications were available to much of the population, often in the form of smartphones, providing instantaneous information, with both positive and negative effects. Research has found that repeated media exposure to traumatic events is associated with mental and physical health problems both at the time of the event and with later traumas (Silver et al., 2021; Zhao & Zhou, 2020). The uncertainty and fear of the pandemic prompted increased use of media for gathering information. In a sample of Chinese college students, many showed symptoms of secondary traumatic stress (similar to PTSD) when indirectly impacted by a traumatic event; Zhao & Zhou, 2020). Sixty-three percent of Americans report that they find their news via Facebook (Keib et al., 2018). Kellerman et al. (2022) suggest that in addition to seeking information that might diminish distress, some people use media to escape from the news and reduce anxiety. It remains to be seen whether these patterns will persist over time.

Digital media played an important role in mental health during the pandemic. The internet was an accessible information source, a line of communication with friends and family, entertainment, and a distraction during a stressful time. Although accurate and current information was important to many, it also added to the anxiety and uncertainty as the pandemic continued. In fact, there was so much information that information overload was a common experience. For example, a search on Google Scholar in March 2023 yielded 1,620,000 hits—and that is only scholarly literature. A more general Google search found 1,380,000,000 sites. A searcher cannot possibly read all the information in cyberspace and may be stressed by the task of deciding which is relevant and reliable for their queries.

The pandemic, the torrent of news, much of it including negative headlines and dire statistics, updated around the clock, led to news fatigue (Fitzpatrick, 2022), with studies revealing that users felt emotional fatigue and distress from reading the news. A conundrum is that participants in the survey also believed the news coverage mitigated the spread of COVID-19. During COVID-19, many people were subjected to upsetting material even if they were not actively seeking it (de Hoog & Verboon, 2020). Social media in particular might be used to communicate with friends and family, but the information about COVID-19 crises and tragedies is likely to be interspersed among the more social material. Hermida (2020) noted that social media can provide immediate, often live, and emotionally layered accounts of a crisis incident. The more news a sample of college students consumed, the more worry they reported; the worry contributed to feelings of hopelessness (Kellerman et al., 2022). In addition, the increase in misinformation and disinformation on this (and other) topics may prompt users to seek even more information in an effort to find accurate news (Kellerman et al., 2022).

Collective Trauma

Trauma has been defined as "the response to a deeply distressing or disturbing event that overwhelms an individual's ability to cope, causing feelings of helplessness" (Chakaryan, 2021, slide 4). When a traumatic event is shared by a group, it is called a collective traumatic event. Hirschberger (2018) eloquently describes this phenomenon: "Collective trauma is a cataclysmic even that shatters the basic fabric of society. Aside from the horrific loss of life, collective trauma is also a crisis of meaning" (p. 1441). There are many features of the pandemic that are shared experiences across the population. Masiero et al. (2020) pointed to the rapid spread of the virus, the high rates of infection, and the number of asymptomatic cases that could unknowingly infect others as features that added to the level of trauma. They also observed that having to make numerous decisions, sometimes with little time to weigh options, was an additional stressor. Many people lost jobs, which had a negative effect on their financial stability, and for those who derive gratification and self-esteem from their work role, those factors can add to the psychological toll. Moreover, even for those who retained their employment, the fear of unemployment (or infection) and the changes in routine (e.g., working from home), can be destabilizing. Finally, in the United States and other countries, the pandemic exaggerated the political and ideological divisions in populations (e.g., debates over masks, vaccines, social distancing, "cures") and added yet another layer of stress, as did the increased disparity of negative consequences on marginalized groups.

Client characteristics that may engender vicarious trauma, burnout, and compassion fatigue in clinicians include impulsive, unpredictable, and manipulative behavior, interpersonal dynamics of the counselor–client relationship, and personal characteristics of the therapist (Litam et al., 2021). The most important approach to protect against vicarious trauma is self-care. There are many ways in which one can accomplish that; knowing what works best for you is important. One essential strategy is to recognize one's limits. If the provider is experiencing secondary trauma, compassion fatigue, or burnout, their effectiveness is compromised, and their own mental health negatively affected. Because the need for mental health services exceeds availability, it is tempting to take more clients, work more hours, engage in more consultation, and so on; clinicians do this work because they care and want to help others. Noticing signs of secondary trauma and/or burnout will alert the counselor to reassess their boundaries. Another important practice is to obtain supervision to address these issues, and possibly to join a group of mental health professionals (including online groups) to gain support and recommendations from others who have similar experiences.

Developmental Factors

As with many mental health issues, symptoms manifest differently at different points in development. Not only do symptoms present in different ways, but the client's stage of development should guide treatment planning to ensure maximum effectiveness. In this section, we approach the impact of COVID-19 across the lifespan.

Children

In 2021, the Academy of Pediatrics declared an emergency due to increasing rates of mental health problems in young people (Dick & Comer, 2022). Worldwide, approximately 8 million children under age 18 lost a parent or primary caregiver to COVID; if secondary caregivers are included, the number rises to 10.5 million (Chatterjee, 2022). In the United States, the National Institute of Health estimates that that over 140,000 children under 18 lost a parent or other caretaker between April 2020 and end of June 2021. A 2022 report found that 70% of children who lost a parent/caregiver were 13 and younger (20% were 4 or younger, and 50% were between 5 and 13; Treglia et al., 2022). Moreover, these losses disproportionately fell on racial, ethnic, and geographic minorities, and in some cases, the distress is compounded by racial discrimination (Thomeer, 2023). Chatterjee points out that in addition to grief, children may experience the consequences of lost income, changing schools, or moving to new communities, and may have elevated fears of getting COVID. The mental health outcomes for children who lose a parent or grandparent (primary caretaker) are severe: school dropout, poor academic performance, decreased self-esteem, acting out by using substances and engaging in sexually risky behaviors, suicidal behaviors, and violence. Keep in mind that the very people these children likely counted on for support and acceptance are the ones who are now gone. It is clear that these young people will need support from mental health professionals in school or in the community, but there is no systematic strategy for detecting them. Schools and agencies must rely on someone to tell them, and it is likely that not all bereaved children will be recognized. Changes in behavior, increased absences, and emotional outbursts may be symptoms of grief and excessive stress. Clinicians must be sensitive to the enormity of the disruption and loss these children are experiencing and realize that treatment is likely to be long-term. See Chapter 5 on grief and loss for a more detailed discussion of this topic.

In addition to these direct experiences, many children were exposed (intentionally or accidentally) to frightening news about COVID. Studies using brain scans to analyze children's responses to negative news showed increased anxiety. However, although some youth exhibited symptoms of PTSD, most did not. It would be valuable to understand what protects some youth from adverse emotional responses. Dick & Comer, (2022) also observed that, particularly on social media, more graphic images and video are included to attract viewers. Viewers are also more likely to view posts that include comments (Keib et al., 2018). When users see a news item, they look at images first and for longer that text. They are more likely to click on a news story accompanied by an image.

Dick and Comer (2022) found that the more media a child saw, the more PTSD symptoms were present. They also demonstrated that children at a distance (San Diego, California) did not differ from those near the traumatic event (Hurricane Irma in Florida) on the association between consuming news and mental health symptoms. The researchers found some evidence of different brain responses to fear and threat and urged parents to closely monitor children's media behavior, especially when a disaster or tragedy dominates the news.

Adolescents

Worldwide, adolescents experienced increases in mental health disorders (anxiety, depression, stress, suicidality, substance abuse) as a result of the pandemic (Jones et al., 2021). In 2021, across all racial/ethnic groups, feelings of sadness and hopelessness were reported in 42% of high school students, 22% had suicidal thoughts, and 29% indicated they experienced poor mental health in the previous month (The Washington Post, 2023). Females and LGBTQ+ teens had significantly higher rates than the overall sample.

Adolescence is a developmental stage in which peer and social relationships increase in importance. Developing an identity and becoming independent from parents are major developmental tasks. The physical distancing regulations imposed in many countries during COVID-19 had a negative effect on the mental health of youth (Marciano et al., 2022). The restrictions caused some to miss important milestones: graduations, proms, starting college or new careers, forming romantic relationships, and perhaps taking steps toward autonomy by getting a driver's license and living independently. The increased pressure on interpersonal relationships, a tendency to be emotionally reactive, and underdeveloped emotional regulation put adolescents at risk for mental disorders (Magson et al., 2021). Garagiola et al. (2022) maintain that despite all the adversities, some adolescents can develop resilience in the context of involved caregivers, having a support network in schools and communities, and possessing an optimistic personality trait. At the same time, the rapid shift to some form of digital learning was unfulfilling for youth, many whose academic interest and performance declined dramatically. The increased need for mental health treatment was accompanied by a concurrent lack of availability of providers.

Longitudinal studies that include pre-COVID and COVID pandemic data are sparse. One such study by Magson et al. (2021) reported findings based on data collected 1 year prior to the outbreak (2019) and again 2 months after stay-at-home and online learning were implemented (March–May 2020). The study was conducted in Australia, in a sample that was 81% White and 79% of middle-high socio-economic status (SES). Australia is an island nation that was able to quickly close borders to forestall infections, and where the highest rate of cases was reported in 2022, 2 years later than the second wave of data were collected. Nevertheless, the findings are enlightening and may provide clues to important factors to investigate. These researchers were examining the ways the pandemic impacted youth anxiety, depression, and life satisfaction. Along with other measures, a COVID-19-related 18-item measure was developed to assess COVID-related stress, as well as four items to assess disruptions in educational settings and two questions related to media exposure. Their findings revealed that all mental health variables were significantly correlated. Regarding distress, the most upsetting circumstance was the inability to see friends, with a friend or family member becoming very sick and/or dying in second place. Also often endorsed was the inability to attend extracurricular activities or social events. Interestingly, worrying about getting COVID or dying of it were not a major source of stress. As expected, results revealed an increase in depressive symptoms, anxiety, and reduced life satisfaction, with greater increases in girls than boys. Age was not a significant moderator; participants with moderate or high levels of COVID-related distress also reported increases in the outcomes (depressive symptoms and anxiety higher, life satisfaction lower).

Media exposure has been implicated in negative mental health effects, but the Magson et al., (2021) research surprisingly found that more exposure to traditional media was associated with decreased anxiety while COVID-related content on social media had no effect. Interpersonal conflict was also examined; the most significant impact on depressive symptoms was conflict with fathers, while conflict with both parents was associated with decreases in life satisfaction. A sense of social connection predicted lower levels of depressive symptoms and anxiety and higher levels of life satisfaction. The change to online learning was not associated with any of the three outcome variables, but more depressive symptoms were reported when online difficulties (e.g., connectivity issues) were present. The final analysis found that participants who observed stay-at-home restrictions showed smaller declines in life satisfaction compared to those who violated those restrictions.

Although this study had its limitations, we think as the only longitudinal study we located, it suggests directions for future research. In some countries that administer questionnaires at regular intervals that include mental health variables, there is still a need for longitudinal and trend studies and inclusion of moderator variables, as in the Magson et al. (2021) research.

Many adolescents increased their use of digital communication as an effective coping strategy. Text messages increased by 83%, phone calls by 72%, social media and video chats by 66%, instant messaging by 48%, and emails by 37%. In addition, 77% of adolescents obtained news from social media (Moreno & Joliff, 2022). Although these practices may have compensated for the isolation and loneliness, it added a stressor in the form of overwhelming information about COVID, much of which was distressing; some of that information was "fake news," and the pressure to distinguish between credible and fake news may have caused fear and worry (Marciano et al., 2022). For youth vulnerable to depression and anxiety, the negative news may reinforce negative beliefs; the cognitive triad (I am powerless, the world is dangerous, and the future is grim; Moreno & Joliff, 2022) are symptoms of depression in cognitive theory; and cognitive behavioral therapy (CBT) is an evidence-based treatment for this disorder. Given the many disruptions in relationships, it is essential that the provider be patient and recognize that the therapeutic relationship may be slow to develop. If the adolescent resists talking about the trauma, art therapy and other creative strategies may be effective.

Adults

Three thousand Canadians 8 years old or older took a survey (November 2020–July 2021) assessing the impact of COVID on their mental health, with a focus on differences across age groups (children, youth, young adults, and adults (Stewart et al., 2023)). Their results indicated that adolescents and young adults had the worst mental health outcomes, although different factors predicted negative mental health outcomes in each age group. They found that the transition from adolescence to adulthood was an especially vulnerable period. In addition, they identified other risk factors: poverty, low levels of education, LGBTQ+ status, having special educational needs, being female or nonbinary, and having a medical or psychiatric illness. They also observed that mental health needs were not met, due to inadequate access to services.

Although some adults are resilient and overcame the mental health challenges that COVID-19 has generated, many did not fare as well. Many studies detect higher than usual levels of PTSD, anxiety, and depression, along with difficulty sleeping, fear of contagion, anger, irritability, and suicidal ideation. We know that health care providers and essential workers are at high risk for exposure to the virus and the mental health impact of the extremely stressful conditions in which they work (Pfefferbaum & North, 2020). Mental health providers can provide support, stress management training and referrals to community resources and can recommend limiting pandemic news. The availability of telemental health is a way for clients to obtain or continue therapy without ignoring restrictions. With continuing or new clients, we suggest a basic screening protocol (anxiety, depression, PTSD, mental status) to ensure that such issues are treated and progress monitored.

In the United States, the discovery of a COVID-19 vaccine was a scientific achievement, but it generated considerable controversy, with some groups lauding the availability of vaccines and others who strongly believed vaccines were unnecessary, dangerous, nefarious tools that violated their freedom of choice. Twenty-eight waves of data obtained from a large nationally representative sample of U.S. adults found that vaccination was associated with lower levels of distress and reductions in perceived risks of infection, hospitalization, and death. There was variation by race/ethnicity, with the largest decline found among American Indian/Alaskan individuals (Koltai et al., 2022). Blanchflower and Bryson (2022) examined U.S. Census data for over 3 million Americans from April 2020 to April 2022. They discovered that as the number of cases in an area increased, mental health decreased. However, as vaccination rates increased, women and men with a college education reported improved mental health, whereas being vaccinated was associated with decreased mental health in less educated men.

For all ages, the explosion of shocking or sensational headlines may lead to "headline stress disorder," an unofficial mental disorder coined by Steven Stosny (2017) to describe the feelings of many of his patients whose engagement with online news led to anxiety, depression, hopelessness, and a sense of having no control over events affecting one's life. Constant exposure to disturbing headlines can cause panic-like symptoms such as agitation and fear. The stress of the barrage of negative headlines can also cause physical symptoms, including gastrointestinal problems, weakened immune system, and more (Rodriquez-Cayro, 2018).

De Hoog and Verboon (2020) used ecological momentary assessment (EMA) to explain the cognitive processes that are employed when negative news is consumed. Although the study had significant limitations (small convenience sample, nonresponse) the findings are informative. The researchers applied Lazarus and Folkmans's (1984) cognitive appraisal theory, which proposes that when someone encounters a stressor (too much information), they make an appraisal (How serious is it? Does it affect me?), which then generates an emotional response. The primary appraisal determines the relevance and severity of the stressor; the secondary appraisal evaluates one's ability to cope with the stressor. These researchers found that women had more adverse emotional reactions than men, but no age differences were detected. The researchers demonstrated that even when the severity is low, the news still influences the emotional reaction, but personal relevance was associated with negative affect.

Another interesting study used *in silico* methodology to examine how social media exposure following a mass trauma (the shooting at Parkland High School in Florida) impacts the population at large (Abdalla et al., 2021). Their results revealed that when news was perused on social media in addition to television, especially when videos or images were present, negative psychological responses were more likely. They concluded that TV exposure increased population-level PTSD and that viewing reports of mass trauma on social media along with TV coverage also increased the symptom level. A study of the elements of features of posts on social media adds to our understanding (Holman et al., 2020). The research examined the effects of both quantity of exposure to the Boston Marathon bombing and the type of images (bloody versus other). Their short-term longitudinal study found that both graphic images and amount of exposure to news about the bombing were associated with mental health problems and impaired functioning

An important element of this situation is that, in many cases, the mental health provider is experiencing the same stressors and pressures as their clients. That makes it particularly difficult to maintain an objective, clinical perspective. For example, shortly after hurricane Irma devastated parts of Puerto Rico, I (SB) attended a conference in the capital city; many attendees were from the area hard hit by the storm. One woman was especially distraught. The town she lived in was practically destroyed, including her home, but the requests for counseling were increasing, and she felt she had to do her job. It is hard to imagine how she might set aside her own pain when attending to clients. The Red Cross often sends disaster mental health teams to such locations—but it typically takes days to get there and some time to organize logistics and have services available. The mental health professions need to address the issue of collective trauma and develop strategies to provide services to the communities while not ignoring the needs of providers.

Vicarious traumatization (also called secondary traumatization, compassion fatigue) refers to the emotional impact of exposure to others' trauma via narratives provided by clients of witnessing such an incident and is an "occupational hazard" of people working in the helping professions. Ironically, it is the compassion and empathy, valuable traits in good counselors, that are the very ones that make them vulnerable to these effects. There are behavioral symptoms such as sleep disturbances, irritability, exhaustion, withdrawal in close relationships, substance abuse. Impatience, conflict, and poor communication with colleagues are interpersonal manifestations of vicarious traumatization, while personal beliefs may be challenged by hopelessness, low self-confidence, hypersensitivity, fear, anxiety, and depression. These symptoms are compounded by the clinician's personal experience of the collective trauma of the COVID-19 pandemic. Again, we stress the importance of ongoing individual and group supervision to prevent these problems or provide support to those struggling.

Elderly

It was clear at the outset that elderly adults were at greater risk of contracting COVID, requiring hospitalization, and ultimately resulting in death. The mental health outcomes however, were much less alarming. Vahia et al. (2020) reported findings from several studies of this age group. We present those findings in Table 2.1. Another study, conducted in China (Li et al., 2020) in late March 2020 with 23,192 participants aged 18–85 (emerging adults [n = 2,045], adults [n = 18,159], and older adults [n = 2,988] examined the types and amount of social support received and resilience on mental health. They controlled for gender and history of chronic disease. Results revealed that that sources of support (family, friends, small groups, communities, organizations, and society overall) and resilience were positively associated with mental health; older adults reported higher levels of mental health than other age groups, but adults had more support than older adults. Another important finding was that the interaction of social support on mental health was significant such that moderate–high levels of social support protected from the negative impact of low levels of resilience.

Worrying about COVD, while not a mental disorder, had a negative impact on mental health (Maxfield & Pituch, 2021), but again researchers found that older adults had lower levels of depression and anxiety than younger adults, and that resilience buffers against loneliness and distress. These researchers included variables not examined in other studies: depression, general anxiety, health anxiety, preparedness for future care needs, and ambivalent ageism (hostile ageism, benevolent ageism, and COVID worry). They found that COVID worry was associated with living alone, generalized anxiety, and benevolent ageism. Hostile ageism was not associated with COVID worry, which was contrary to expectations. Also interesting was the finding that neither gathering information nor concrete planning were associated with COVID worry. Note that the sample was 85% White and cannot be considered representative of the population.

What are the implications of this body of research for counselors? First, it seems that although the medical risks for the elderly were emphasized in public health messaging, the "paradox of aging" (Li et al., 2020) appears to apply to the COVID pandemic. That is, older adults tend to have better mental health than younger people. Given the consistent message that older age is a risk factor for getting COVID, it's not surprising that worry about COVID was greater among the older aged participants than younger cohorts, although their mental health did not decline (Maxfield & Pituch, 2021). This does not mean that counseling and therapy are not needed. Research findings describe patterns in groups of people, but there is considerable variation among individuals in those groups. A strategy that is used to treat elders with dementia that appears applicable to elders in the community is technology-enhanced reminiscence therapy (Manav & Simsek, 2019), during which clients recall and tell stories about earlier period in their lives, often evoking positive memories. There are online groups and virtual reality techniques that can provide support and reduce loneliness. Elderly clients may need assistance with technology, which, in addition to facilitating access to online opportunities, provides cognitive stimulation and interaction with others, which are likely to enhance well-being.

Online support groups provide social support and help alleviate loneliness, which are important to elder mental health at all times including during the pandemic. Staying in touch with family and friends using online conferencing or Facetime are also ways to enhance social support. A study of 591 older adults (M_{age} = 68.18, SD = 10.75) revealed that older adults recognize the advantages of using technology and that more use of technology was associated with greater perceived well-being and lower rates of depression (Chopik, 2016) via reduced loneliness. However, seniors may not have the technological skills to access online resources. Helping an elder client find classes or tutoring to learn those skills can be extremely beneficial.

These studies were conducted in the earlier months of the pandemic. The situation may have changed as the duration extended and the numbers of cases and deaths climbed. As noted, COVID-19 is a collective trauma, and the stressors that accumulated in the population were also felt among this age group. The research reported in Table 2.1 was conducted with older adults living in the community and does not provide any insight about those in more controlled settings such as nursing homes and assisted living facilities, or those with prior medical conditions, including dementia. Vahia et al. (2020) observed that technology can be useful in promoting physical exercise, reducing isolation and loneliness, and supporting spiritual activities, and, when necessary, providing online therapy such as CBT.

Assessment

During the pandemic, it was clear that many clients had mental health needs. Because there is a shortage of providers, it is important to be as efficient as possible. It is imperative to take a history of past mental health diagnoses and/or ask whether these symptoms are the result of COVID or are the continuation of a preexisting condition. If the client has received prior treatment, ask for permission to contact that provider to get their perception of what has been helpful with the client in the past. If the clinician is going to conduct their own

TABLE 2.1. **Studies of the Impact of COVID-19 on Older Adults Residing in the Community (2020)**

Location	Source	Sample Size	Age Range	%Depression	%Anxiety	*TRSD*	Loneliness
US	CDC (Czeisler et al., 2020)	5,412	18–24 (n = 731)	5.8	6.2	9.2	
			25–45 (n = 1,911)	52.3	49.1	46.0	
			46–64 (n = 895)	32.5	35.3	36.0	
			65+ (n = 933)	14.4	16.1	17.2	
Spain	González-Sanguino et al. (2020)	3,840	18–39 / 40–59	The older group had lower scores on depression, anxiety, and PTSD. Women had higher scores than men.			
US/Canada	Klaiber et al. (2021)	776	18–39 (n = 330) / 40–59 (n = 253) / > 60 (n = 193)	Participants in the two older groups had less negative and more positive feelings than the youngest group, although all had similar level of stress.			
US	Maxfield and Pituch (2021)	4855	18–82	Depression, anxiety, and health anxiety lower in older participants.			
							Suicide Attempt
Canada	Stewart et al. (2023)	3,140	< 8 (n = 192)	4.2 parent report	5.2		0.5
			8–18 (n = 289)	35 self-report	31		4.4
			19–29 (n = 586)	56 self-report	55		4.5
			30+ (n = 1,936)	55 self-report	38		1.4
Netherlands	Van Tilberg et al. (2021)	1,679	65–102	Mental health indicators unchanged			Increased

assessment of common issues, we suggest the following well-known, short measures with good psychometric properties:

Stress

The most widely used measure for assessing global stress level is the Perceived Stress Scale (Baik et al., 2019). The original scale had 14 items, but a 10-item scale was created by deleting items with the lowest factor loading. Higher scores on two scales (positive and negative) indicate the degree of stress. This test is widely available online (e.g., https://www.bemindfulonline.com/test-your-stress or https://www.mdapp.co/perceived-stress-scale-pss-calculator-389/) and can be scored and interpreted by the client.

Anxiety

The Generalized Anxiety Disorder-7 is another self-report measure that is short, reliable, and valid and is used in both research and clinical settings. The items reflect the presence and severity of symptoms of anxiety. It has a valid Spanish translation in addition to the English version. Higher scores represent more severe anxiety (Baik et al., 2019).

Depression

There are several measures for symptoms of depression. The Patient Health Questionnaire-9 uses items that describe the diagnostic criteria for depression (DSM-5-TR version). It also is available and validated in English and Spanish. The Center for Epidemiologic Studies of Depression from the

National Institute of Mental Health (CES-D) is available online (http://www.chcr.brown.edu/pcoc/cesdscale.pdf), as is the CES-DC (children's version; https://www.brightfutures.org/mentalhealth/pdf/professionals/bridges/ces_dc.pdf). Finally, there is the Beck Depression Inventory, which can be found online at multiple sites. It has 21 items, and higher scores indicate more severe depression. Some versions (e.g., https://www.ohsu.edu/sites/default/files/2019-06/Beck%20Depression%20Inventory.pdf) are self-scored with an explanation of scores provided. We find this measure to be useful to measure progress in treatment in addition to use as a diagnostic tool.

PTSD

There are a number of ways to assess for PTSD, including interview protocol and self-report measures. The Davidson Scale is linked to the DSM-V criteria and contains both a checklist (for screening) and 24 Likert scale items with response options ranging from "none at all" to "6 or more times a week/severe (https://www.div12.org/wp-content/uploads/2014/11/PSS-SR5.pdf; author's permission is required). A listing of PTSD assessment tools, including references, additional information, and directions to obtain permission, can be found at https://www.apa.org/ptsd-guideline/assessment.

Treatment Approaches

The restrictions imposed during the pandemic resulted in a rapid adoption of telemental health practices, using various online communication tools to replace face-to-face treatment. Social distancing and stay-at-home requirements propelled the shift to telemental health, but it is likely that some clients and practitioners will continue to use distance services now that these pandemic restrictions have been rescinded. The switch to digital modes of treatment was appealing because it addressed many existing challenges in delivering in-person therapy: time constraints, transportation difficulties, high costs, and concerns about stigma (Hull & Mahan, 2017). However, for many new users (clients and clinicians) of online modalities (real-time interactive formats), a period of adjustment was necessary to become comfortable and proficient using these tools.

Prior to COVID-19, most practitioners had not received training in best practices for using the technology in this way, and not all entities that license practitioners require such training. Shore et al. (2018) identified various resources and training opportunities for clinicians to consider so that the online treatment they provide is as equivalent to in-person treatment as possible. There is solid evidence that online treatment results are quite similar to those achieved in face-to-face treatment (Dueweke et al., 2020; Sweeney et al., 2019). A review and meta-analysis of smartphone interventions for anxiety concluded that the studies in their analysis demonstrated that greater improvement was reported in smartphone interventions than in control conditions (Firth et al., 2017).

Shore et al. (2018) offered recommendations for clinicians doing telemental health:

- Ensure that the details (name, location, age) provided by potential new clients are verified.
- Because sessions are online, some clients wish to contact the provider between sessions (via email, text, etc.). The provider should specify their policy about such contact.
- A protocol for managing emergencies must be in place prior to the start of treatment. This is why it is so important to verify the location of the client; local emergency services may need to be contacted in urgent situations.
- Have a plan for digital interruptions (e.g., loss of internet connection) and share that with clients.

- Select a platform that ensures data privacy and security. In Europe, the General Data Protection Regulation provides guidelines. This is a challenging task, but it behooves providers to carefully research the programs these use to ensure they provide secure and confidential service and that they will not use or sell information to other parties.
- Carefully consider how you arrange the physical location from which you conduct online sessions. A professional and welcoming environment puts clients at ease.
- Discuss the importance of the client connecting from a private place. This is particularly important if the client is a minor. Meeting with the caregiver and discussing the importance of privacy may be helpful; there are cases, however, when the home is crowded, and private locations are not available. It may be possible to use a headset and makeshift screen to improve privacy and/or to schedule sessions for a time when there is the least activity in the household.
- Take cultural considerations into account as you would with all clients. The digital format may be unfamiliar in some cultural groups and may arouse suspicion in others. Having an open discussion about cultural differences in initial sessions, exhibit cultural humility, and check with the client about the acceptability of techniques or formats.

In telemental health, security of data and communication is of the utmost importance. Clinicians who conduct telemental health should investigate methods to protect all communication and data and use only the most secure platforms. Andersson (2022) advises providers to use only technologies that include encryption and/or require two-step authentication to access the platform.

In addition to synchronous virtual therapy sessions, asynchronous text therapy has also shown positive outcomes (Hull & Mahan, 2017). An advantage of this format is that the client and clinician can each participate at a time and place that is convenient for both. Almost half rated effectiveness of the treatment as somewhat or much better. Andersson (2022) summarized quantitative and qualitative studies that found therapeutic alliance is as high in online formats as in face-to-face environments. This is important because, overall, positive outcomes are associated with high therapeutic alliance.

There is a paucity of research evaluating the efficacy of specific apps or platforms, and given the large number of these, it is unlikely that conclusive evidence will be available in the short-term. We encourage clinicians to do due diligence in making decisions about what digital tools they will use with as much information as is available.

One approach that does have empirical support is CBT (Mahoney et al., 2021; Rauschenberg et al., 2021). There are various ways CBT can be offered online. There are self-guided programs that do not involve a professional at all and mixed-format approaches that have some face-to-face meetings interspersed with digital interactions with a clinician. Other programs use asynchronous communication between client and counselor, which gives both an opportunity to formulate their responses and the therapist time to review notes and earlier conversations. For example, a randomized controlled trial in Oman compared outcomes of six weekly sessions of online CBT therapy during COVID with a control group (self-help) that received a newsletter with similar content. The results demonstrated that the intervention group had greater symptom reduction that those in the control group (Al-Alawi et al., 2021).

CBT treatment components typically include psychoeducation (reading assigned content), "awareness training though self-monitoring and writing exercises, relaxation training, positive self-verbalisation, social skills training through behavioural experiments, time management and relapse prevention" (Ruwaard, 2013, p. 142). In a series of randomized controlled studies by Ruwaard, CBT was found to be efficacious for work-related stress, depression, panic disorder, and bulimia. Since participants volunteered to be part of the research, he also used anonymized records from a mental health clinic to evaluate online CBT for a variety of disorders in a naturalistic context. Findings supported the positive outcomes for all disorders. However, providers who provide mental health services to minority and low-income communities have been reluctant to utilize mental health technologies, even when doing so would be beneficial for those clients (Martinez-Martin et al., 2020). Furthermore, the populations used to develop and test new apps or tools are less likely to include minority and marginalized groups, so caution is needed when recommending such an app to minority clients.

Ethical Issues

Professional organizations for mental health professionals have established ethical standards for practitioners in those fields. Although wording varies, there are foundational tenets that underlie all these documents. A perspective on ethics that was a response to the widespread impact of the pandemic was proposed by Mifsud and Herlihy (2022), who argue that the current standards are not adequate for crises that effect multiple layers (individuals, families, communities, countries) in multiple spheres (economic, political, financial, cultural) at the same time. They also contend that existing ethical codes embody Eurocentric worldviews emphasizing individualism and autonomy and discounting communality and intuition. For example, the ACA's ethical code Standard A.1.a. urges autonomy and self-determination, which contrasts with collectivist perspectives and inter-dependence so relevant to the current context. They propose that the focus on individual treatment is insufficient in such circumstances. They urge professions to seek collective interventions in a culturally sensitive manner. These scholars propose a different view of ethics that focuses not on situations but on characteristics of the counselor.

The American Psychological Association's code of ethics was examined through the pandemic lens by Chenneville and Schwartz-Mette (2020). They review the five overarching principles reflected in the code (beneficence and non-malfeasance, fidelity and responsibility, integrity, justice, and respect for people's rights and dignity) and offer guidance on applying those principles to the standards during and following the pandemic. The need for and risks associated with telemental health (including the need for technological support and necessary hardware and software) are underscored, as is the need for therapists to prepare for unanticipated absence (or death) so client services are not interrupted. Self-awareness on the part of clinicians is also highlighted as a basic requirement for practicing in an ethical manner.

During the pandemic, many regulations were adjusted to facilitate the provision of services during the emergency. For example, in the United States, HIPPA rules were relaxed so that those who provided services via telehealth in good faith would not be penalized (Martinez-Martin et al., 2020). These scholars point out that HIPPA regulations apply to "covered entities," which do not include apps and technologies that collect data from users, creating a risk for misuse of that information. In addition, the changes in HIPPA regulations mean that the client is responsible for finding and interpreting an app or platform's privacy policy. Although the COVID pandemic is no longer an emergency, Martinez-Martin et al. stress the importance of having a regulatory agency charged with overseeing protocol and practices and adverse outcome data for digital mental health tools.

Early in the pandemic, there were circumstances in which mental health clinicians were required to provide services in settings that did not have adequate protocol or protective equipment. That situation has largely resolved, but it reminds counselors that they have ethical principles that guide their work. Do no harm is a basic tenet; there may be times when the provider must refuse to engage in practices that may harm clients (or themselves). Hopefully, a supervisor will realize that despite the need to serve clients, it is unethical to put clinicians in a position that could inflict harm.

The news media and various agencies and established companies have reported on data breaches of what was supposed to be secure, protected data. Knowing that, counselors need to be aware that no site or app is impenetrable, and users must take extreme caution when storing client information online. In addition, clients need to understand that apps also collect data; they also need to be vigilant and weigh the value gained from the app against the kind of information it collects. A case in point is that of BetterHelp, owners of a number of mental health apps, that has been ordered to follow strict requirements to ensure that data they collect will not be shared with social media sites. The order can be found here: https://www.ftc.gov/business-guidance/blog/2023/03/ftc-says-online-counseling-service-betterhelp-pushed-people-handing-over-health-information-broke, and it provides an excellent model for all mental health apps to follow. A useful discussion of this issue can be found at https://www.latimes.com/business/technology/story/2023-05-02/mental-health-apps-privacy-risk-what-to-look-for. The U.S. Department of Health and Human Services has several relevant documents under its HIPPA for Professionals pages.

A case that is pertinent to this discussion is a federal inquiry into the practices of BetterHelp. They are under scrutiny for allegedly sharing private information with third parties. The court documents describe steps and practices that telehealth services should provide to clients, beginning on page 2, which serves as an excellent guideline for professionals and potential clients moving to tele-mental health.

One of the issues that came to the forefront as a result of COVID is that most states restrict counselors from practicing across state lines. Here's a scenario: An ongoing client has been displaced by COVID and is now living in another state with relatives. In most states (other than during COVID when such restrictions were relaxed), that counselor could not provide telemental health services to the client unless they were also licensed in the client's state. This has added momentum to pass compact legislation, which would allow licensed counselors in a compact state to practice in other states that have passed the legislation. At the time of this writing, 17 states had passed legislation that would be effective at the end of 2023 (ACA, n.d.).

All professional ethical codes include principles that relate to counselor or other mental health professional-only practice in areas for which they have been trained. In an emergency, clinicians are able to provide services in areas for which they are not sufficiently trained, providing information about those limits as part of informed consent. A useful resource for clinicians and supervisors Williamson and Williamson's (2020) book, one of few that focuses on distance counseling in great detail.

NOTE TO SCHOOL COUNSELORS

Schools are often the first point of contact with students who exhibit mental health concerns, but the pandemic removed the consistency and support that schools provide. School counselors are the people at school whose job includes promoting wellness, offering short-term counseling (individual and group), and making referrals to community resources. It is common knowledge that the pandemic disrupted the lives of students in many ways: adjusting to online learning, experiencing parental unemployment, fear of infection, and losing a loved one. In some cases, the death of a parent (or grandparent or guardian) means the child is orphaned. Estimates vary and tend not to be updated, but sources mention about 265,000 children losing primary caregivers, of whom 65% were from minority groups (Sparks, 2023).

School counselors may be the only mental health professionals in the school; 70%–80% of youth who obtain mental health services do so in school. The absence of face-to-face interaction with students compounded the difficulty in recognizing which students may need more support and services. Although most schools ultimately made some form of videoconferencing available, families in some areas lacked devices and connectivity and thus could not utilize those tools. In addition, many schools and districts experienced a shortage of school counselors, increasing the burden on those who are still on board. In some areas, when schools began returning to in-person

(Continued)

or hybrid formats, staff shortages were so prevalent that counselors were assigned non-counseling duties (substitute teaching, lunch duty, doing administrative tasks, etc.), further limiting their availability for attending to mental health needs of students (Alexander et al., 2022). It is common for school counselors to meet with students during class time; the heightened worry about academic declines caused some teachers to refuse to allow their students to leave the classroom and/or to provide time for counselors to deliver classroom guidance lessons on mental health topics.

Pincus et al., (2020) suggest a variety of strategies that school counselors might use to manage the mental health needs of students during and post COVID. Universal screening, using such measures as the Adverse Childhood Experiences (ACE) questionnaire, and others such as the Generalized Anxiety Disorder Seven-Item Scale (GAD-7), the Screening, Brief Intervention and Referral to Treatment (SBIRT), the School Refusal Assessment Scale, Beck Anxiety Inventory for Youth, Spence Children's Anxiety Scale, and others, would provide useful data for planning interventions. They argue that school counselors are trained in the use of these instruments and that administering such screening tools would identify students most in need of intervention. Alvarez et al. (2022) also recommend universal screening as part of a multitiered system of support (MTSS), although they suggest the Student Risk Screen Scale and the Child and Adolescent Trauma Screen in identification of students needing immediate services. They also propose that SEL programs be incorporated into tier 1 initiatives.

An opposing view is that of Racine et al. (2020), who oppose the use of the ACE as a universal screener. They point out that the experience of responding to the questionnaire may trigger revictimization or retraumatization experiences. In addition, they believe exclusive focus on ACEs does not provide a broad assessment of other risk factors or resilience and is not useful for the clinician. Finally, the ACE questionnaire has only minimal evidence of adequate psychometric properties.

We agree that identifying students with mental health problems is a daunting task. However, with the current political environment in which education is under scrutiny, and with parents objecting to such widely used curricula as social emotional learning, it is likely that conducting a universal mental health screening (or even lessons) would generate criticism and be prohibited. What is realistic in the current climate? One option is for counselors to incorporate trauma-informed practices in their comprehensive programs and to exert leadership in promoting and delivering training for all school staff about this approach to working with youth, many of whom will have had traumatic experiences during and after COVID (Alvarez et al., 2022; Dollarhide, 2003). A special issue of *School Mental Health* (March, 2016) is an excellent source of material on trauma-informed schools; the introduction by Overstreet and Chafouleas (2016) provides an excellent overview.

Summary

- The COVID-19 pandemic resulted in both immediate and long-term consequences for mental health. Although rates of hospitalizations and deaths (as of October 2023) have diminished, new variants appear, and the issue cannot be dismissed.
- The shortage of mental health providers is critical and was exacerbated by the pandemic; many people with acute needs for treatment are unable to get services.
- Media (both print and digital) have been sources of important current information but have also disseminated misinformation and disinformation. The quantity of new alerts (and alarms) has contributed to increases in anxiety and depression in the population
- The pandemic was a shared trauma, and recovery can be a slow process.
- Mental health professionals were also affected by the pandemic and associated stressors; self-care and support are necessary to be able to provide care to others. One major risk for clinicians is taking on too many clients. They need to avoid burnout by having a manageable caseload and taking time for respite when needed.

- Restrictions (school closures, etc.) disproportionately affected adolescents and young adults, for whom peer relationships are primary. However, digital technology enabled them to sustain contact, although in a different format.
- Telemental health, which increased dramatically during COVID, is here to stay. Clinicians must be well trained in this modality, especially regarding security and privacy. They also need to be familiar with online self-help or mixed-format platforms in order to guide clients to make good choices of resources.

Additional Resources

In Print for Counselors

- https://herbalebook.com/products/cbt-toolbox-for-children-and-adolescents-over-220-worksheets-exercises-for-trauma-adhd-autism-anxiety-depression-conduct-disorders?fbclid=IwAR3KYm6RO_Qi_wTD3EzZyyar2uorHZWxLKB_MdAVSgNEQ9Q3uy2-XpiKQjQ

Film and Television

- https://electricliterature.com/7-books-about-COVID-lockdown-pandemic/
- https://mashable.com/feature/sundance-pandemic-movies
- https://www.businessinsider.com/guides/learning/books-about-covid-19-pandemic#a-fantastical-pandemic-story-that-follows-real-life-events-6
- https://www.businessinsider.com/guides/learning/books-about-covid-19-pandemic#a-pandemic-story-that-uses-a-metaphor-to-teach-children-about-patience-22

Books for Children

- *Today I Feel ... (Angry, Anxious, Sad)* by Dr. Amy West
- *Everyone Feels (Anxious, Sad, Angry)* by Dr. Daniela Owen
- *Calling the Wind* by Trudy Ludwig

Exercises

1. In a small group, design a presentation or webinar (slide deck and script) for teachers regarding how they might respond to kids affected by COVID.
2. Create a similar presentation geared to parents.
3. Create and record a 30-second PSA to raise awareness of COVID-related mental health needs.

4. Create a poster to raise awareness of the mental health impact of COVID.

5. Create a case study based on an actual client or composite to use for case conceptualization and treatment planning.

6. Locate statistics on rates of infection, hot spots, deaths, vaccination rates, and so forth in your town/county/state and create infographics to present those data.

7. Create a listing of state laws providing mental health services for teens (see https://www.washingtonpost.com/opinions/2023/04/01/teen-mental-health-state-programs/).

8. Consider how to identify kids who most need counseling. Prepare a proposal to school officials with your plan.

————— PART II —————

PROBLEMATIC
STATUSES

CHAPTER 3

LGBTQIA+

Being lesbian, gay, bisexual, transgender, or queer/questioning is not a disorder. That sentence could not have been written before 1973, when homosexuality was still listed in the *Diagnostic and Statistical Manual of Mental Disorders* (DSM-II) as a clinical disorder. It was not until 1973 that the board of directors of the American Psychiatric Association voted to remove homosexuality from the DSM; in 1974, a vote of the membership supported that decision. However, there continued to be diagnoses that implied that anything other than a heterosexual orientation was pathological. The diagnosis of *ego-dystonic homosexuality* was included in the DSM-III (published in 1980). This diagnosis pathologized a psychological state that is largely the consequence of the prevailing negative societal attitudes toward LGBTQIA+ status.

In such a cultural climate, most individuals who become aware of their nonheterosexual orientation experience a period in which their sexual orientation is ego dystonic. Finally, in 1986, that diagnosis was deleted from the DSM-III-R, and the American Psychiatric Association endorsed the change.

Ego-Dystonic: a condition that is unacceptable to the self.

There is an intolerance and discrimination in contemporary society. One only needs to look at current sociopolitical events in the news. The National Board for Certified Counselors (NBCC) indicated that within the first 5 months of 2023, there were at least 321 anti-LGBTQIA+ bills introduced or debated (as reported by the American Civil Liberties Union [ACLU]; NBCC, 2023a). With respect to the mental health field, given the history and evolution of the DSM, there is evidence that treatment providers also hold negative stereotypes that interfere with the therapeutic process. Researchers in the early 2000s found that providers had more difficulty recalling information provided by LGBTQIA+ clients, avoided topics that were disconcerting for the therapist, and did not accurately assess the relevance of sexual orientation to the client's presenting problem (Cochran, 2001). Twenty-plus years later, in 2023, another group of researchers found similar themes with a study of transgender and gender-diverse (TGD) people. Puckett et al. (2023) found that therapists having insufficient understanding of TGD identities resulted in potentially harmful practices.

In addition, LGBTQIA+ youth are a particularly vulnerable population and have been found to have higher rates of depression, anxiety, and suicidality that their non-LGBTQIA+ peers (NBCC, 2023a). An awareness of the impact of current events on adolescents is essential for all counselors. NBCC reports that greater than 70% of LGBTQIA+ youth (and 86% of transgender and nonbinary youth) have reported that the current legal debates and actions that have focused on restricting rights of LGBTQIA+ individuals have negatively impacted their mental health (NBCC, 2023a). The purpose of this chapter, then, is to inform and sensitize counselors so that they can provide quality services, and at the very least do no harm.

CASE STUDY

Jerry was raised in a small community where activities revolved around a conservative church. He was the only son in the family, with two older sisters. Throughout school, Jerry socialized and dated girls, although he did not enjoy the little physical contact he had with them. He had lots of friends and often invited them to spend the night. He was aroused by the presence of males but never acted on his desires. He describes his adolescent thoughts about his homosexual interests as "violent denial." He had repeatedly heard from family, friends, and church sermons about the evils of homosexuality, and he believed that religious fervor was a worthy substitute for sexual passion. In fact, he convinced himself that his chaste behavior with girls was about serving God and remaining pure, as he had been taught. He was saving himself for marriage, the only allowable context for sexual behavior.

Jerry remembers learning very early that his homosexual interests were unacceptable, when he was discovered at about age 6 looking at the men's underwear pages in a Sears catalog. He was told that such behavior was "wrong" and that he shouldn't be looking at "such things." He remembers later realizing that it probably would have been okay to be looking at the women's section.

When he was 18 years old, Jerry had his first gay sexual experience. He was so distraught over the incident that he considered killing himself. Instead, he went to the youth pastor of his church and disclosed his fears of being gay. He entered counseling with the pastor's wife with the goal of becoming heterosexual. The counseling had positive benefits, as the focus was on the root causes of the behavior rather than on demonic possession. He had an opportunity to sort out some of his feelings about his relationships with his parents, which he found helpful. In addition, Jerry was instructed by the Bible passages that were believed to condemn homosexuality, and he learned to combat the lustful thoughts with prayer. He was told he could be "cured" by learning to ignore his impure thoughts until they had no influence.

At about this time, the youth pastor took Jerry and several other youth to an "exorcism" in an old church. He understood that the purpose of the ritual was to "cast out demons," which in his case meant his homosexual desires. He was frightened by the behavior of some of the other youth, who struggled with the demons he witnessed. When it was his turn, however, nothing happened. Jerry's interpretation of this "failure" at the time was that he did not have enough faith, which was more reason to despise himself.

Jerry moved out of state for a period of time and then returned to his small community when he was about 20. When he came back, a group of friends invited him to go "gay bashing" at a local park. This actually provided him with important information—a place where gay men could be found. Jerry then began cruising the park on his own and had sexual encounters with men he found there. He continued to struggle with his identity: Being gay meant going to hell, and he did not feel good about who he was. He battled his own homophobia. At one point, he had mononucleosis and panicked, fearing he had AIDS. He eventually concluded that he would not "win" his struggle against his "animal lust, his dark side," so he gave in to those impulses and set aside God and church, which he believed were incompatible with his nature.

When Jerry started counseling at age 28, he was still struggling to accept his sexuality. It was difficult for him at first to believe that I did not judge or condemn him. By this time, Jerry had been able to have sexual relationships with men, but they were separate from personal relationships. He had not learned how to integrate his sexual ("dark") side with his nonsexual ("good") side to form meaningful intimate relationships, and this was one of his goals for counseling. By this time, Jerry had already disclosed his sexual orientation to both of his sisters, who took the information well and conveyed that their foremost desire was for Jerry to be happy. In fact, both of them engaged in various matchmaking efforts in an attempt to be helpful.

Early in counseling, Jerry was adamant that he could never tell either of his parents that he is gay. He truly believed that the knowledge that they have a gay son would kill them, and his mother was already in poor health. Several years later, he did come out to his mother, who was in counseling at the time. She was disappointed, but loving nevertheless. She made sure Jerry was on her church's prayer lists. She was welcoming to men her son was in relationships with.

Jerry took much longer to tell his father. His stepmother suspected and confronted Jerry, who admitted his orientation to her. She advised him that telling his father would "kill him," so he continued to keep his secret. When

Jerry's father finally was told, his father was bereft and focused his anger on Jerry's mother, whom he blamed for this outcome. To this day, although Jerry and his father do communicate, his father never wants information about Jerry's relationships and has never visited him (although he visits Jerry's sisters, at much greater distance and despite their less-than-perfect behaviors). Jerry accepts that this is his father's problem and is sad that his father is missing out on knowing his son.

Jerry is now living with his partner in a committed relationship. He misses religion in his life and thinks he may someday find a church where he feels comfortable. His partner's family is very accepting of him, and he is grateful to be treated as a member of the family rather than as a pariah. He still has challenges related to his sexuality. He has difficulty enjoying sex and recognizes that the voice of his childhood saying this is evil is still present at some level. Nevertheless, he is more and more comfortable with himself and is continuing to grow and flourish.

Definitions and Description

The term *LGBTQIA+* (or other combination of similar letters) is an inclusive term attempting to refer to or represent all identities of the community who are lesbian, gay, bisexual, pansexual, transgender, transexual, queer, questioning, intersex, asexual, or ally (County of San Mateo, n.d.; University of California [UC] Davis, LGBTQIA Resource Center, 2023):

- *Lesbian*: Usually, someone who identifies as a woman, whose primary sexual and affectional orientation is toward people of the same gender. However, some nonbinary people also identify as lesbians, often because they have some connection to womanhood and are primarily attracted to women.
- *Gay*: A term used to describe a man who is attracted to men, but often used and embraced by women to describe their same-sex relationships as well. A sexual and affectional orientation toward people of the same gender.
- *Bisexual or bi*: A person whose primary sexual and affectional orientation is toward people of the same and other genders or toward people regardless of their gender. Some people may use *bisexual* and *pansexual* interchangeably.
- *Pansexual or pan*: A person who experiences sexual, romantic, physical, and/or spiritual attraction for members of all gender identities/expressions.
- *Transgender*: A term for people whose gender identity is different from their assigned sex at birth. An adjective used most often as an umbrella term and frequently abbreviated to "trans." Identifying as transgender, or trans, means that one's internal knowledge of gender is different from conventional or cultural expectations based on the sex that person was assigned at birth. While it may refer to a woman who was assigned male at birth or a man who was assigned female at birth, *transgender* is an umbrella term that can also describe someone who identifies as a gender other than woman or man, such as nonbinary, genderqueer, genderfluid, no gender or multiple genders, or some other gender identity.
- *Transexual*: A person whose gender identity is different from their designated sex at birth and has taken steps of physical transition so that their body is congruent to both their gender identity and the conventional concept of sexually male and female bodies.
- *Queer*: An umbrella term to refer to all LGBTQIA+ people; also a political statement, as well as a sexual orientation, which advocates breaking binary thinking and seeing both sexual orientation and gender identity as potentially fluid. Historically, queer has been used as an epithet/slur against the LGBTQIA+ community. Some people have reclaimed the word *queer*

and self-identify in opposition to assimilation. For some, this reclamation is a celebration of not fitting into social norms. Not all people who identify as LGBTQIA use "queer" to describe themselves. For example, those of earlier generations are typically averse to self-identifying as queer. The term is often considered hateful when used by those who do not identify as LGBTQIA.

- *Questioning*: A person in the process of questioning or analyzing their sexual orientation, gender identity, or gender expression.
- *Intersex*: An umbrella term to describe a wide range of natural body variations that do not fit neatly into conventional definitions of male or female. Intersex variations may include, but are not limited to, variations in chromosome compositions, hormone concentrations, and external and internal characteristics. Many visibly intersex people are mutilated in infancy and early childhood by doctors to make their sex characteristics conform to society's idea of what normal bodies should look like. Intersex people are relatively common, although society's denial of their existence has allowed very little room for intersex issues to be discussed publicly. *Hermaphrodite* is an outdated and offensive term that has been used to describe intersex people in the past. People with intersex conditions should not be assumed to be transgender.
- *Asexual*: A broad spectrum of sexual orientations generally characterized by feeling varying degrees of sexual attraction or a desire for partnered sexuality. Asexuality is distinct from celibacy, which is the deliberate abstention from sexual activity, despite sexual desire. Some asexual people do have sex and do experience varying levels of sexual attraction. There are many diverse ways of being asexual. A person who does not experience sexual attraction can experience other forms of attraction such as romantic attraction, physical attraction, and emotional attraction, as these are separate aspects of a person's identity. These may or may not correlate—for instance, some people are physically and romantically attracted to women. However, others might be physically attracted to all genders and only emotionally attracted to men.
- *Ally or allyship*: The action of working to end oppression through support of, and as an advocate for, a group other than one's own. LGBTQIA allyship is the practice of confronting heterosexism, sexism, genderism, allosexism, and monosexism in oneself and others out of self-interest and a concern for the well-being of lesbian, gay, bisexual, transgender, queer, intersex, and asexual people. Is founded on the understanding that dismantling heterosexism, monosexism, trans oppression, trans misogyny, cissexism, and allosexism is a social justice issue.

LGBTQIA+ have sometimes been called an *invisible minority* because their minority status may not be obvious or readily apparent. Like other minorities, they comprise a small proportion of the general population, and are subjected to discrimination and oppression based on this status. Unlike most other minorities LGBTQIA+ individuals must decide whether to reveal this aspect of their identity (Garnets, 2002).

There are other terms that are important in this chapter. *Homophobia* refers to oppression, discrimination, and fear (and possibly hatred) toward members of the LGBTQIA+ community. *Heterosexism* is the belief that heterosexuality is the only acceptable sexual orientation. Heterosexism discounts and/or excludes the needs and life experiences of the LGBTQIA+ community—and gives advantage to heterosexual people (UC Davis, LGBTQIA Resource Center, 2023). *Allosexism* is the belief or assumption that everyone experiences sexual attraction. *Monosexism* is the belief or assumption that people are attracted to only one gender. *Genderism* is the belief that people need to conform to their gender assigned at birth and that there is a binary gender system (only female and male).

We have only scratched the surface of some of the language we consider vital for the helping professional. As a language-based society, having the proper language to speak to clients about their gender and sexual identities will help them to feel seen and validated (GLSEN, n.d.a.). Not using the proper language, not having enough education about current language and terminology, and lacking understanding of LGBTQIA+ lives and experiences can lead to clients feeling disconnected and misunderstood by their counselor. Puckett et al. (2023) found that clients who endorsed this feeling of disconnection and being misunderstood also reported feeling hopeless that therapy would be able to help them within anything they were facing.

Prevalence

Research attempting to assess the prevalence of LGBTQIA+ status relies on self-disclosure of sexual and gender identity and/or behaviors by participants, who may be less than forthcoming given the societal stigma still associated with LGBTQIA+ status. The widely cited statistic of 10% of the population being homosexual was based on Kinsey's landmark study of sexual behavior more than 50 years ago (Kinsey et al., 1948; Kinsey et al., 1953). However, Kinsey's participants were not randomly selected and were interviewed face-to-face, and his methods of determining homosexuality are subject to debate. Only recently have studies used general population surveys and anonymous reporting. In a recent Gallup poll, the percentage of adults in the United States who self-identify as LGBTQIA+ was at just over 7%. This is more than double the percentage from just a decade earlier, and approximately 21% of Generation Z (who have reached adulthood) identify as LGBTQIA+ (Jones, 2022). More specifically, nearly one is six Gen Z adults identify as bisexual.

Jones (2022) attributes this change in identification to Americans reportedly accepting LGBTQIA+ people more, and to the fact that LGBTQIA+ individuals perhaps having more legal protection against discrimination than in previous generations. However, when one looks at legislation being presented in recent years, we are not sure this protection will continue. What is obvious, however, is that younger generations are more likely to self-identify. We do not believe that there are just more LGBTQIA+ people; it just seems that younger generations are more comfortable than older generations in being out (see Table 3.1).

TABLE 3.1. Americans' Self-Identification as LGBTQIA+, by Generation (Jones, 2022)

	LBTQIA+	Straight/Heterosexual	No Response
Generation Z (born 1997–2003)	20.8%	75.7%	3.5%
Millennials (born 1981–1996)	10.5%	82.5%	7.1%
Generation X (born 1965–1980)	4.2%	89.3%	6.5%
Baby boomers (born 1946–1964)	2.6%	90.7%	6.8%
Traditionalists (born before 1946)	0.8%	92.2%	7.1%

Developmental Influences

The primary focus of this section is adolescence, as it is the period of life in which sexual orientation and associated challenges are most salient. Adolescence has been defined as the stage of life that marks the transition from childhood to adulthood. The major life tasks at this stage are developing an identity and attaining autonomy, laying the foundation for finding intimacy and a sense of belonging in young adulthood. LGBTQIA+ adolescents are presented with challenges that are different from those experienced by the sexual majority. They must accomplish their developmental tasks while adjusting to a socially stigmatized identity. When these challenges are confronted within a supportive and accepting cultural environment, the deleterious impact of being different can be minimized. Without such support, LGBTQIA+ adolescents are vulnerable to internalizing a negative sense of self that has lifelong consequences both for the individual and for our society.

Physical, cognitive, emotional, and social changes are striking during adolescence. During this period, the young adolescent may experience dramatic shifts between longing to remain close to family and their need for privacy and strivings for autonomy (Marans & Cohen, 1991). As the adolescent disengages from the intensity of relationships within the family, their attention and energy are increasingly focused on peer relationships. These changes affect the development of an emerging identity, including sexual identity. This occurs whether the adolescent is among LGBTQIA+ or not. The aim of this section is not to reiterate "normal" adolescent development, but to focus on those aspects of adolescent development that are particular to LGBTQIA+ adolescents.

The developmental tasks of LGBTQIA+ adolescents (e.g., of identity, autonomy, belongingness, and intimacy) are complicated by both intrapsychic and interpersonal factors. LGBTQIA+ adolescents may focus their erotic and romantic involvements on members of the same sex. Some become aware of the different-ness of their attractions at a much earlier time in their lives (Tharinger & Wells, 2000); for others this awareness becomes clear only during adolescence or later. Discovering one's different-ness complicates the feelings of estrangement that are typical of adolescence by possibly adding a sense of alienation from peers and family and feelings of shame and secrecy. "Incorporating into one's own self-image the negative feelings associated with the label 'homosexual' ... can cripple hopes and dreams for a productive future. Internalized homophobia may also help explain why gay youth are believed to attempt suicide at rates that are much higher than the rates among their heterosexual peers" (Baker, 2002, p. 6). Because of the need for secrecy about their sexual orientation, many LGBTQIA+ youth lack contact with peers who experience similar feelings, and they may also lack adult role models, thus increasing the sense of isolation. Unlike with heterosexual adolescents, those in the LGBTQIA+ community may have few socially sanctioned opportunities for dating, for open pair bonding, or for sexual experimentation.

Studies beginning in the 1970s have shown that adolescents are engaging in a greater range of sexual behaviors at younger ages than earlier generations. Self-identification as LGBTQIA+ also appears to be occurring at younger ages (Wildman, 2000). Intermittent same-sex sexual behaviors between adolescents do not define those individuals as gay, nor do they necessarily lead to a gay identity. To the benefit of those in the LGBTQIA+ community, cultural barriers against homosexuality have decreased, which allows for achievement of life goals and open social relationships at home, school, and work. This may accelerate the self-identification of LGBTQIA+ youth.

Integration of one's sexual identity into all social roles has been conceptualized as the final outcome of identity development for LGBTQIA+ individuals. It is seen as essential to healthy psychosocial adjustment and psychological well-being (Rostosky & Riggle, 2002). "An individual exploring homosexual interests in adolescence who has a history and repertoire of successful adaptation skills as well as a history of secure attachment will navigate the process—all things being equal—more successfully than the adolescent with a history of poor relational and coping abilities" (Tharinger & Wells, 2000, p. 162). Developmental models of homosexual identity formation have been described by various authors over time (Cass, 1979; Coleman, 1982; Troiden, 1989), which provides a framework for understanding the unique processes experienced by these youths. The disadvantage of these models, however, is the inclination to view them as inflexible, with the expectation that all youth will follow the same linear stages of development. As such, they can be detrimental, just as the assumption of heterosexuality is often detrimental to the developing gay or lesbian child. Further mitigating the usefulness of the developmental models is the fact that some heterosexual youths engage in homosexual behaviors, crushes, and affiliations, and some homosexual youths behave in similar heterosexual ways before their sexual identities have crystallized. With these cautions in mind, Cass's and Troiden's models are outlined.

The first of stage of Cass's model is *identity confusion*, which is when an individual recognizes their thoughts and behaviors as homosexual and is distressed by that awareness. They may seek other explanations or rationalizations for those behaviors and may begin to seek information on homosexuality. The next stage is *identity comparison*, in which the person accepts the possibility of being homosexual. In this stage, the person may accept that they have engaged in homosexual behaviors while still rejecting a homosexual identity. The third stage is *identity tolerance*, characterized by the individual's understanding that they are probably homosexual. In this stage, the person recognizes that being homosexual involves social and emotional components in addition to sexual desire. Typically, persons actively seek out other LGBTQIA+ persons and begins to experience being part of the LGBTQIA+ community. In the next stage, *identity acceptance*, people accept that they are homosexual and become increasing involved with the gay community. This stage is often accompanied by anger toward the antigay elements of society and deceasing interaction with heterosexuals. In stage 5, individuals often adopt a black-and-white view of society (gay or not gay) and seek to immerse themselves in the gay community. It is in this stage that disclosure of sexual orientation to family and others occurs. It is often also at this stage that confrontation with heterosexual society takes place. In the final stage, known as *identity synthesis*, the person has integrated their LGBTQIA+ status with other aspects of identity. Their sexual identity is still important, but there is a more balanced approach to relationships.

Troiden (1989) points to the seminal work of Kinsey by acknowledging that the dichotomous labels of "heterosexual" and "homosexual" are artifacts that do not reflect the reality of sexuality for many people. Individuals vary widely in the degree to which they are attracted to the same or to the opposite sex. In that context, Troiden differentiates between the terms *self-concept* and *identity*. He defines self-concept as a global term that refers to the mental image that one has of themselves. Identity, on the other hand, has a situational context: One is a teacher, a garden club member, a criminal, a Sunday school teacher, and so on. "A homosexual identity is a perception of self as homosexual in relation to romantic or sexual situations" (Troiden, 1989, p. 46). He describes three components of LGBTQIA+ identity: *self-identity* is the view individuals have of themselves as LGBTQIA+ in relation to romantic or sexual situations; *perceived identity* occurs when the individual believes that others know they are LGBTQIA+; and *presented identity* occurs when the individuals announce or present themselves as LGBTQIA+. An LGBTQIA+ identity is most fully realized in situations in which these three identities coincide, "where an agreement exists between who people think they are, who they claim they are, and how others view them" (p. 47).

In describing his stage model of LGBTQIA+ identity formation, Troiden (1989) points out that his postulated stages are general patterns and are not necessarily experienced in a linear fashion. Those people who go through all four stages generally settle into a committed nonheterosexual or noncisgender identity while others may drift away from these stages at any point and ultimately not commit themselves to a nonheterosexual or noncisgender identity.

Stage 1, *sensitization* begins before puberty when individuals have social experiences that give meaning and relevance to their later sexual or gender identity. They begin to see themselves as different from their peers. During this stage, the experience of being different focuses on social and gender roles, rather than specifically on sexuality. The sensitization stage lays a foundation of meaning for the experiences of later stages, in that the nonheterosexual- or noncisgender-identified person later reinterprets past experience as early indicators of a nonheterosexual or noncisgender path.

Stage 2 is *identity confusion*. In most cases after the onset of puberty, consideration is given to the idea that feelings and behaviors could be regarded as nonheterosexual or non-cisgender. No longer able to assume heterosexuality or cisgender identity, the individual experiences ambiguity, turmoil and uncertainty about who they are. "By middle or late adolescence, a perception of self as 'probably' homosexual [sic] begins to emerge" (Troiden, 1989, p. 53). The stigmatization of nonheterosexuality or noncisgender identity, along with inaccurate and inadequate information, a lack of role models, and inaccessibility to others with similar feelings, contributes to the confusion of this stage. Genital and emotional experiences lead to a perception of self as sexually different, not just socially different. A variety of defensive "stigma-management" responses typically occur during this stage, such as denial, heterosexual or cisgender experimentation, psychotherapy to change their orientation, or even taking on anti-LGBTQIA+ attitudes and behaviors.

Stage 3 is *identity assumption*. Occurring typically during or after late adolescence, identity assumption involves self-definition as LGBTQIA+, associating with other LGBTQIA+ individuals, sexual experimentation, and involvement in LGBTQIA+ culture. For lesbians, this stage is usually arrived at in the context of a love relationship, while for a majority of gay males, it is experienced through sexual contacts with other males. Identity assumption brings on negative aspects of membership in a stigmatized group. This can precipitate defensive strategies such as passing as heterosexual or cisgender by concealing sexual or gender preferences from others who might be critical or condemning, or adopting stereotyped behaviors that are gender inappropriate. Affiliating with other people from the LGBTQIA+ community reduces social isolation and provides opportunities for exposure to positive role models, learning strategies for coping with stigma, and feeling support from others.

In the final stage, *commitment*, one realizes that it is less costly to maintain an LGBTQIA+ identity than to try to hide or change it. This involves self-acceptance and comfort with the role and the identity. Internal indications of this stage are the fusion of sexuality, gender, and emotions that allows for entering love relationships, satisfaction with the LGBTQIA+ identity, and increased happiness with this self-definition. Externally, this stage is indicated by entrance into a love relationship, disclosure to others, and adopting more effective stigma-management strategies. Cass's and Troiden's stage models are summarized and compared in Table 3.2.

Peer Relationships

It is during early childhood, before understanding what sexual orientation means, that most people begin to sense how society views homosexuality (Baker, 2002). When children are exposed to antigay rhetoric, they learn that it is acceptable to harass and vilify those in the LGBTQIA+ community. As those in the LGBTQIA+ community gradually become aware that they are different, they learn that this difference is bad and shameful. They become frightened of what their feelings and attractions will mean for their lives. Those youth who are able to keep their feelings hidden are less likely to be targets of taunting and victimization. Thus, being "in the closet" often leads to decreased involvement in school and extracurricular activities. Having only a small network of friends while hiding one's sexuality from parents, siblings, teachers, and peers reinforces a sense of being marginalized (Tharinger & Wells, 2000).

Disclosing one's sexual attractions to others can be a very risky business. Particularly during the identity confusion stage, but continuing in later stages, as previously explained, many keep their feelings secret in order to avoid rejection, harassment, physical abuse by peers and family members. Those who do disclose may choose first to reveal their attractions to a close friend, hoping for understanding and acceptance. Savin-Williams (1998) studied 180 college-aged gay males' recollections of adolescent experiences. He found that fully 50% first disclosed their sexual attractions to a female friend, while one third disclosed to a male best friend. The sexual orientation of the male friends varied; some were known or assumed to be heterosexual, while others

TABLE 3.2. Classic Models of Homosexual Identity Development

Cass (1979)		Troiden (1989)	
Stage	Description	Stage	Description
Identity confusion	Recognizes one's thoughts, behaviors as homosexual; is distressed by that awareness	Sensitization	Prepubescent social experiences lead to awareness of being different from others of same gender.
Identity comparison	Accepts possibility of being homosexual but rejects identity	Identity confusion	After puberty, one recognizes feelings and behaviors are probably homosexual, leading to turmoil and uncertainty.
Identity tolerance	Accepts probability of being homosexual; broadens understanding	Identity assumption	During or after late adolescence, defines self as homosexual, associates with homosexuals, experiments sexually; experiences being stigmatized.
Identity acceptance	Accepts homosexual identity, becomes involved in gay community; rejects heterosexual society; comes out	Commitment	Accepts and is comfortable with homosexual identity. Fusion of erotic and emotional components; enters love relationship.
Identity synthesis	Homosexuality integrated with other elements of identity		

were gay friends or gay sexual partners. The remaining youths made their first disclosure either to family members or to a supportive adult, such as a therapist.

Intrapsychic Effects

In general, it is believed that theories of development apply to all individuals, regardless of later sexual identity. In looking at the unique challenges to the development of people in the LGBTQIA+ community, it is useful to consider the impact of early childhood attachment on their ability to integrate a healthy sexual identity. As Tharinger and Wells (2000) point out, there is little evidence to suggest that the quality of earliest attachment relationships to caregivers differs between gay and nongay children. As the child grows, and the evidence suggesting same-sex attractions mounts, however, there is a potential for disruption of the attachment as both parties (parent and child) come to terms with this emerging stigmatized reality. The ability of a child to adjust to their LGBTQIA+ status is influenced by the early attachment experiences. In their provocative work, Tharinger and Wells looked at LGBTQIA+ individuals who, upon disclosure of their attractions to parents, experienced rejection. Those with secure attachment histories experienced the rejection of parents with greater difficulty than those whose attachment experience was insecure. Integrating the new reality (rejection) that was different from their previous secure attachment was difficult. The parental rejection is so upsetting to the previously secure child that future development may be compromised. For those with histories of insecure parental attachment, upon experiencing the rejection of their parents because of their sexual attractions, they integrated the rejection as "more of the same," and they seemed to not have as much difficulty with the rejection as their securely attached peers. It may be that those with secure early attachment experiences are more prone to acting out than are those whose attachment is insecure. This appears to be only a temporary phenomenon, however, as there is general agreement that secure attachment is a better foundation for healthy psychological and emotional development than is insecure attachment.

Acting Out

Although many LGBTQIA+ youth have fared well and even flourished in school, evidence indicates that, as a group, these students are at higher risk in several important ways. LGBTQIA+ youth who reported high levels of victimization at school had higher levels of substance use, suicidal behaviors, and sexual risk taking than similarly victimized heterosexual peers (Bontempo & D'Augelli, 2002). LGBTQIA+ youth attempt suicide at a rate that is three times that of their heterosexual peers (GLSEN, n.d.b.), and their attempts are more lethal, with three times as many requiring medical intervention. In 1989, suicide was the leading cause of death among LGBTQIA+ youth (Besner & Spungin, 1995), and LGBTQIA+ youth accounted for up to 30% of all completed adolescent suicides (American Academy of Pediatrics, 1993; Morrison & L'Heureux, 2001; O'Conor, 1994). LGBTQIA+ adolescents display suicidal ideation, plan and attempt earlier than heterosexual adolescents, and progress faster from suicidal ideation to plan (Luk et al., 2021).

LGBTQIA+ students are three times as likely to miss school than their heterosexual or gender-normative classmates, often due to fears of harassment and physical harm at school due to their sexual orientation or gender expression (GLSEN, n.d.b.). They also drop out of school at a disproportionate rate (Herr, 1997). Further, these students have been less successful academically compared to heterosexual students (GLSEN, 2022). LGBTQIA+ students who experienced discrimination at school had lower GPAs, were more likely to have been disciplined at school, and had lower levels of self-esteem and sense of belonging—and higher levels of depression (GLSEN, 2022).

The Massachusetts Youth Risk Behavior Survey found significantly higher rates of substance abuse among nonheterosexual youth compared to other youth (Human Rights Watch [HRW], 2001). The survey found that these adolescents were more likely to use drugs prior to the age of 13 and to have a higher lifetime use of illegal drugs (Siecus, 2001). Risky sexual behavior has also been found to be more prevalent in LGBTQIA+ adolescents (HRW, 2001). LGBTQIA+ youth are over-represented among the homeless, with studies finding from 16% to 40% of homeless youth identifying as LGBTQIA+. These youth are at increased risk for sexually transmitted diseases because many resort to trading sex for survival needs.

School Issues

According to GLSEN's (n.d.b.) School Climate Survey in 2021, nearly 82% of LGBTQIA+ students feel unsafe in school because of a perceived hostile attitude toward their actual or perceived personal characteristics. Schools can be a hostile environment, and the majority of LGBTQIA+ students routinely hear anti-LGBTQIA+ language—and they experience victimization and discrimination while at school. As mentioned, a large number of LGBTQIA+ students miss school and avoid school activities.

The School Climate Survey also reported that 90% of LGBTQIA+ students heard homophobic remarks, and 92% heard negative remarks about gender expression (from students and teachers or other school staff). Only approximately 10% reported that school personnel intervened when hearing a homophobic remark or negative remark about gender expression; 76% of LGBTQIA+ students experienced verbal harassment at school, and 31% were physically harassed at school.

We do not yet know how much impact recent legislation around "parents' bills of rights" will have on the school climate, but it does not appear favorable in terms of increasing feelings of safety for LGBTQIA+ students in schools.

Family Issues

Disclosure of sexual orientation to parents and other family members is a significant milestone in the life of LGBTQIA+ adolescents, but it is also a major event for parents. Parental reactions to the disclosure vary, from responses that are loving and supportive to those that reject the sexual orientation, or the person. Often the negative responses from parents are rooted in the erroneous belief that they are responsible for their child's sexual attractions. "Families react with shame and guilt to homosexuality in a child partly because of the widespread belief that homosexuality is the result of bad parenting" (Hetrick & Martin, 1987, p. 41.) The conflict that results from this belief can be damaging to the youth and to the family and may become a source of family violence or even ejection of the adolescent from the home. One study (Hunter, 1990) found that more than half (61%) of the violence that all LGBTQIA+ youths experience occurs in the home; another (Pilkington & D'Augelli, 1995) found that one third of their sample of LGBTQIA+ youth had been verbally abused because of their sexuality, and 10% physically assaulted, in the home. In her review of this lamentable situation, Morrow (1993) points out that family members, like LGBTQIA+ youths themselves, suffer from a lack of accurate information about homosexuality. Furthermore, many family members may experience a normal period of grief over losing the previously presumed heterosexuality of their child. Given time, these families can learn better coping skills in dealing with their child's homosexuality.

In his proposals for family therapy as a modality to assist in the coming out process, Lasala (2000) reiterates that it is considered psychologically healthy for LGBTQIA+ youths to come out of the closet. He also notes the shock, disappointment, and shame that many parents feel when they learn of a son or daughter's sexual orientation. Disclosure often precipitates a painful family crisis, which can lead to serious disruption of relationships among family members. Parents must grieve and obtain accurate information about the LGBTQIA+ community. LGBTQIA+ individuals need support as they struggle to cope with their parents' negative reactions. Lasala suggests that during family therapy, family members should be coached to maintain noncombative communication following the disclosure, even if contacts are initially brief and superficial.

LGBTQIA+ Adults

Like their heterosexual or cisgender peers, adulthood for those in the LGBTQIA+ community is usually focused on work and family and balancing the two. For the LGBTQIA+ community, the issues they may face in adulthood are very much a function of the historical period in which they developed. To Kimmel and Sang (1995), the impact of the demonstrations at the Stonewall bar in 1969 and the later AIDS epidemic were profound. Stonewall "began to change the social construction of homosexuality from a personal pathology to minority group membership" (Kimmel & Sang, 1995, p. 190). LGBTQIA+ Pride Month is celebrated in June each year in honor of the Stonewall uprising.

Stonewall Riots: On June 27, 1969, police raided a popular gay bar (Stonewall Inn) in New York City. Patrons resisted, and a "riot" ensued. This event marked the beginning of the "gay liberation movement."

Close to 50 years later, in 2016, the Pulse nightclub shooting was one of the deadliest mass shootings in the history of the United States, and certainly the deadliest attack on the LGBTQIA+ community. On June 12, 2016, a gunman opened fire in the Pulse nightclub, a gay club in Orlando, Florida, killing 49 people and injuring more than 50. It was "Latin night" at the nightclub, and the majority of people killed were LGBTQIA+ people of color.

Since the Pulse nightclub shooting, other events have had a significant impact on the LGBTQIA+ community and have impacted the issues that LGBTQIA+ adults face. While president of the United States, Donald Trump banned transgender Americans from serving in the armed forces. Various states and organizations have banned trans students and athletes from competing in school sports. Many states have adopted or attempted to adopt anti-LGBTQIA+ legislation. However, the U.S. Supreme Court affirmed that LGBTQIA+ people are protected under the Civil Rights Act from discrimination in the workplace (NPR, 2021).

Some gay men and lesbians do not come out until middle adulthood and may have been in heterosexual marriages. Their adult experience will be different from those of adults who came out in adolescence and early adulthood and have lived their lives as a member of the LGBTQIA+ community. Those who do not disclose their homosexuality until middle adulthood may feel the need to learn new social skills and may face turmoil from the effects of the disclosure on family members.

For midlife LGBTQIA+ individuals, social support and a sense of belonging may come from friends and the LGBTQIA+ community to a greater degree than from family. Even for those who have been out to their families for years, there may be a sense that they cannot be fully understood or fully themselves except by others like themselves.

Parenting

According to the 2021 American Community Survey, there were 1,209,462 households identified as headed by same-sex couples (711,129 married couples, 498,333 unmarried partner couples; U.S. Census Bureau, 2023). Only in recent years has parenting been an option for LGBTQIA+ individuals and couples. Previously, parenthood was considered the domain of heterosexuals. Gay men and lesbian couples who were parents generally had children from previous heterosexual relationships or had become single parents by choice. Gay families were often subject to discrimination, ranging from unkind remarks to loss of legal custody. Adoption by someone from the LGBTQIA+ community was rarely allowed. While society has not yet advanced to full acceptance of alternative models of the family, there are more and more LGBTQIA+ people who choose to raise children. This section will present some of the unique challenges faced by those individuals, some of which may bring them to the counselor's office.

First, it is important to address the widespread misconceptions about LGBTQIA+ parents. Children of sexual or gender minority parents fare as well as, or better than, children raised by straight parents (Hart, 2023). What has been found is that it is the warm relationship with parents (or lack thereof) that affects a child's adjustment, not the sexual orientation or gender identity of the parents. In addition, children of same-sex parents are no more likely to be homosexual or bisexual than children from heterosexual families (Schumm & Crawford, 2019).

Different issues emerge in families depending on the way children came into the family. Some families headed by same-sex parents were created when a LGBTQIA+ person had children in a previous heterosexual relationship or marriage and then formed a new relationship with a same-sex partner. In other cases, gay men or lesbians become parents via artificial insemination, surrogacy, or adoption. Because families with LGBTQIA+ parents are still stigmatized, not least by a sometimes very complicated legal recognition of their status as a family (Shapiro, 2020), LGBTQIA+ parents may be less confident in the role of parents, particularly when they are not the child's biological parent. The nonbiological parent, who may have a complicated legal parental status, may be reluctant to invest fully in the parental role, fearing they will lose the child if the relationship ends or the biological parent dies (Martin, 1998). This emotional distance is likely to have an effect on children and may create problems in the relationship.

In families in which children were born in the context of a heterosexual marriage, the challenge, in addition to the task of helping the child deal with parental divorce, may be telling the child in an age-appropriate manner that the parent is gay, lesbian, transgender, or other sexual minority. The parent may fear rejection by their children if they tell them about their status. If this disclosure comes closely on the announcement about a divorce or separation, children may feel emotionally overwhelmed. Depending on the age of children, they may be aware of the social stigma of being a member of the LGBTQIA+ community and may fear the consequences for their own social relationships. How and when to come out to children is a delicate decision, and Martin

(1998) advocates that disclosure wait until custody arrangements are secure and the parents are able to present the information about their status in a positive way.

For those who chose parenting via donor insemination, surrogacy, or adoption, there are unique issues to be addressed. Aware of the numerous decisions to be made in these situations, some may seek assistance from a counselor. For couples who elect to have a child via insemination or surrogacy, there are numerous decisions about the identity of the donor and to whom that should be revealed. If the sperm donor is known to the couple, his role with respect to the child must be defined. If the donor is anonymous, the developing child will not have access to answers about their biological father. In the case of a surrogate mother, she cannot be anonymous, and her role must also be defined. For LGBTQIA+ individuals who choose adoption, finding an adoption agency that is knowledgeable about this population is essential. In some states, both parents may not be legally recognized, which can create a new set of challenges. Counselors can help clients work through the decision-making processes and the feelings associated with all these concerns.

It is also important for counselors to remember that when the child of a same-sex couple is referred for counseling, the sexual orientation of the parents may not be a central issue (Martin, 1998). Although it is important for the counselor to pay attention to how the family configuration may be related to the presenting issue, it is also important to avoid assuming that whatever problem there is must be caused by the sexual orientation of the parents.

LGBTQIA+ Elderly

Older adults often feel that ageism is commonplace, and that elders are devalued in American society. For the older LGBTQIA+ person, the discrimination and prejudice has dual sources. As with LGBTQIA+ persons in middle adulthood, the issues for LGBTQIA+ adults will vary with the historical context in which they have lived. Prior to the Stonewall riots in 1969, there was a social climate that stigmatized gays and lesbians as perverted and evil and forced them to conceal their identity or contend with prevalent discrimination. Recall that until 1973, homosexuality was listed as a psychiatric disorder.

The coming out process can be seen as a major developmental transition (Reid, 1973) that provides inner resources and develops strength, which can then be utilized to adapt to other challenges, such as those associated with aging. Friend (1991) has proposed a theory of successful aging for gay men and lesbians, in which achieving a positive identity as an openly gay man or lesbian provides an advantage for adaptation to the physical, psychological, and social changes that are inherent in the aging process. He suggests that because the social environment for older gay men and lesbians was one of negative evaluation, those individuals who were able to reject that evaluation and create a positive personal identity as a gay or lesbian have strength of character and self-esteem that transfers to other life challenges. Friend calls those who have achieved this positive personal identity "affirmative" individuals because they have adjusted well despite a less-than-supportive social context. For those older gay men and lesbians who accepted the negative evaluation promoted by the social environment, Friend posits two outcomes: (a) keeping one's sexual identity a secret and living with internalized homophobia and self-hate and (b) attempting to live their lives as heterosexuals.

Research has found that older gay men and lesbians vary in their adaptation to aging, as do their heterosexual contemporaries. There are, however, several unique aspects of aging that confront older gay men. The gay subculture often idolized youth (Reid, 1973), so older gay men see themselves as old at a younger age than do their straight peers. If LGBTQIA+ elders never had children, they may miss the support and assistance that children often provide aging parents. They may have to confront archaic policies of hospitals and nursing homes that do not consider them to be family, and the absence of legal status may marginalize their role in end-of-life decision-making for partners.

Younger LGBTQIA+ people today are more likely to access or receive affirmative support, as opposed to LGBTQIA+ elders (NBCC, 2023b). LGBTQIA+ elders are more likely to feel isolated and therefore suffer the physical and emotional effects of isolation. Also, because of barriers to employment and affirmative health care, older LGBTQIA+ clients are more likely to seek unlicensed medical care. Specifically, older transwomen may have received harmful medical treatments or injections (NBCC, 2023b).

It is suggested that counselors keep a developmental perspective in mind when working with older LGBTQIA+ clients. The counselor must consider the individual developmental stage (e.g. Erikson's integrity versus despair), the developmental stage of a couple for the partnered client, and any discrepancies between the developmental stages of a couple. Considering these aspects of development would be useful for working with any older client but are particularly important with aging LGBTQIA+ clients.

Loneliness is an issue for many older adults as friends and partners die. Sang (1992) pointed out that older lesbian women often prefer to socialize with other lesbians and may not have access to that social group. Sang recommends that the counselor explore with the older lesbian client who is lonely whether she is isolated because of real circumstances or because she fears exploring new relationships due to fears of rejection or limited social skills. For the trans community, there are no known neighborhoods in the United States where transpeople can live (and live safely) among other members of the transgender or gender nonbinary community. This means that safety may only be expected in their own living space (which is still not a guarantee; NBCC, 2023b).

Assessment

Because LGBTQIA+ status is not a disorder, assessment is not an issue. Any assessment the counselor might use would relate to the reason the person is seeking treatment. However, the clinician must be alert to the impact of sexual orientation on the presenting problem. One must also be sensitive to subtle ways assessment forms may reflect heterosexism; forms that ask for name of spouse convey the message that marriage is the only acceptable form of coupleship, thereby discounting the gay clientele. Checking assessment forms and other documents for discriminatory wording is essential to convey a message of acceptance.

Treatment

Below are some guidelines and models for practice.

Guidelines for Effective Treatment of LGBTQIA+ Clients

The American Psychological Association (2021) published guidelines that provide context and information for providing services to LGBTQIA+ clients. These guidelines are consistent with ethical principles of counselors and with the policies of other mental health professional organizations. The counselor or social worker who follows these guidelines is assured of ethical practice with this clientele. We have left the word *psychologists* used in the guidelines as authored, but the reader can easily substitute the word *counselor* or *helping professional* and find them applicable. The American Psychological Association has developed guidelines for practice with sexual minority persons (APA, 2021) and guidelines for practice with transgender and gender nonconforming people (APA, 2015).

The guidelines for practice with sexual minority persons are as follows:

- Psychologists understand that people have diverse sexual orientations that intersect with other identities and contexts.
- Psychologists distinguish issues of sexual orientation from those of gender identity and expression when working with sexual minority persons.
- Psychologists strive to affirm bi+ identities and examine their mono-sexist biases.
- Psychologists understand that sexual minority orientations are not mental illnesses and that efforts to change sexual orientations cause harm.
- Psychologists recognize the influence of institutional discrimination that exists for sexual minority persons and the need to promote social change.
- Psychologists understand the influence that distal minority stressors have on sexual minority persons and the need to promote social change.
- Psychologists recognize the influence that proximal minority stressors have on the mental, physical, and psychosocial health of sexual minority persons.
- Psychologists recognize the positive aspects of being a sexual minority person and the individual and collective ways that sexual minority persons display resilience and resistance to stigma and oppression.
- Psychologists strive to be knowledgeable about and respect diverse relationships among sexual minority persons.
- Psychologists recognize the importance and complexity of sexual health in the lives of sexual minority persons.
- Psychologists strive to understand sexual minority persons' relationships with their families of origin, as well as their families of choice.
- Psychologists strive to understand the experiences, challenges, and strengths faced by sexual minority parents and their children.
- Psychologists strive to understand the educational and school system experiences that impact sexual minority students in K–12 and college/university settings.
- Psychologists strive to understand career development and workplace issues for sexual minority persons.
- Psychologists strive to educate themselves and others on psychological issues relevant to sexual minority persons and to utilize that knowledge to improve training programs and educational systems.
- Psychologists strive to take an affirming stance toward sexual minority persons and communities in all aspects of planning, conduct, dissemination, and application of research to reduce health disparities and promote psychological health and well-being.

The guidelines for practice with transgender or gender nonconforming people are as follows:

- Psychologists understand that gender is a nonbinary construct that allows for a range of gender identities and that a person's gender identity may not align with sex assigned at birth.
- Psychologists understand that gender identity and sexual orientation are distinct but interrelated constructs.
- Psychologists seek to understand how gender identity intersects with the other cultural identities of transgender and gender nonconforming (TGNC) people.
- Psychologists are aware of how their attitudes about and knowledge of gender identity and gender expression may affect the quality of care they provide to TGNC people and their families.
- Psychologists recognize how stigma, prejudice, discrimination, and violence affect the health and well-being of TGNC people.

- Psychologists strive to recognize the influence of institutional barriers on the lives of TGNC people and to assist in developing TGNC-affirmative environments.
- Psychologists understand the need to promote social change that reduces the negative effects of stigma on the health and well-being of TGNC people.
- Psychologists working with gender-questioning and TGNC youth understand the different developmental needs of children and adolescents and that not all youth will persist in a TGNC identity into adulthood.
- Psychologists strive to understand both the particular challenges that TGNC elders experience and the resilience they can develop.
- Psychologists strive to understand how mental health concerns may or may not be related to a TGNC person's gender identity and the psychological effects of minority stress.
- Psychologists recognize that TGNC people are more likely to experience positive life outcomes when they receive social support or trans-affirmative care.
- Psychologists strive to understand the effects that changes in gender identity and gender expression have on the romantic and sexual relationships of TGNC people.
- Psychologists seek to understand how parenting and family formation among TGNC people take a variety of forms.
- Psychologists recognize the potential benefits of an interdisciplinary approach when providing care to TGNC people and strive to work collaboratively with other providers.
- Psychologists respect the welfare and rights of TGNC participants in research and strive to represent results accurately and avoid misuse or misrepresentation of findings.
- Psychologists seek to prepare trainees in psychology to work competently with TGNC people.

Affirmative Practice

Affirmative practice models provide guidelines for working with the LGBTQIA+ community. An absence of homophobia is not enough to practice affirmatively with the LGBTQIA+ community. Practicing affirmatively requires that clinicians validate and celebrate LGBTQIA+ identities. The clinician works with LGBTQIA+ clients to help them develop positive identities. The practice affirms LGBTQIA+ identity as a human experience that is as positive and valid of an experience as heterosexuality or being gender normative (Crisp, 2006). It is intended for the clinician to counteract any lifelong messages of homophobia, heterosexism, or genderism.

Appleby and Anastas (1998) provide six principles toward this type of practice, specific to sexuality:

- Do not assume that a client is heterosexual.
- Believe that homophobia in the client and society is the problem rather than sexual orientation.
- Accept an identity as a gay, lesbian, or bisexual person as a positive outcome of the helping process.
- Work with clients to decrease internalized homophobia that they may be experiencing so that clients can achieve a positive identity as a gay or lesbian person.
- Become knowledgeable about different theories of the coming-out process for gay men and lesbians.
- Deal with one's own homophobia and heterosexual bias.

Welcoming LGBTQIA+ Clients

LGBTQIA+ individuals are likely to be cautious about revealing their sexual orientation or gender expression to a counselor for fear they will be rejected or judged. They may be uncertain about the counselor's commitment to confidentiality. To avert some of the fear associated with client self-disclosure, the counselor may wish to provide evidence of their openness to discussion. One way to do this is to include posters or other material that proclaims one's commitment to diversity, specifically including the LGBTQIA+ community. Reading materials and literature, when available, should include content that addresses this clientele. The counselor's professional disclosure statement should be written so as to make it clear that the counselor is willing to work with clients of all diverse groups.

Clients will be alert to subtle ways the counselor may communicate heterosexism or genderism. For example, in an initial interview, counselors may inquire about romantic relationships. Asking a female client about a "boyfriend" or a male about a "girlfriend" conveys the assumption that same-gender relationships are not acceptable. The counselor can avoid that perception by referring to "romantic interests" or "significant others" in questions about this area of functioning.

Puckett et al. (2023) found that counselors can help facilitate coping by simply listening and being a witness to clients' internal experiences. Clients felt affirmed when their counselors provided empathy and validation of their experiences. As with all other types of counseling, the relationship between therapist and client is of upmost importance. Pucket et al. (2023) provide some additional suggestions:

- Integrate aspects of the client's identity or the systems and context in which they are living.
- Highlight how clients' experiences may be connected to systems of oppression.
- Stay informed about political and social events that are related to or impact the LGBTQIA+ community and acknowledge these in session, if appropriate. Discuss how these events may impact their well-being.

A counselor or other mental health professional should strive to increase the comfort of all clients. Counselors should ensure that their offices and work settings are welcoming and respectful to all people. Display LGBTQIA+-affirmative resources and signage and eliminate any items that may relay anti-LGBTQIA+ attitudes. Pay close attention to names and pronouns that are used, and ask when appropriate. Be careful not to assume gender identity or expression and use inclusive language when possible. Model allyship. Counselor information on websites, business cards, and email signatures can be changed to include the counselor's pronouns. If counseling an individual who is transgender, the professional should not "dead-name" their client (to call a transgender person by their birth name when they have changed their name as a part of their gender transition). A counselor may want to give some attention to paperwork, questionnaires, and forms that are used as a part of their work and attempt to communicate respect through subtle changes in language. Paperwork requesting demographic information should be inclusive and cover a range of gender identities. When possible, the environment could be altered to be more inclusive (e.g., gender-neutral restrooms).

Conversion or Reparative Therapy = Explicitly Condemned

Conversion or reparative therapy is an intervention with the goal of changing a homosexual orientation to a heterosexual one. We primarily mention this because of the history of its use over time, but it is indeed a condemned practice, yet we still surprisingly hear of its use. A coalition of 10 organizations, including the American Counseling Association, the American Psychological Association (2005), the American Academy of Pediatrics, and several educational professional organizations published a fact sheet in response to the promotion of conversion or reparative therapies.

The publication includes this statement: "Health and mental health professional organizations do not support efforts to change young people's sexual orientation through 'reparative therapy' and have raised serious concerns about its potential to do harm" (p. 6).

Issues of Diversity

Cultural attitudes regarding LGBTQIA+ people are important considerations when working with individuals with diverse cultural backgrounds. Remember that individuals within a culture vary widely in their identification with the cultural beliefs and practices, so counselors must avoid making any assumptions based solely on an individual's culture. Knowing about cultural differences does allow the counselor to inquire sensitively about how cultural factors may be involved.

Ethnic Minorities and LGBTQIA+ Status

Ethnic minority LGBTQIA+ persons are "minorities within minorities" (Greene, 1997, p. 232). For some, their experience coping with racism and discrimination as a person of color may have provided skills with which to manage the additional burden of LGBTQIA+ status. On the other hand, they may find themselves the victims of racism within the LGBTQIA+ community and homophobia within the cultural community, essentially limiting their ability to experience a secure sense of belonging to either group.

Native and Indigenous Americans

Native American conceptions of homosexuality are quite different from those of the majority culture. These differences are reflected in the 168 native languages currently spoken in the United States that have words for people who are neither male nor female (Tafoya, 1997). Because the native terms were not directly translatable into English, the term *two-spirited* is now used by many to describe those who have both male and female spirits (Jacobs et al., 1997). In most native cultures, two-spiritedness is not solely a function of sexual orientation, but it includes one's social and spiritual identity. Those native youth who are in contact with or influenced by the dominant culture may feel forced to decide if they are either homosexual or heterosexual. In fact, Tafoya notes that, perhaps as a reflection of the more fluid concepts of sexuality and relationships, there is a higher reported rate of heterosexual experience in American Indian gays and lesbians than in other ethnic groups.

Tafoya (1997) also notes that in pre-Columbian times, two-spirited people were highly valued in many native tribes and were accorded positions of high status. With the advent of European culture and values, many of which were inculcated in vulnerable youth via the federal boarding school system, some tribes have adopted the homophobic attitudes of the dominant culture.

Black and African Americans

Being both a person of color and LGBTQIA+, and holding multiple marginalized identities, can magnify discrimination (Human Rights Campaign, 2019). In African American communities, family ties are typically strong and extensive, as the notion of family includes aunts, uncles, grandparents, and so on to a greater degree than in some other groups. In addition, gender roles have been quite flexible, perhaps as a legacy of the more egalitarian African cultures, and also as a response to racism, which made it difficult for African American males to find employment and take on the stereotypical role of provider in the dominant European culture (Greene, 1997). Religion plays a large role in the lives of many African Americans.

Greene (1997) reported that Black and African American gays and lesbians view the Black and African American community as very homophobic. One explanation for that attitude is the strong influence of Christian religious groups that use selective biblical references to justify this position. In addition, the perceived shortage of potential African American marriageable males may support a bias against gays, while the importance of bearing children would mitigate against lesbians. The Human Rights Campaign (2019) reports that 47% of Black or African American LGBTQIA+ youth have been taunted or mocked by a family member, and 59% say their families make them feel bad because of their identity. Only 19% say they can be themselves at home, and only 26% have had a family member get involved in the LGBTQIA+ community (being an ally).

These negative attitudes toward LGBTQIA+ individuals in the African American community discourages many from coming out to their African American families and friends, thus depriving them of important sources of support. Because their allegiance to the African American community is primary for many, they may be reluctant to identify with the LGBTQIA+ community, thus lacking support there as well. Interestingly, in their study of intimate relationships in African American lesbians and gay males, Peplau et al. (1997) found that one third of their participants were in inter-racial relationships, with gay men more likely to be in inter-racial relationships than lesbian women, and that such relationships are more common among homosexual than heterosexual African Americans. These researchers speculate that when gay or lesbian African Americans move into urban areas with more active LGBTQIA+ communities, they are more likely to meet and form partnerships with those of other races.

Latinx Americans

In addition to differences in country of origin, Latinx in the United States differ on the degree of acculturation to the majority culture. Thus, readers must be cautious about making assumptions based on these generalizations.

Two characteristics of Latinx culture bear on the current issue: the centrality of family and the relatively rigid gender roles. One clue to the cultural attitudes toward LGBTQIA+ status is found in the language. There are no words to for lesbian or gay men that do not have pejorative implications. According to Greene (1997), same-sex sexual contact, especially among males, is not always met with disapproval, but overt expression of a gay or lesbian identity is unacceptable.

Some experts believe that homophobia in the Latinx community is stronger than that in the dominant culture. For some Latinx people, being openly gay or lesbian is seen as a betrayal of the family and the culture. On the other hand, families often tolerate a family member who is gay or lesbian, allowing them to maintain family ties without acknowledging or accepting their LGBTQIA+ identity. The fear of being ostracized from family and culture can coexist with a desire to express one's sexual identity, causing significant stress for such individuals.

Morales (1992) describes *states* (as opposed to stages, which imply an orderly and linear progression) experienced by Latinx LGBTQIA+ people as they attempt to resolve their multiple identities:

- *Denial of conflicts*: The individual minimizes or denies the discrimination they experience as a dual minority (ethnic and sexual). In this state, they may have an idealized picture of an accepting society in which they are welcome. For those who seek counseling in this state, Morales (1992) recommends helping the client create a more realistic picture of their position in society and helping them reframe their multiple identities as assets.
- *Bisexual versus gay or lesbian*: In this state, some Latinx LGBTQIA+ persons choose to identify as bisexual, believing that this identity is less negatively treated. Some also view sexuality

more broadly than behavior and may consider themselves bisexual even though all their partners have been of their own sex. A further reason for identification as bisexual is that the gay and lesbian community may be seen as racist. A counselor can assist clients in this state by helping them recognize the depression and hopelessness inherent in this state and by helping them find a supportive community where they can feel safe as both a sexual and ethnic minority.

- *Conflicts in allegiances*: When uncertain about whether one can integrate ethnic and LGBTQIA+ identities, one strategy is to attempt to separate the two to avoid anxiety. The tension that accompanies this conflict can be debilitating, so the counselor working with clients in this state will want to help them see a multicultural perspective in which they can operate from the identity that best fits the given situation and context.
- *Establishing priorities in allegiances*: In this state, LGBTQIA+ Latinx's primary identity is their ethnic identity. Typically, they express anger at rejection by the LGBTQIA+ community because of their ethnicity. When a client is in this state, the counselor might focus on how the person identifies themself, encouraging Latinx rather than "minority," which suggests oppression. The counselor might also encourage developing a social network with other Latinx gays and lesbians and seeking support from others.
- *Integrating the various communities*: In this state, the focus is on how to integrate the multiple identities into a multicultural perspective. For some LGBTQIA+ Latinx, the risk of coming out and revealing yet another status that may result in mistreatment or rejection is a major one. The counselor can validate clients' skill in making judgments about where, when, and to whom to come out, while also encouraging clients to rely on the support systems they have created.

Morales (1992) stressed that individuals may revisit these states multiple times and may in fact present elements of more than one trait at any given time.

Asian Americans

Most of what has been discussed in the literature about LGBTQIA+ Asian Americans is based on those with Chinese or Japanese ancestry. Applicability to other Asian groups is uncertain. In traditional Asian cultures, obedience to family, respect for elders, and clear gender and generational distinctions are important cultural features. Men pass on the family name by marrying and having children, and women are identified with their roles of daughter, wife, and mother. Sex is a taboo topic and is not discussed openly. Although men may have sexual relations with other men, they are not necessarily considered gay. A gay or lesbian identity is viewed as a threat to traditional values and roles. Bringing shame to the family is to be avoided at all costs (Greene, 1997). Therefore, a gay or lesbian Asian American would likely struggle with the conflicts inherent in being both Asian American and LGBTQIA+.

Chan (1995) emphasizes the distinction between public and private selves, which is an important feature of Chinese culture. The public self is prescribed by one's roles within the family. Interestingly, in the two main Chinese languages, individual names are rarely used. People are referred to by the family role: first daughter, third son, little sister. In the same vein, there is no concept of sexual identity in traditional Chinese culture, in that sex is part of the private self. One's sexuality must not interfere with one's prescribed role in the family.

As a result of these values, Chan (1995) believes Asian American gays and lesbians are more likely to come out to non-Asians. In her study, many participants had not come out to their parents although they had been out to others for an average of 6 years.

Jewish Americans

Persons of the Jewish faith and LGBTQIA+ people have several commonalities, the most obvious of which is their physical invisibility. That is, neither is readily identifiable, which provides the option to "pass." The ability brings with it an internal struggle over whether to proclaim one's identity (either cultural or sexual) publicly and risk the racism and discrimination, or to avoid discrimination by denying one's identity. As Dworkin (1997) so aptly put it, "A Jew struggles with the Christian assumptions of society and a lesbian struggles with the heterosexual assumptions of society. Jews experience oppression at the hands of the dominant culture, and so do lesbians" (p. 75).

Religious (Orthodox) Jews condemn homosexuality, but the more liberal traditions (conservative and reform) often welcome LGBTQIA+ congregants, although they may be excluded from important roles in the synagogue. One reason for the opposition to homosexuality is the strong need to increase the community and bear children, which those in the LGBTQIA+ are assumed not to do. There are now LGBTQIA+ synagogues that integrate new prayers with the traditional liturgy. These prayers acknowledge that people from the LGBTQIA+ community also died in the Holocaust and also acknowledge the loss of life to AIDS.

There is an excellent resource online for those who may be looking for synagogues, rabbis, or other Jewish organizations that display a commitment to belonging and equality for the LGBTQIA+ community: Keshet (https://www.keshetonline.org/).

Persons With Disabilities

It is essential to keep in mind several factors when thinking about or working with LGBTQIA+ persons with disabilities. First, neither of these statuses (ability or sexual orientation) is a psychological disorder. Second, the focus of counseling for these persons may be neither the disability nor the sexual orientation. Although both disability and LGBTQIA+ status are often misunderstood, and both may be the target of discrimination and stigmatization, it is essential not to make assumptions when such a client comes for counseling. Finally, while both of these statuses may be invisible, it is also possible that one is apparent and the other not, so it is important to inquire about all potentially relevant information when conducting intake interviews with all clients.

Much of the scant literature addressing LGBTQIA+ individuals with disabilities focuses on a specific subgroup (e.g., lesbians with physical disabilities or deaf gay men). Most of the implications for counselors apply across disabilities, so in the interest of space, our discussion will be quite general in this regard. We include some useful references at the end of the chapter.

From their in-depth interviews with 25 White lesbian women with physical disabilities, Hunt et al. (2006) learned about their experiences with counseling. While some reported experiences were positive and others negative, themes were extracted that inform counselors about what factors were important to this clientele. First, the overall counseling skills of the clinician were of central importance. The cultural sensitivity of counselors was noted by many participants, who desired to be completely understood by the counselor and to feel confident that the counselor could be helpful. Several of the participants had experiences with counselors who seemed to hold stereotypical views of lesbians or disabled people, and other counselors did not appear to have needed information. Other clients arrived at first appointments to find information forms that subtly reflect assumptions of heterosexuality, which offended the participants.

One theme expressed by participants we think is particularly important for counselors to heed. They did not expect counselors to be knowledgeable about every disability—there are simply too many—but they did value an overall appreciation of how disabilities affect individuals, and most of all a willingness to learn on the part of the counselor. Participants did not want to spend their counseling sessions educating clinicians about their disabilities, but they expected the counselor to read or consult once the disability was identified. Another behavior that was highly valued by participants in the Hunt et al. (2006) study was a willingness to advocate for disabled lesbian clients and to teach clients how to advocate for themselves. Also important for counselors to know is that although some participants found the counselor's sexual orientation or disability status to be important, most did not mention it. It appeared that their acceptance of these clients was what mattered more.

In terms of identified problems, sometimes offices were not user-friendly, either in terms of accessibility, or written materials (for visually impaired clients), and assessment procedures were not applicable to disabled persons. Finally, because many individuals with disabilities have limited incomes, adjustments in fees were greatly appreciated.

Boden (1992) also worked with disabled lesbians and provides insight about dynamics that are unique to LGBTQIA+ people whose disabilities were either congenital or evident in early childhood. When the disabled person was growing up, she developed a sense of being different as a result of her disability. This sense of being different sometimes was internalized to mean being defective. When the developing person then realizes she is a lesbian, feelings around the earlier awareness of how others responded to the disability may be reawakened.

Another aspect of disabilities of importance to LGBTQIA+ individuals is the reduced number of potential life partners (Lawson, 2005). Lawson observes that having an autistic spectrum disorder and being a lesbian does not have to be a problem, but "it might present us with extra difficulties that require some navigation" (p. 83).

Persons whose disabilities are developmental and cognitive in nature are often excluded from the discourse on disabilities: "Theories about *disability* are really theories about *physical disability*" (Thompson et al., 2001, p. 55). These authors contend that people with developmental disabilities are generally not accepted by either the disabled community or the LGBTQIA+ community, depriving them of much needed support. They also are not provided with adequate and accurate sexual information, which is sorely needed. The absence of appropriate sex education is also a problem for deaf individuals, some of whom are members of the LGBTQIA+ community. Swartz (1993) found sex knowledge of deaf college freshmen was less than that or the hearing peers, consistent with the alleged absence of sex education for this population.

There appears to be a commonly held myth that disabled persons are **asexual**, and certainly cannot be homosexual (O'Toole & Bregante, 1992; Shakespeare, 1999; Thompson et al., 2001). In fact, Appleby (1994) was critical of the lesbian community, which she believed was not inclusive of disabled lesbians, due in part to the acceptance of this myth. Partners of disabled persons are often assumed to be caretakers. This assumption of asexuality often means that disabled LGBTQIA+ persons do not receive important and needed information about sexuality from medical providers. Shakespeare (1999) observed that individual gay and lesbians with disabilities varied in the salience of each status in their self-image. In general, the stronger identity was with the status that appeared earlier in life, so if the person was disabled as a child, they were more likely to identify as disabled, but if the disability emerged after the sexual identity had been disclosed to others, the LGBTQIA+ status was likely to be more prominent in the individual's self-identity. For some, having dealt with one difference was helpful in facing another. Many of his participants (22 disabled gay men and lesbians) observed that the LGBTQIA+ community is not particularly welcoming to those with disabilities. That position is supported by Nora Rae Bednarski, who is wheelchair bound (Hays, 2001) and has personally experienced the insensitivity and inaccessibility of LGBTQIA+ events. Further, many disabled people do not reveal their sexual orientation because of fears about the effect of the disclosure on caregivers or residential institutions on which they depend.

Counselor Issues

In a sincere effort to be inclusive and nonjudgmental, counselors may take the position that since LGBTQIA+ status is neither a disorder nor a problem, they should not inquire about sexual orientation, nor focus on it in counseling. While such a position is understandable, it can also be short-sighted and harmful to the client. Many other issues (family relationships, depression, abuse, even career concerns) should be addressed in context, and LGBTQIA+ status is part of the context. As long as this remains a stigmatized attribute, counselors will do their clients a disservice if they do not examine the impact on other aspects of client functioning.

Most identity development models describe the coming-out process as an essential task in reaching the most integrated developmental stages. It may follow that counselors would encourage clients to take that important step. It is crucial that clients not feel pressured to come out before they are ready and prepared for the consequences. First, clients should feel clear about their identity before coming out, particularly to those whose possible rejection would be traumatic. Clients also need help in finding the optimal time and situations in which to make this disclosure. Despite its importance to the individual, the client should assess the receptiveness of the persons to whom they are disclosing (avoiding times of high stress, poor health, etc.). Clients need to be well prepared for possible anger and distress from loved ones, particularly following an initial disclosure. What is critical here is that the counselor self-monitor to be sure that it is the client's needs and agenda that drive the decision, not the counselor's.

As with all the other issues in the book, counselors who are part of the LGBTQIA+ community themselves must be conscious of how that affects their reactions to clients and must be clear that they are not imposing their own agenda on others. When (or if) disclosing their status to clients, counselors must be sure that the disclosure is appropriate, for the client's benefit, and not the focus of clinical attention. We strongly recommend that all counselors seek supervision, but particularly when they work with clients whose issues have a personal meaning for the counselor.

NOTE TO SCHOOL COUNSELORS

While protection of rights is an important element of the role of schools with LGBTQIA+ adolescents, school counselors are in a position to make a significant contribution to the welfare of these students. In fact, school counselors may be the first school person to be approached by LGBTQIA+ youth (HRW, 2001). This box will discuss the special responsibilities of school counselors to this group of their constituents.

The American School Counseling Association (ASCA, 2022) takes the position that

> school counselors promote equal opportunity and respect for students regardless of sexual orientation, gender identity or gender expression. School counselors recognize the school experience can be significantly more difficult for students with marginalized identities. School counselors work to eliminate barriers impeding LGBTQ+ student development and achievement. (para. 1)

As student advocates and mental health professionals, school counselors should be at the forefront of promoting acceptance of diversity in schools and are in a unique position to take the leadership in promoting a safe and supportive school climate for LGBTQIA+ students (Bauman & Sach-Kapp, 1998; Monier & Lewis, 2000). Counselors have a number of avenues by which they can positively impact the school experience of LGBTQIA+ youth and, by extension, all students (Anderson, 1994; Besner & Spungin, 1995; Reynolds & Koski, 1994).

(Continued)

The ASCA's position statement regarding LGBTQIA+ youth clearly defines the school counselor's role. We will list some of the activities that ASCA specifies as the school counselor's role, but we encourage you to view the resource directly on ASCA's website. ASCA has continued to update and revise the posted position statement since 1995. The most recent update was 2022. School counselors do the following:

- Counsel students with questions about their sexual orientation and gender identity as well as students' feelings about the identity of others in an accepting and nonjudgmental manner.
- Advocate for equitable educational and extracurricular opportunities for all students regardless of sexual orientation, gender identity or gender expression.
- Advocate for transgender, nonbinary and gender-expansive students regarding access of building facilities (e.g., ensuring a safe environment for restroom use and changing) and gender presentation (e.g., wearing a dress or pants for an orchestra or vocal performance).
- Promote policies that effectively reduce the use of offensive language, harassment, and bullying and improve school climate.
- Address absenteeism, lowered educational aspirations and academic achievement, and low psychological well-being as a result of victimization and feeling unsafe at school.
- Provide a safe space for LGBTQIA+ students and allies such as genders and sexualities alliance clubs.
- Promote sensitivity and acceptance of diversity among all students and staff to include LGBTQIA+ students and diverse family systems.
- Advocate for the rights of families to access and participate in their student's education and school activities without discrimination.
- Support an inclusive curriculum at all grade levels.
- Model language that is inclusive of sexual orientation and gender identity.
- Advocate for adoption of school policies that address discrimination and promoting violence-prevention programs to create a safe and supportive school environment.
- Support students in addressing possible discrimination by staff members.
- Encourage staff training on inclusive practices, an affirming school environment, accurate information, and risk factors for LGBTQ+ students.
- Support families whose children are coming out by helping them navigate these important developmental milestones in ways that protect LGBTQIA+ students from harm and help families stay together.
- Identify LGBTQIA+ community resources for students and families and assess the quality and inclusiveness of these resources before referring to such resources.

School counselors are already in the role of consultant to teachers and administrators. In this capacity, they can assist teachers in developing lessons and strategies that are more inclusive of people from the LGBTQIA+ community and in devising classroom management approaches to deal with unacceptable behavior toward these students. As student advocates, counselors must insist that discriminatory behavior toward any student, including LGBTQIA+ students, be confronted and disciplinary action taken. They must insist that all students' rights are respected and their welfare promoted, and they must intervene when this does not happen.

Counselors could be proponents of and leaders in providing in-service training to teachers and staff to raise awareness, provide information, and dispel misinformation. This training can be an opportunity to sensitize the adults in the school about the impact of language. Evidence is accumulating to support the benefits of staff training. A study by Laura Szalacha (Sadowski, 2001) found that more than twice as many students perceived that LGBTQIA+ students had faculty support in schools that provided staff training than in schools that had not.

Counselors must work with administrators to ensure that such training be required so that staff who attend do not fear being labeled and so that those most in need of the training must participate.

School counselors can also be leaders in diversity training and programming for students within the school and can promote the value of including LGBTQIA+ issues in such training (Bauman & Sachs-Kapp, 1998). Bauman and Sachs-Kapp describe a powerful workshop conducted for and by students on this important topic. Experiential exercises were included along with informational presentations so that students were engaged and involved. Anecdotal comments by student participants revealed that the workshop had a significant impact.

In their consultant role, counselors can initiate task forces within their schools to focus on these issues and should be actively and visibly involved in efforts to improve climate for LGBTQIA+ students, including publishing clear policies of nondiscrimination. Counselors can speak out when they become aware of incidents or policies that are detrimental to LGBTQIA+ youth. Due to their professional training and sensitivity, counselors may be alert to the more subtle cues that exclude LGBTQIA+ clients and can be vigilant and assertive in raising awareness of the negative consequences of such practices. Students who see that counselors take an active and visible stance regarding LGBTQIA+ students are more likely to approach them for assistance.

We acknowledge and note that recent legislation in some states in the United States discourage and/or prohibit school counselors from being able to serve LGBTQIA+ youth and schools in the school counselor's role. This is a clear case of legislation being proposed and passed that ignores the data, input, and guidelines set by a professional organization.

Confidentiality and privacy concerns must be explicitly addressed if LGBTQIA+ youth are to feel safe approaching school counselors with these issues. Two actions are important for counselors to take with respect to confidentiality: informing students of any limits to student–counselor confidentiality and advocating strongly for explicit policies that prohibit disclosure of students' sexual orientation or gender identity (HRW, 2001). Counselors need to make it clear that they are willing and able to work with LGBTQIA+ youth by having visible indicators prominently displayed that convey their openness to diversity in general and LGBTQIA+ issues in particular. Their offices make statements about their openness, and if posters and/or symbols reflect acceptance of LGBTQIA+ students, these will be recognized.

In addition to individual counseling that allows LGBTQIA+ students to discuss their concerns with a nonjudgmental professional, group counseling can be a very effective format for working with students. In-school support groups provide a safe and supportive environment within the school for discussion of the particular issues that arise in the school setting (Muller & Hartman, 1998). The discovery that they are not alone can be a very healing experience for all students, but particularly for LGBTQIA+ youth who often feel isolated within the school milieu. An extremely small percentage (6% at high school and 3% at middle school) of the counselors in Monier and Lewis's (2000) study had started such support groups, and approximately half at each level indicated they do not plan to do so. In addition to group counseling, gay-straight alliances (GSAs) have been found to be important in changing school climate. Counselors should be advocates for gay-straight alliances in schools and can take comfort in Szalacha's finding (Sadowski, 2001) that schools with GSAs were considered safer for LGBTQIA+ students by three times.

To provide effective services to LGBTQIA+ students, schools counselors must be well informed and connected to community resources to which students can be referred. Referrals are most effective when they include more than just a telephone number. Offering information about organizations and services conveys to youth that the counselor is personally interested enough to seek out this information.

While school counselors cannot provide ongoing family therapy to families of LGBTQIA+ students, they can utilize their knowledge of family issues to assist interested parents in obtaining information and support and recommending family therapy when indicated. Talking with parents about their distress and fears, and normalizing them, can be an important contribution. It is essential that school counselors have information readily available about PFLAG (formerly known as the Parents, Families, and Friends of Lesbians and Gays) and other resources that are appropriate for parents, including family therapists with expertise in helping families through this adjustment.

(Continued)

The importance of school counselors' role in working with LGBTQIA+ youth is obvious, but lack of training and skill may inhibit counselors from taking this responsibility (Monier & Lewis, 2000; Sears, 1992). There have been several studies that have examined school counselors' preparedness and competency for working with LGBTQIA+ students (Abreu et al., 2020; Shi & Doud, 2017; Simons, 2018). Overall, school counselors perceive themselves as having a low level of competency for working with LGBTQIA+ clients and often lack transgender-specific training. In an earlier study, Fontaine (1998) found that only 8% of school counselors rated themselves as highly competent.

The importance of school counselors' role in working with LGBTQIA+ youth is obvious, but lack of training and skill may inhibit counselors from taking this responsibility (Monier & Lewis, 2000; Sears, 1992). There have been several studies that have examined school counselors' preparedness and competency for working with LGBTQIA+ students (Abreu et al., 2020; Shi & Doud, 2017; Simons, 2018). Overall, school counselors perceive themselves as having a low level of competency for working with LGBTQIA+ clients and often lack transgender-specific training. In an earlier study, Fontaine (1998) found that only 8% of school counselors rated themselves as highly competent.

Historically, graduate training programs for school counselors have not seemed to be providing sufficient training in working with LGBTQIA+ youth, and many counselors received the majority of their training at seminars and workshops (Abreu et al., 2020; Monier & Lewis, 2000; Shi & Doud, 2017). Shi and Doud (2017) call for the training for school counselors in working with this population starting in graduate school but emphasize that school counselors should take every opportunity postgraduation to learn more through conferences and workshops. It is important for counselor to pursue and obtain specialized training for themselves in addition to training for teachers and administrators and other school staff (Abreu et al., 2020). Counselors can take the initiative in insisting that such training be provided by professional organizations and their local districts and actively soliciting such training.

We have not addressed the particular issues of LGBTQIA+ youth of color, who have "double minority" status. One would expect that these youth would experience increased risk and negative outcomes as a result of experiencing discrimination on more than one dimension of identity. However, a study of LGBTQIA+ youth of color found that while they earned lower grades than their heterosexual counterparts, the difference in grades was significant only for White youth (Russell & Truong, 2001). The researchers speculate that minority youth of color may have more experience with prejudice and discrimination than White youth and that this prior experience serves to inoculate them against the toxic effects of added discrimination. White youth may experience minority status for the first time, and their negative school outcomes may reflect the absence of coping strategies for dealing with discrimination.

If the mission of school counselors is to contribute to the academic, personal, and career success of all students in schools, it is imperative that they accept and exercise their responsibility for working with and for LGBTQIA+ youth. This responsibility extends to taking leadership in promoting an inclusive school climate in which acceptance of differences is the norm and in assuring that LGBTQIA+ youth are protected and welcomed in schools, which are such an influential social environment for developing adolescents. This responsibility is a weighty one. From comments supplied by some respondents in Monier and Lewis's (2000) survey, it is clear that some counselors fear the reactions of parents and other educators should they take visible actions on behalf of LGBTQIA+ students. They perceive the larger social context to be unsupportive of LGBTQIA+ individuals in general and critical of any efforts by school personnel, including counselors, to support this population. This fear will potentially be higher, given the status of recent anti-LGBTQIA+ state legislation. Hopefully, school counselors are strongly rooted in their professional codes of ethics and their primary commitment to student welfare and will accept their responsibilities to LGBTQIA+ students.

Ethical Concerns

One of the most challenging ethical dilemmas a counselor may face is more likely to arise when working with LGBTQIA+ clients. We refer here to the ACA's 2014 Code of Ethics, principle B.2.c:

B.2.c. Contagious, Life-Threatening Diseases

When clients disclose that they have a disease commonly known to be both communicable and life threatening, counselors may be justified in disclosing information to identifiable third parties, if the parties are known to be at serious and foreseeable risk of contracting the disease. Prior to making a disclosure, counselors assess the intent of clients to inform the third parties about their disease or to engage in any behaviors that may be harmful to an identifiable third party. Counselors adhere to relevant state laws concerning disclosure about disease status. (p. 7)

If a client were to disclose that they are HIV positive and having unprotected sexual relations with a partner who does not know of the HIV status, what does this ethical code say? First, it may be the case that the role of the counselor is to assist the client in telling the partner. It has been our experience that clients do not feel good about keeping this secret; they are terrified of losing the relationship and fear that will happen. In many cases, with support (and perhaps rehearsal) the client will make the disclosure, and the counselor will not need to break confidentiality.

In the event that does not happen, the counselor must confirm the diagnosis before taking any further steps. It is possible that the client may believe they are HIV positive but has never been tested. In that case, the counselor must urge the client to get accurate test results. In other cases, the diagnosis is confirmed. If the client agrees to use effective protection, is the counselor obligated to take any further steps? The use of the term *high risk* in the ethical code suggests that if the counselor is certain that the client will not engage in unprotected sex, the counselor does not have to inform the partner. However, in such a situation, it is essential that the counselor seek consultation. In fact, most professional organizations offer free consultation on ethical matters, and this would certainly be a situation in which to take advantage of that service.

Summary

- LGBTQIA+ status is not a disorder, which is important for counselors to remember. However, despite advances in public awareness, LGBTQIA+ individuals continue to experience discrimination.
- LGBTQIA+ clients seek counseling for a variety of reasons; the counselor must be sensitive to ways in which their sexual orientation, gender identity, or gender expression impacts other areas. At the same time, the counselor must not assume that these topics will be the focus of counseling.
- Development of sexual or gender identity and the coming-out process is a major developmental milestone for many LGBTQIA+ clients. Counselors must be aware that, particularly for adolescents, support and acceptance are critical. Screening for such disorders as depression and addictions is prudent with adolescents who struggle to navigate this process.
- Issues for adults and older adults vary with the historical context. For many, the absence of legal status as a couple creates challenges in parenting and end-of-life issues. The counselor can serve as a support and a resource for essential information.
- For ethnic minority LGBTQIA+ individuals, there may be some conflict around identifying as a dual minority and a sense that the LGBTQIA+ community is not accepting of ethnic minorities. Morales (1992) provides a model to help conceptualize these challenges.
- Reparation or conversion therapy exists despite professional condemnation. The counselor must be aware of this approach in order to provide accurate information to clients. Some clients may seek counseling from other therapists after such an experience, and the counselor must understand the ways in which the experience may have been harmful.
- Guidelines for effective therapy with LGBTQIA+ clients are available, and the ethical counselor will be cognizant of these principles.

Additional Resources

On the Web

- https://saigecounseling.org/ is the website for SAIGE: Society for Sexual, Affectional, Intersex, and Gender Expansive Identities: Counselors and Related Professionals Serving Sexual, Affectional, Intersex, and Gender Expansive Communities. This organization was formerly known as ALGBTIC and is a division of the American Counseling Association.

- http://www.pflag.org/ is the site for Parents and Friends of Lesbians and Gays (PFLAG).

- https://www.glsen.org is the site for GLSEN, which has excellent information on topics of importance, including the national school climate survey, as well as information about starting chapters (gay-straight alliances) in schools.

- https://www.hrc.org/ is the site for Human Rights Campaign. This organization's mission is to end discrimination against LGBTQIA+ people and realize a world that achieves fairness and equity for everyone.

- https://www.schoolcounselor.org/Standards-Positions/Position-Statements/ASCA-Position-Statements/The-School-Counselor-and-LGBTQ-Youth is the site for the ASCA's position, rationale, and role of the school counselor with LGBTQIA+ youth.

- https://www.thetrevorproject.org/ is the website for The Trevor Project, provides information and support to LGBTQIA+ youth.

- https://www.thetaskforce.org/ is the site for the National LGBTQ Task Force, which works toward justice for LGTBQIA+ people and their families through change-inducing initiatives.

- https://glaad.org/ is the website for GLAAD, an LGBTQIA+ media advocacy organization.

- https://www.sageusa.org/ is the website for an organization that offers advocacy and services for LGBTQIA+ elders.

- https://www.wpath.org/ is the website for the World Professional Association for Transgender Health (WPATH).

- www.deafqueer.org is a website for deaf gay men and has links to resources, a chat, and other features that might be of interest to deaf gay clients.

In Print for Counselors

- *LGBQQIA Competencies* (2013) and *Transgender Competencies* (2010), both available from SAIGE at https://saigecounseling.org/competencies-2/.

- *The Queer and Transgender Resilience Workbook: Skills for Navigating Sexual Orientation and Gender Expression* by Anneliese A. Singh (2018). A workbook that could be used with clients—also available in a Kindle edition.

- *Group Counseling With LGBTQI Persons* by Kristopher M. Goodrich and Melissa Luke (2015). A good resource that provides strengths-based group counseling strategies.

- *A Clinician's Guide to Gender-Affirming Care: Working With Transgender and Gender Nonconforming clients* by Sand C. Chang, Anneliese A. Singh, and Lore M. Dickey (2018). A good resource regarding an affirmation approach.

- *Affirmative Counseling With LGBTQI+ People* by Misty M. Ginicola, Cheri Smith, and Joel M. Filmore (2017).

- *Standards of Care for the Health of Transgender and Gender Diverse People* by the World Professional Association of Transgender Health (2022). This publication is now in its eighth edition and is currently published in the *International Journal of Transgender Health,* which can be found at the website for the World Professional Association of Transgender Health: https://www.wpath.org/.

- *Casebook for Counseling: Lesbian, Gay, Bisexual, and Transgender Persons and Their Families* by Sari H. Dworkin and Mark Pope (2014). Great resource that contains 31 case studies with LGBTQIA clients.

- *Counseling Gay Men and Lesbians: Journey to the End of the Rainbow* edited by S. H. Dworkin & F. J. Gutiérrez. Although it is a 1992 edition, the variety of specialized topics covered in the book is valuable to the counselor.

- *Homosexuality and the Family,* edited by Frederick Bozett (1989) has good information for anyone working with gay fathers.

- *The Sharon Kowalski Case: Lesbian and Gay Rights on Trial* by Casey Charles (2003), an HIV positive gay lawyer and English professor.

- *Why Can't Sharon Kowalski Come Home?* by Karen Thompson.

- "The Law Governing LGBTQ-Parent Families in the United States" (2020), by Julie Shapiro, provides a fairly good summary of the legal issues that LGBTQIA+ families may face. It is found as a chapter in *LGBTQ-Parent Families,* edited by Abbie Goldberg and Katherine Allen, published by Springer.

In Print for Clients

- *The Book of Pride: LGBTQ Heroes Who Changed the World* by Mason Funk (2019). A series of interviews with leader, activists, and others who have witnessed the gay rights movement since the 1960s.

- *GLBTQ** by Kelly Huegel is written from the perspective of one who struggled personally with this issue at that age. It is a handbook written in a frank and conversational voice that speaks to many of the questions youth may have.

- *Gay Relationships* by Tina Tessina, addresses many of the specific questions that may be important to a client newly out.

- *The Best Little Boy in the World* was published by John Reid in 1973. He later revealed he was actually Andrew Tobias, a well-known financial guru. The book tells the story of a boy coming to terms with being gay and is an insightful personal account of one person's struggle.

- *The Best Little Boy in the World Grows Up* by A. Tobias describes the personal and political aspects of life as a gay man in America.

- *Becoming a Man: Half a Life Story* by Paul Monette is another memoir of the struggle to accept oneself as gay that won the National Book Award in 1992.

- *A Face in the Crowd*, edited by John Peterson and Martin Bedogne, is a lovely photo-essay book, written after the death of Matthew Shepard, which has moving photos and brief stories.

- *Queer Crips: Disabled Gay Men and Their Stories* (2003) by Bob Guter and John R. Killacky provides personal perspectives on being gay and disabled.

- *Sex, Sexuality and the Autistic Spectrum* by Wendy Lawson is also a personal account.

- *School Experiences of Gay and Lesbian Youth: The Invisible Minority* by Harris. We strongly recommend this book for school counselors, in which the school experiences of LGBTQIA+ youth are described in an excellent collection of articles.

- *Love Makes a Family* by Sophie Beer (2018) and *It's Okay to be a Unicorn* by Jason Tharp (2020) are children's books.

Films and Television

- *Call Me by Your Name* (2017), staring Timothee Chalamet and Armie Hammer, is a romantic, coming-of-age story based on a 2007 novel of the same name.

- *Dallas Buyers Club* (2013), starring Matthew McConaughey, is the story of a man who is diagnosed with AIDS in the mid-1980s when HIV/AIDS was widely misunderstood.

- *The Power of the Dog* (2021), starring Benedict Cumberbatch, Kirsten Dunst, and Jesse Plemons, tells the story of a complex 1920s Montana rancher.

- *The Danish Girl* (2015), starring Eddie Redmayne, is based on a novel of the same name published in 2000. It is based on one of the first known recipients of gender-affirming surgery.

- *Philadelphia* (1993), starring Tom Hanks, is a mainstream film that broached the difficult subjects of AIDS. The issues are still current and the treatment is timeless.

- *Laramie Project* (2002) is about the horrific murder of Mathew Shepard in 1998 that shocked the nation. With actors playing the roles of various townspeople, this film highlights both the tragedy and the increased awareness that resulted from this terrible crime.

- *Brokeback Mountain* (2005) raised the public consciousness of what has been a painful secret for many gay people, and hopefully has helped normalize LGBTQIA+ status. It is well worth watching.

- *Transamerica* (2005) and *Boys Don't Cry* (1999) portray the marginalized transgender group and are both extremely well done.

Exercises

1. Attend an event or visit the local chapter of PFLAG or another local organization that supports LGBTQIA+ individuals and/or their families. Write a brief paper describing what you learned.

2. Imagine a client comes to see you wanting conversion therapy. What would you say? How might you explore with the client their motivation in seeking such therapy?

3. Describe how you will make it clear to potential clients and referral sources that you are open to working with clients of minority sexual orientations.

4. Imagine you have an adult client who learns that their child is gay or lesbian. List some possible goals for the counseling.

5. Generate a list of gay-friendly churches, physicians, and lawyers in your community to whom you might refer clients who had those needs. How will you go about this task?

6. Plan a presentation to teachers about kids who have two moms or dads. Help the teachers think about how to make sure both parents are treated as such. Help them develop appropriate responses to kids who ask about Johnny or Judy's two moms or two dads.

7. Assume you are working with an adolescent who recognizes they are gay or lesbian and wants your help telling their parents. How would you work with this client?

8. Find out more about intersex conditions and prepare a brief report to your classmates. Or do the same for transgender surgery.

9. Watch *Transamerica* and/or *Boys Don't Cry* and discuss your reactions with your classmates.

10. Think about what might be different if you were to do couples counseling with a same-sex couple compared to a heterosexual couple.

CHAPTER 4

People Experiencing Homelessness

At first glance, homelessness may seem more of a social problem than a mental health issue. While there are certainly many political and social policy considerations regarding homelessness, there are also important roles for mental health professionals at all levels, who have important clinical and advocacy roles with this population. Mental health professionals are needed to work with individuals and families experiencing homelessness, as 21% of people who are homeless have severe mental illness, 16% have chronic substance abuse problems, and 8% are victims of domestic violence (Williams, 2023), with many having multiple disorders. The clinician's standard repertoire of skills and techniques will be applicable to people who are homeless, but they will also need to develop specific skills and rely on collaboration and consultation to do so. Although working with this population may be challenging, "your work with people who are homeless can be quite rewarding" (p. 20).

CASE STUDY

Although many mental health professionals do not anticipate working with the population of people who are homeless, it is possible that a client with whom you have a relationship becomes homeless. Few who knew her as an educated and respected professional would have expected Amanda to become homeless. Amanda brings a unique perspective to the issue of homelessness as she has a master's degree in school counseling and worked in that capacity for 10 years. Amanda became homeless herself after a series of tragic events in her life, including a divorce, losing custody of her children, and multiple deaths of loved ones in a short period of time. One of those losses was her stepdaughter, who died of a heroin overdose while experiencing homelessness. Amanda became severely depressed and eventually turned to substances to ameliorate her suffering. These problems ultimately caused her to lose her job (and income); the resulting eviction was the immediate precipitant for becoming a person experiencing homelessness. Although she had family and friends who might have provided temporary housing, she believed that they expected her to address her substance use and mental health issues before they would be willing to help. She was on her own.

When working as a school counselor, Amanda recognized that some children with whom she worked were experiencing homelessness (both sheltered and unsheltered). To assist those children and families, she became very familiar with the services and types of assistance that were available. Having knowledge of resources in the community enabled her to take care of her basic survival needs during the 2 years she was experiencing

(Continued)

homelessness; she could also help other people who were homeless access available resources and services. When Amanda was experiencing homelessness, she still had a car, which became her dwelling place. That added an element of safety, as the car had doors she could lock and provided a consistent place to spend the night and store her belongings. Although fortunately she was not personally the target of violence or assault, she witnessed such acts and noted that women and adolescents were particularly vulnerable. Her car provided protection.

The city in which Amanda lives is in the desert southwest, where temperatures during the summer can be extremely high and sometimes lethal for individuals. Recognizing the vulnerability of the population of people who are homeless, she used her own food allotment to buy and deliver bottles of water to various locations where they were known to congregate. Although she was experiencing homelessness herself, she was concerned for the safety of others. She became known as a welcome source of assistance; in addition to water, she offered a nonjudgmental listening ear and developed trust with other people experiencing homelessness. The recipients of her care clearly benefited from her generosity; it also helped to bolster her self-esteem.

After about 6 months of being homeless, Amanda joined a residential program for substance abusers, where she remained for 6 months. She commented that shorter programs (detox, 30 days inpatient, etc.) were not sufficient to result in lasting change. She was aware that there would be restrictions and monitoring in the facility and signed up because she knew that was necessary for her. When she completed her 6-month stay, she moved to a gospel rescue mission, whose motto is "homeless to wholeness" and whose mission is "hope, shelter, transformation." This organization offers a faith-based program and has about 300 programs and affiliates around the United States. Those in the program were required to remain clean and sober, and the local facility provided the care and support Amanda needed to continue her journey.

Amanda described her journey in Facebook (FB) posts, and we include some here because it is her story, and in her own words. Her FB posts were generally uplifting and optimistic quotations and images, memorials to lost loved ones on their birthdays, and photos of her creative and appetizing culinary creations, but some referred to her experience of homelessness.

> The Journey 2020: A year ago, I was at a park praying for a miracle. I was homeless, living in my car, broken and alone. Even in the depths of sadness, I chose to see the beauty in nature. I am not ashamed to tell my story and be open about my struggles. Maybe this can help someone suffering in the same way. Today is a new day. Today I have a roof over my head. Today, I have a secure job. Today, I have my dignity. Today, I strive to be what God would want me to be. Everything is possible with faith and perseverance.
>
> The Journey: It's been four years this month that I made water deliveries to the homeless. As the epidemic of homelessness, fentanyl use, and overdose rises, we often don't know what to do. Perhaps we can't solve the problem on a world level. However, I believe we can treat those suffering with addiction and homelessness with dignity and respect. A bottle of water, a bite to eat and a listening ear goes a long way. I have been there. Thirsty, hungry and lonely. And we can pray for resolution and have faith that a power beyond will restore humanity.
>
> When I was homeless, there were times that I went hungry wishing that someone would rescue me. It doesn't matter (in my eyes) what made anyone homeless. Everyone needs to eat. I delivered 48 sodas And 5 pizzas today. It took seconds for everyone to tear through it. Thank the good lord that I don't have to suffer with hunger anymore.

Amanda is currently working as a counselor in an organization that assists people in the criminal justice system; the rates of homelessness in that population are disproportionately high. The transition from the system to society is a particularly dangerous time for returning to substances and/or having untreated mental illness. Helping these individuals make better choices, assisting them in locating needed services, is gratifying. The agency for which Amanda works also offers substance abuse treatment and counseling for victims of domestic violence; these issues are over-represented among the homeless. Amanda feels her journey is now on a solid and positive path. Although she may want to work with children again in the future, she is confident that she brings a meaningful understanding and compassion to her current clientele and is certain that this is what she needs to be doing at this point in her journey. Her knowledge of resources allowed her to receive assistance from the state to pay for her treatment.

In many encampments of people who are homeless, a type of community develops in which some take care of each other, but attacks and violence also happen. High rates of serious mental illness and substance abuse result in unpredictable and sometimes aggressive behavior. Adolescents are particularly vulnerable and may be preyed upon. Amanda observed how grateful young people are for attention, increasing the likelihood that they may succumb to drugs or sex to gain and maintain that attention. Families who are homeless may have had their children placed in care, and/or the family members are split among different shelters. Keep in mind that many children who are homeless have already experienced multiple *adverse childhood experiences* (ACEs) and separating them from family is yet another trauma. Trauma is pervasive among people who are homeless. See Chapter 6 on trauma for a more detailed discussion of that topic.

Amanda had advice for mental health professionals who are interested in working with people who are homeless. She stressed that the two most important qualities are being nonjudgmental and being willing to listen. Many of the people who are homeless have had negative experiences with authorities or agency personnel and are likely to be slow to trust any professional and to be put off by bureaucratic procedures. They are not likely to come to a counseling office seeking services; clinicians need to work with them where they are—both geographically and psychologically. That is a departure from the carefully appointed office designed to convey a calm and welcoming ambiance, and counselors needs to adjust their approach to the unconventional context. They also need to recognize that it will take a long time to develop a trusting relationship and the actual treatment will come later. It is helpful for the clinician to demonstrate their commitment by serving as a quasi-case manager, assisting people with accessing services and resources—perhaps bringing a laptop to facilitate online applications.

Experts debate whether a *housing first* or *treatment first* policy is more effective. In Amanda's case, treatment allowed her to regain her mental health so that she was then able to live independently. Even when shelters are available (most cities have an extreme shortage), not all people who are homeless will want that option. Shelters have curfews and substance-free requirements, and many are not ready to commit to those expectations.

Amanda reminds us that some people hide their homeless status given the negative judgments that are associated with it. It is important for counselors to recognize the signs that suggest possible homelessness. In children, being withdrawn, wearing the same (often bedraggled) clothes repeatedly, and having frequent absences are clues that should be explored.

In addition to providing services, mental health professionals might become advocates for the homeless, both within the system and in soliciting small contributions to improve some aspects of their lives. Amanda provided much-needed water and food. Others have arranged for free services (e.g., barbers, basic medical supplies, delivering toys, etc.) to make a difference.

Amanda's journey has been a challenging one. It is a reminder to me that this can happen to anyone, and mental health professionals need to develop compassion and understanding for these members of our society. Amanda's story also reminds us that homelessness is not inevitably permanent or chronic; mental health professionals have an important role to play. Her journey is inspiring.

Definitions and Terminology

The term *homeless*, although generally understood, is not the only term in use. Although homelessness is the term most associated with these living situations, some prefer the terms *unsheltered*, *houseless*, or *unhoused*, which are arguably less stigmatizing. (Robbins, 2022). They argue that people who are homeless may not have conventional homes, but for them, those dwellings or locations where they are situated are home. While the general term *homeless* includes those who are in transitional housing or shelters, those who are unhoused or unsheltered do not have a stable indoor place to sleep.

Person-first language (i.e., person experiencing homelessness) acknowledges their humanity, avoids labeling, is less stigmatizing, and implies that their living situation does not define them nor is it necessarily permanent. For consistency, we will use the term *person who is homeless* or *person experiencing homelessness* in this chapter.

Different agencies use slightly different definitions of homelessness to determine eligibility for their services. The Social Security Administration definition reads:

Homeless/Transient (Living Arrangement): An individual with no permanent living arrangement, i.e., no fixed place of residence, is considered homeless or transient. Someone who is transient is neither a member of a household nor a resident of an institution. For example:

- Someone who sleeps in doorways, overnight shelters, parks, bus stations, etc.
- A person who stays with a succession of friends or relatives and has no permanent living arrangement on the first moment of the month

The U.S. Department of Housing and Urban Development also has a definition that guides their decisions about eligibility for various housing programs (Legal Information Institute, n.d.). Substance Abuse and Mental Health Services Administration (SAMHSA; n.d.)'s definition is quite specific, so we include it verbatim here (https://soarworks.samhsa.gov/article/definitions-of-homelessness):

The definition of those who are experiencing homelessness includes:

- An individual or family who lacks a fixed, regular, and adequate nighttime residence, such as those living in emergency shelters, transitional housing, or places not meant for habitation, or
- An individual or family who will imminently lose their primary nighttime residence (within 14 days), provided that no subsequent housing has been identified and the individual/family lacks support networks or resources needed to obtain housing, or
- Unaccompanied youth under 25 years of age, or families with children and youth who qualify under other Federal statutes, such as the Runaway and Homeless Youth Act, have not had a lease or ownership interest in a housing unit in the last 60 or more days, have had two or more moves in the last 60 days, and who are likely to continue to be unstably housed because of disability or multiple barriers to employment, or
- An individual or family who is fleeing or attempting to flee domestic violence, has no other residence, and lacks the resources or support networks to obtain other permanent housing.

SAMSHA also provide a definition of those at risk for homelessness:
The definition of those who are at risk of homelessness includes individuals and families who:

- Have an annual income below 30 percent of the median family income for the area, as determined by HUD, and
- Do not have sufficient resources or support networks, immediately available to prevent them from moving to an emergency shelter or place not meant for habitation, and
- Exhibit one or more risk factors of homelessness, including recent housing instability or exiting a publicly funded institution or system of care such as foster care or a mental health facility.

The definitions of homeless used by federal agencies and legislation matter, especially for children and youth who are homeless. The Homeless Children and Youth Act of 2017 (H.R. 1511/S. 611) is an attempt to modify the Housing and Urban Developmenet definition, which restricts local entities from devising assistance tailored to local needs. One important criterion in the federal definition—that people who are homeless are those living in shelters or living outside—excludes many youths and families who are staying in motels, moving from one "couch" to another, facing impending eviction (with appropriate documentation). Note that the definitions are broader and would classify more vulnerable youth and families as homeless and eligible for assistance. Supporters of this legislation believe the HUD definition should be aligned with those of other federal agencies. They also note that housing alone is insufficient—support services for health, education, employment, and so forth are necessary to encourage progress toward self-sufficiency (Campaign for Children, 2017). At the time of this writing, the legislation that would expand the definition still had not passed, despite being reintroduced in both the House and Senate.

The homeless population is not homogenous. One factor on which homeless persons vary is the stage of homelessness, described by Belcher et al. (1991). The first stage, *marginal homelessness*, refers to those who are not usually counted among the homeless but who access many of the services used by people who are homeless, such as soup kitchens and food pantries. Their housing status may be quite tenuous, due to reliance on friends and family who may not be willing or able to continue those supports indefinitely. The *recently homeless* group includes those who have been homeless for less than 9 months and who identify with the general community rather than with people who are homeless. They still have hope that their situation is temporary, and although interactions with family members may currently be negative, they remain hopeful that those relationships can be repaired. The *chronic homeless* have been homeless for more than a year and have accepted homelessness as their normative condition. This group tends to be suspicious of and alienated from the mainstream population. They are the most challenging clients for mental health professionals.

Prevalence

The problem of homelessness has become critical in the United States, with many cities experiencing increases in homelessness at a time when resources area scarce. Approximately 582,462 Americans were homeless in 2022, 28% of whom were families with children, 22% were chronically homeless, 6% were veterans, and 5% were unaccompanied individuals under age 25. This is the highest number of those experiencing homelessness since data collection began (National Alliance to End Homelessness, n.d.). Sixty percent of homeless were in sheltered settings (e.g., emergency shelters) while 40% were unsheltered and living in such places as the street, abandoned buildings, and other unsuitable places (De Sousa et al., 2023). This crisis is important to mental health professionals, as 21% of homeless have severe mental illness, 16% have chronic substance abuse problems, and 8% are victims of domestic violence (Williams, 2023). These rates vary by state and by location within each state.

Rates also vary by demographic factors. Men represent 68% of homeless individuals. Small in number, transgendered individuals' rate of homelessness has increased 231% since 2015. Although numerically White people comprise the majority of those experiencing homelessness, Black people have a rate of homelessness that is four times as high, and Native Hawaiian and Pacific Islanders have the highest rate of all race/ethnic groups.

A variety of factors have been implicated in this growing problem: inflation, increased cost of housing, increased drug use, inadequate wages for entry-level jobs, and so on. During the pandemic, there was funding for programs that assisted this population (e.g., eviction moratoria, rental assistance housing vouchers), but those funds have not been renewed, so the situation is likely to become more dire. Data from 2016 indicate that 27,000 children are in foster care because of housing instability, and 130,000 children in foster care are prevented from rejoining their families due to families' lack of housing (Campaign for Children, 2017).

Theoretical Frameworks

When mental health professionals think about how to provide services to the homeless population, several well-known theories may be helpful. We briefly review Maslow's hierarchy of needs and Bronfenbrenner's bioecological systems theory next. We discuss Erikson's stages of psychosocial development in the section on children and adolescents.

Maslow's (1987) hierarchy is a well-known model of human needs. It is presented as a pyramid with more basic needs at the lower levels (deficiency needs) and more growth-oriented needs at the top. Maslow himself acknowledged the progress from bottom to top is not a linear process (i.e., one can return to lower levels and/or skip to higher levels depending on life circumstances). The levels seem particularly relevant to counseling people experiencing homelessness. The lowest levels are essential and must be fulfilled before other needs are addressed. The mental health professional will need to assist the client in accessing resources. There is some disagreement in the literature regarding the best approach: housing first or treatment first. Maslow's model suggests housing first is more appropriate and helpful. In addition to some type of shelter, food, water, clothing, medication, hygiene products, and so forth should be priorities. The clinician must be aware of course of these essentials and be prepared to assist the person who is homeless in accessing these resources. The debate over the best approach appears immaterial. Both are necessary. For example, a program in Houston, Texas, is a collaboration between government entities, the private sector, housing authorities, foundations, faith groups, and nonprofits. A person who is homeless is given a home with basic furnishings and is the lease holder with a key. They also receive a subsidy for the rent and needed services, including mental health treatment (Eichenbaum & Nichols, 2023).

The next level, safety needs, are also fundamental. Among other concerns, people who are homeless, especially those sleeping rough, are vulnerable to becoming victims of violence. Kushel (2022) notes than in 2021, 85 persons experiencing homelessness were murdered, breaking prior records. Kushel expressed concern that the public often has the false perception that persons who are homeless are criminals, which may contribute to or cause violent attacks against them. In addition to protection from harm (police availability), safety needs include employment, health care, schools, and financial stability. Love and belonging, although higher in the pyramid, may be present at all levels. See Figure 4.1 for a visual presentation of Maslow's hierarchy. Alfred Adler, noted psychiatrist, also proposed that love and belonging are a basic human need, as is social interest.

Above the belonginess and love level is *esteem*, feeling respected and valued, and having pride in one's accomplishments. This can be a challenge for people who are homeless, but counselors can model treating people who are homeless with dignity and respect as they assist clients in obtaining employment or increasing their education, both of which are sources of esteem. They can address them by Mr. or another appropriate title and ask permission before using their preferred first name. The top of the pyramid contains self-actualization needs, which include the need to "be all you can be" (i.e., achieving one's potential). Theoretically, this need can be met when the lower levels (physiological, safety, belongingness, and esteem) have been satisfied. For some people who are homeless, clinicians might encourage them to consider self-actualization an aspirational goal and work with them to imagine what that would look like.

While Maslow's theory applies to the individuals' needs, the biopsychosocial theory of Urie Bronfenbrenner situates the individual in the center of a series of concentric circles, each of which influences development. Although the theory was presented as a description of child development, it has been useful for understanding people at all stages of development. The individual (including biological and genetic predispositions and traits) at the center is surrounded by the ever-broader layers of influence, called systems. This conceptualization is relevant to working with people who are homeless; to have an impact, the professional will need to intervene in multiple systems. The *microsystem* is the most proximal to the person who is homeless and includes their

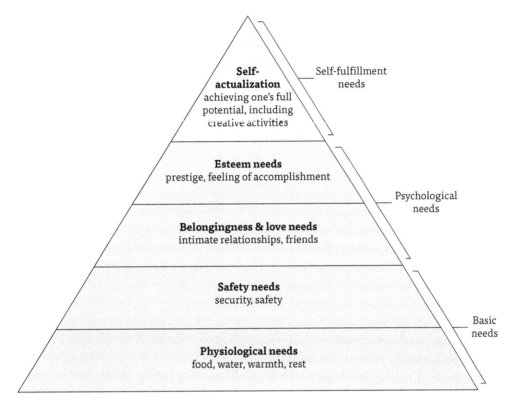

FIGURE 4.1 Maslow's hierarchy of needs.

immediate environment (family, friends, schoolmates, coworkers, religious groups, etc.) with whom they interact directly. That system may be restricted to other people who are homeless as other relationships may have been damaged or destroyed, especially in cases in which serious mental illness and/or substance abuse are involved. The *mesosystem* includes the interactions between components of the microsystem. The *exosystem* includes such systems as government, education, political systems, economic systems, the legal and criminal justice systems, and media. All of these systems are influential for people who are homeless. For example, the news has almost daily reports of city governments demolishing or otherwise removing homeless encampments. Although it is understandable that such communities can be unsightly and interfere with local businesses (e.g., Phoenix, Los Angeles), there is typically no mention of alterative accommodations. There are far more people needing shelters than available beds. Kushel (2022) noted that people who are homeless are often involved in the criminal justice system. People leaving jail or prison may not be well prepared or equipped to rejoin their communities without assistance, and so become homeless. According to Kushel, some people who are homeless are arrested for petty crimes (stealing food) and get entangled in another system that is difficult to navigate. In addition, the current lack of affordable housing, increasing rents, high rates of poverty, and inadequate wages for entry-level employment make it difficult for people who are homeless to find a path back to stability. In the *macrosystem* are the values and cultural norms of society. It is arguably the case that the current social norms in the United States are not favorable toward people who are homeless, mentally ill, or abusing substances. As a result, services are operating with insufficient funding at a time when the homeless population is growing. The outermost layer is the *chronosystem*, which contains both the time in one's life and the historical context.

We will discuss the developmental effects of being homeless next. The current historical period, with marked divisions among people with different beliefs, provides the backdrop for all the inner layers. In addition, although the acute pandemic appears to be over, the effects of the years-long presence of COVID-19 and its attendant changes in society is still with us. It is likely that some of the people experiencing homelessness have experienced both direct and indirect consequences of that period.

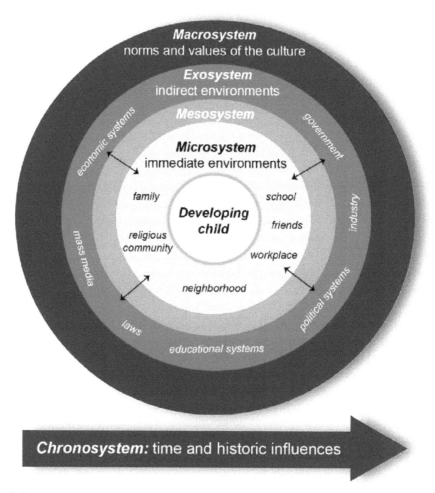

FIGURE 4.2 Bronfenbrenner's bioecological model of human development.

Developmental Aspects

One approach to examining how homelessness interacts with development is to consider how progress through each of Erikson's developmental stages might be affected when a person is homeless. The impact upon development actually begins prior to birth, for the homeless mother may not obtain prenatal health care, may lack proper nutrition, may be exposed to toxins in the environment, and in short may not provide the optimal intra-uterine environment for the developing fetus (McGeough et al., 2020). Homeless infants are four times as likely as other infants to need special care at birth (National Center for Homeless Education, 2013). If the mother has problems with substance abuse, these prenatal conditions can be further complicated. For the infant born into a homeless family, they may already have experienced harmful effects of homelessness prior to birth.

Erik Erikson's stages of psychosocial development (Orenstein & Lewis, 2022) are a useful framework for understanding changes over the lifespan. The first stage of psychosocial development occurs during the first year of life. During that time, infants develop a sense of trust if their needs for food and physical comfort are met. The mother who is homeless, who is likely to be a young, single parent, may expend all her emotional resources and physical energy trying to meet basic survival needs (see Maslow's hierarchy). In such a situation, the mother may be too stressed and exhausted to respond to her children's emotional and psychological needs. Children who are homeless at this stage of development are prone to such problems as insecure attachment, poor self-esteem, and aggressive behaviors (DiBiase & Waddell, 1995). Nutritional standards may suffer. The child is less likely to receive immunizations at recommended ages and is more likely to have elevated levels of lead in their blood. If the mother is residing in a shelter, communicable diseases are more prevalent, sanitation may be substandard, and light and noise may disrupt sleep. Thus, the infant's earliest needs are in danger of not being met, and the first stage of psychosocial development is prone to a negative outcome. This means that even if circumstances improve, the child who is homeless in the 1st year or so of life is at a developmental disadvantage, which will make later stages harder to negotiate successfully.

In the next stage, autonomy versus shame and doubt, the toddler (age 1–3) explores the environment and discovers a sense of independence. In many environments in which the homeless struggle to survive, the necessary exploration is hampered by the need to restrict movement to protect against dangerous situations. Crowded conditions also serve to hamper the child's need to explore. Several research studies have found that preschool children ages 2–5 who are homeless exhibit numerous developmental delays, including short attention spans, withdrawal, aggression, immature behaviors, immature motor development, as well as language and cognitive disabilities (Koblinskey et al., 2000). Consider that the homeless mother may be too preoccupied with basic survival to provide warm and consistent nurturance for the child, and the situation is even bleaker.

Children who are homeless during preschool and elementary school years may find their parents less playful and responsive than they would be in better circumstances. Children in families that are homeless are more likely to have a variety of health problems (Gargiulo, 2006; Weinreb et al., 1998) than their housed peers, which increases school absences. Frequent changes of location are disruptive to children's educational progress as well as their ability to establish stable friendship patterns. Studies have found that 52% of students experiencing homelessness are performing below grade level in reading, and 57% achieve below grade level in math (Rahman et al., 2015). Children who are homeless are more likely to exhibit emotional and behavioral problems at school (Masten et al., 1993) and may have diagnosable mental disorders as well. Homeless young children are more likely to have learning disabilities or to have intellectual disabilities than children in the general population (Gargiulo, 2006). Programs to remediate some of these difficulties are harder to access when there are frequent relocations, so the child is less likely to receive needed educational and psychological services than peers in stable homes. Again, homeless children are likely to have additional obstacles to confront in their development and to have fewer consistent resources to assist them.

Adolescents may be homeless with their families but are also homeless without supervision in greater numbers. Haber and Toro (2004) categorize homeless adolescents as *runaways* (left home without parental permission), *throwaways* (forced out of the home by parents), and *street youth* (who have been part of the street culture for a period of time). These authors say that at least 7.6%

of adolescents are homeless at some point during this developmental period. They tend to gravitate to large cities. Most adolescents who are homeless without families are 13 or older, but some homeless children without families have been found as young as 9 years old. As with adults, more males than females are homeless in adolescence, and African Americans, Native Americans, and those who are low income are over-represented among adolescent homeless.

A slightly different model of youth homelessness was used by researchers who studied service utilization by youth who are homeless (Carlson et al., 2006). They propose five stages. The first stage is the *immigrant* stage, when youth first encounter the street culture. In the *initiation* stage, the youth learn the culture from mentors. Next is the *stasis* stage, in which the youth is now part of the street culture and economy. For many, there comes a *disequilibrium* stage, which is a period of crisis that makes street life more tenuous. This is followed by the *extrication* stage for those who then attempt to leave the street culture. Carlson and her colleagues discovered that most participants in their sample of 185 youth and adolescents did access services when they were available, although they were surprised at the low rate of shelter use. Only half of those in the sample utilized medical services while on the streets. Those in the *stasis* stage were least likely to utilize any services.

Studies of adolescents who are homeless find that there has often been a pattern of residential instability in their families of origin, and previous institutional placement (e.g., foster care, group homes) is not unusual in this group. Histories of neglect and physical and sexual abuse are often reported. In fact, some adolescents left home as a way to stop the abuse. Adolescents may be particularly vulnerable to homelessness upon release from placements when they may fear returning to the situation in which their problems originated. Adolescents experiencing homelessness exhibit numerous learning problems; about 43% have been retained in a grade in school, with 11% having failed more than one grade (Smollar, 2001). It is also the case that many adolescents who become homeless did not attend school regularly when living at home. Adolescents who are homeless have higher rates of mood disorders and suicide attempts than matched groups of housed peers, and also have higher rates of substance abuse disorders, sexual activity, and disruptive behavior.

Homeless adolescents may come from unstable backgrounds, but the condition of being homeless exposes them to numerous additional risks. They are at high risk for such health problems as hepatitis, asthma and pneumonia, and scabies (Smollar, 2001). They are likely to form associations with deviant peer groups, which leads to antisocial behavior and exacerbates existing problems (Milburn et al., 2006). They may engage in illegal activities such as theft or prostitution in order to provide food and shelter, and they may be physically or sexually victimized. What happens, then, is that homelessness compounds the harm experienced in earlier family environments, often leading to a variety of serious legal, behavioral, and psychological problems that continue into adulthood. Many adults who are homeless report having been homeless in adolescence as well, so the prospect of recovery from these circumstances is poor.

Adolescents may experience discrimination based on their status as homeless or their race, ethnicity, or sexual orientation (Milburn et al., 2006). Discrimination may come from other homeless youth, family, police, and service providers. Milburn et al. predicted that the experience of discrimination might be an impetus to exit homelessness and return to stable housing. They interviewed 227 recently homeless adolescents in California, 60% of whom were female, 83% racial/ethnic minorities, and 16% LGBTQIA+. They found that discrimination was related only to sexual minority status; there were no significant differences in rates of discrimination by race or ethnicity. Also, for all groups except the sexual minority adolescents, reports of discrimination decreased at the 6-month follow-up interview. The only discrimination that was associated with homeless status was discrimination by families; those who reported discrimination by family members at baseline were more than twice as likely to have returned to stable housing within 6 months than others in the sample, although they did not necessarily return to live with their families.

Shelters are available in some communities for adolescent runaways, but most youth do not get services from the shelter system. One estimate is that only one in every 12 youth who experiences homelessness contacts a shelter. Smollar (2001) makes an interesting observation: Many adolescents who experience homelessness were unable to accomplish earlier developmental tasks that lead to a sense of competency and industry. The very fact of running away from home may be the first experience of having control and accomplishing a goal. Some of these youths do develop skills needed to survive on the streets and gain esteem from other youth experiencing homelessness based on these skills. Unfortunately, these skills (shoplifting, stealing, panhandling, hustling, etc.) are not those that provide esteem in mainstream society. Thus, the skills they acquire interfere with any efforts to reintegrate into society. Similarly, adolescents who had difficulty forming close relationships with family and peers when living at home may find the camaraderie of the streets to be very appealing, further distancing them from the mainstream.

For young adults who, according to Erikson's theory should be focused on forming enduring intimate relationships and establishing a career path, homelessness is likely to interfere with that developmental trajectory. In fact, as energy is devoted to survival (think of the bottom layer of Maslow's hierarchy), there is little left to focus on more traditional age-related tasks. Thus, homelessness interferes with development across the life span, and those who are homeless for more than a brief period are likely to confront numerous challenges. Without intervention, it is likely that homelessness becomes intergenerational, and as the numbers grow, society may be forced to address this problem with more resources and more broadly based programming. In-depth interviews with 31 young adults who were homeless in Arizona revealed that barriers to exiting homelessness included insufficient resources, difficulties getting and keeping employment, perceived discrimination by law enforcement, transportation problems, and legal issues. Further, personal issues such as mental and physical health problems and lack of money management skills were additional obstacles to exiting homelessness (Sample & Ferguson, 2020).

Digital Media

In the digital age, smartphones, tablets, and laptops are ubiquitous. Perhaps surprisingly, digital media plays an important role in the lives of people who are homeless. In an Australian study, Humphry (2019) found that 95% of her participants, all of whom were experiencing homelessness, owned a mobile phone; smartphones accounted for 77% of those phones. Similar rates were found in other samples (Heaslip et al., 2021; Rhoades et al., 2017), with older people generally having lower rates. Rhoades et al. (2017) observed that rates of cell phone ownership were slightly higher in the homeless population than in comparable samples in the general population. In this section, we discuss the ways in which digital devices are valuable tools for people experiencing homelessness and point out challenges that may keep them from utilizing these advantages.

Digital media contain important information about resources, services, food banks, health care facilities, housing assistance programs, and employment and training opportunities. For some of these resources, applications must be submitted online, so having a device (usually a mobile phone) with internet access is useful. Although ownership of mobile phones among people who are homeless is common, they may not be able to afford the associated costs: data plans, access to Wi-Fi, and so on. One way to manage this is to purchase a *burner phone,* a less expensive option, which comes with prepaid minutes and is typically used for a brief period of time. Humphry (2019) indicated that this is the preferred option for many people who are homeless. While this is an advantage, the user will not have a consistent phone number that can be used to reach them. Consider someone who has applied for a job, and the potential employer needs to contact them to inform them of the status of their application. Family members may wish to check on the person who is homeless and, particularly if they move from one location to another, being able to reach them by phone is a useful way to do so. Using these temporary phones, with different numbers, is problematic.

Digital media enables people who are experiencing homelessness to communicate with family and friends and use social networks, email, and messaging apps. Having a way to communicate with others reduces social isolation, which contributes to mental health disorders (Thurman et al., 2021). Communication was the top use for mobile phones, followed by contacting support services (Humphry, 2019). Job searches can be conducted online, and applications submitted. There are also numerous free online educational and skill training tutorials, videos, and courses. This is an excellent way to gain new skills and knowledge and enhance or improve existing skills. There are also apps to send notifications of appointments, medication reminders, and encouraging messages that some will find helpful. Since the expansion of digital mental health services during the pandemic, people who are homeless can engage in counseling and therapy without having to manage transportation issues. The continued use of telehealth for mental health services is expected and hopefully will expand outpatient treatment options for this population. In fact, Heaslip et al. (2021) reported that people experiencing homelessness are five times more likely to seek online help than people with stable housing, although this activity decreases by 2% for each month of homelessness.

An interesting research study was conducted in two parts with a convenience sample of people experiencing homelessness. The first part was conducted over a 4-month period and the second for 1 month (Thurman et al., 2021). The 31 participants were an average of 42.7 years old (68% male, 68% White) and had been experiencing homelessness for an average of 7.4 years (including one participant who had been experiencing homelessness for 30 years!). Eighty-one percent of participants were unsheltered. Inclusion criteria included having a chronic health condition and having been given a prescription for medication. Of those with health conditions, 23% had anxiety or depression, 16% had been diagnosed with bipolar disorder, and 13% suffered from a brain injury. At the start of the study, all participants received a smartphone with unlimited text, calling, and data and public transportation. Quotations from participants about having technology were enlightening. These are direct quotations from the article: "The new phone is so amazing. It will take you around the world," "It's like a life assistant," and "Phones are so important to have nowadays. You really have to have one to be able to keep track of everything." On the other hand, Marler (2021), who based on his observations on 80 individuals experiencing homelessness and interviews with five of those participants, observed that when instances of strangers assisting others needing help were publicized on social media, some of the participants developed the belief that they could use social media and crowdfunding to get financial assistance. This strategy was not successful. Some of the participants in this study did use social media to connect with others but were reluctant to reveal that they were experiencing homelessness and/or were jobless in the interest of privacy and safety by exposing themselves online (allowing people with whom they had hostile relationships to know personal details about their lives).

In another study, researchers interviewed 87 young adults (18–21 years old, 75% Black, 14% LGBTQIA+) who were experiencing homelessness. More than half of the participants used the internet daily (via smartphones or public computers); those with smartphones were three times as likely to do so. Participants were interviewed about their experiences before they experienced homelessness and during the period they did experience homelessness. Data included survey responses and interviews. Researchers asked about the potential for a website specific to homeless youth, and all expressed interest. They suggested youth be involved in website development to ensure it would be relevant to their needs and recommended using social media and other digital tools to publicize it. Topics they thought should be included were housing, food, jobs, health, education, services, and important phone numbers. They also thought it would be valuable to have a secure web-based storage site for important documents to ensure the information they contained would not be lost.

Many people experiencing homelessness value access to entertainment—streaming videos, online games, and so forth. These can be distractions from or ways to reduce stress (Heaslip et al., 2021). Marler (2021) points out that for people experiencing homelessness, "digital leisure" (i.e., using the internet for entertainment and passing time) is one way to cope with the stress of current circumstances. He argues that there is evidence that engaging in such leisure activities is associated with improved mental health and well-being and contends that such activities are as beneficial as other activities more often discussed and studied.

An important benefit of access to online resources is the large number and varied platforms that offer mental health information, self-help programs, counseling services, and support groups or communities. Many are free to use, although some offer enhanced affordances for a fee. (See Chapter 2 in Bauman and Rivers [2023] for recommendations for apps and sites for mental health.) Mobile phones have the ability to contact emergency services when needed. Practitioners need to be familiar with these resources and assist people experiencing homelessness in making the best choices, particularly in self-help apps.

The most obvious challenge to using digital resources is lack of access. Not only is cost a factor, but having access to reliable connections may be a barrier. Some public spaces (e.g., libraries, agencies, some shelters) have computers available to the public, but many have time limits for usage and may have wait times for availability (Marler, 2021). In addition, other rules at some facilities (e.g., enforcing quiet) might discourage those who enjoy sharing the screen with a friend and discussing the content. In addition to access, these devices need to be charged, and finding a place to do so is another obstacle that must be overcome. The living situations of people who are homeless are often vulnerable to theft, given limited places to store devices securely, and loss or breakage can also disrupt access.

Some people who are homeless, particularly older individuals, may not have skills to use digital devices or platforms and would require training to be able to use them effectively. It is essential that they understand the importance of data security and privacy to avoid being targeted by cyber-criminals or trolls. Others may be hampered by discrimination. In a Canadian study (Zerger et al., 2014), people experiencing homelessness in their sample of 231 diverse participants found that 61% perceived discrimination based on their status, while 51% reported discrimination based on race/ethnicity, and mental health status and substance abuse was the basis for discrimination for 44%. Others who perceived discrimination were immigrants and those whose homelessness was chronic.

Mental health practitioners may work with people experiencing homelessness when an existing client finds themselves in that situation. Others may choose to work with this population in agencies or organizations that are dedicated to assisting people experiencing homelessness in improving their life and well-being. This section is background information that might facilitate understanding and lead to stronger therapeutic alliance. Given the high rates of mental illness and substance abuse among people who are homeless, there is a pressing need for mental health professionals to assess children exhibiting symptoms of possible disorders.

Assessment

To detect homelessness, sophisticated assessment tools are not required. However, two diagnoses for which those experiencing homelessness are at high risk should be investigated whenever possible. Substance use disorders have very high prevalence rates in those experiencing homelessness, and determining whether treatment for that disorder is needed and available should be part of any needs assessment for an individual experiencing homelessness. Mental disorders (e.g., mood disorders and schizophrenia) are also frequently detected and should be screened for routinely. Agencies serving homeless populations ideally should gather as much information as possible so that programs can be planned to maximize strengths (e.g., prior education and work experiences, family bonds) to remediate deficiencies. Programs that provide housing support without other services are unlikely to have the kind of effect anticipated, as homelessness creates additional problems (see the discussion about trauma) that must be treated over a long period.

Treatment Options and Considerations

It is not homelessness per se that most helping professionals will treat. Because associated conditions—substance abuse and mental disorders or family violence—are more likely to bring the client to a helping professional, the reader is directed to the relevant chapters for information on treatment. It is important to keep in mind that treatment for any disorder is not likely to be effective unless it is part of an integrative service approach that considers all the needs of an individual or family and includes extensive follow-up and support services. The helping professional will need to create a network of collaboration to address the many and varied needs of this population.

A major concern for those experiencing homelessness who are severely mentally ill is the lack of availability of services, from outpatient to long-term institutional care. Comprehensive, integrated systems of services for this population should include readily available on-site mental health care. Helping professionals, in their role as advocates, might explore this possibility in their own communities. It is encouraging that both self-help and professional counseling can be obtained online, which may provide access to some who might otherwise not get any assistance at all.

Issues of Diversity

Data from 2004 indicated that 40% of those experiencing homelessness were African American, 40% Caucasian, 11% Hispanic, 8% Native American, and 1% Other (National Homelessness Law Center, 2022). Among the homeless, about 33% of men are veterans, compared to 23% in the overall population. About 47% of homeless men served during the Vietnam era, 67% were in the military for at least 3 years, 33% were stationed in a combat zone, and 89% were honorably discharged from the service (National Coalition for Homeless Veterans, n.d.) About 25% of the single homeless adults are severely and chronically mentally ill. However, it is estimated that only 5%–7 % of the mentally ill experiencing homelessness need to be institutionalized. Sexual minority youth are over-represented among those experiencing homelessness, with studies finding 20%–40% of youth experiencing homelessness identifying as sexual minority (Ray, 2006). A more nuanced study of youth with several marginalized identities found that low parent caring was an important predictor of youth experiencing unstable housing (Houghtaling et al., 2024). The extent of discrimination against sexual minority homeless youth is such that Milburn et al. (2006) recommend that shelters and services allocate specific spaces for sexual minority youth so that their safety can be assured. Another group that is over-represented among those experiencing homelessness is individuals with HIV/AIDS; 3.3% of people experiencing homelessness are HIV positive compared to 1.8% of those with stable housing (Thakarar et al., 2016).

In many ways, working with the homeless population epitomizes issues of diversity in helping professions. Employed counselors are members of mainstream society; they are professionals worthy of respect. They may represent a minority ethnic or racial group, a sexual or religious minority, but they are not homeless, and in most cases, have never been homeless or had significant contact with those experiencing homelessness. Helping professionals must acknowledge their biases and limitations and work to develop awareness and attitudes that do not impair their ability to work with this population. Those experiencing homelessness who are also members of other diverse groups may experience a heightened sense that the clinician comes from another planet and cannot have any empathy or understanding for their plight. Individuals experiencing homelessness are likely to assume (often correctly) that counselors judge them and don't believe they are worthy of assistance.

While developing empathy and understanding for individuals who have different experiences and hold vastly different values is no easy task, recognizing the barriers and acknowledging them ("I've never experienced homelessness and can't imagine what it would be like to live under the highway like you do") is a step in the right direction. Also, it is essential that the counselor realize that while they may not share life experiences with those who experience homelessness, we all have had experiences that engender the same emotional responses: loneliness, incompetence, estrangement, anger, distrust, frustration, loss of hope, depression, and so on. We may not be able to identify with the day-to-day experiences of the homeless, but the feelings are ones that all human beings feel. They may be more intense, or more chronic, but tapping into your own feelings may help increase your empathy for these clients, and thus increase your ability to provide a useful service.

Our final point regarding those experiencing homelessness as a diverse group in our society is this: Finding assets amid the debris that is the person's current life is necessary and important. What strengths does the person have (or had in the past) that can be enhanced and amplified to assist them in their current situation? Most times, the deficits are so apparent and flagrant that valuable characteristics and strengths are ignored (or assumed not to exist), depriving people experiencing homelessness of an opportunity to generate a more balanced view of themselves. Noticing strengths is an important component of counseling people experiencing homelessness and is a small step toward reducing the hopelessness that so often keeps these individuals down.

Counselor Issues

Counselors, like many people in contemporary America, may find people experiencing homelessness frightening, repulsive, or otherwise deplorable. There is a widespread misconception that people experiencing homelessness are all drunks and drug addicts who do not want to work and that their condition is a matter of choice. In other words, if they would just sober up and get a job like the rest of us, they would be productive members of society.

These attitudes obviously would interfere with one's ability to be helpful to individuals experiencing homelessness. Hopefully, reading this chapter and consulting some of the additional resources will help mental health professionals recognize the harm in such beliefs. Recognizing that people experiencing homelessness may no longer be able to conform to mainstream standards for hygiene and appearance may increase tolerance for differences.

Clients who are homeless, if they can somehow be engaged in counseling, exhibit other behaviors that can be very frustrating for counselors. People experiencing homelessness may have trouble keeping appointments. Living situations and transportation problems often interfere, and people experiencing homelessness may not be attuned to keeping a calendar or schedule. One homeless man who had been terminated from his counseling program because of frequent no-shows told me that he requested a standing appointment on the same day and time every week (which seemed to be a reasonable request). He was told that was not possible, and he found it too hard to manage varying appointments. Counselors might assist these people by accessing case management services to help them get transportation rather than criticize them for being irresponsible. Counselors might also arrange to provide services at a homeless shelter or agency close to where homeless people congregate to minimize transportation difficulties.

All counselors working with people experiencing homelessness need to be very mindful of the learned helplessness pattern that is so pervasive in this population. People experiencing homelessness may enter counseling to meet the requirements of a service, or if it is residential, to get a respite from the streets, but they are likely to be hopeless about their situation and to believe they are incapable of making changes. They also may lack the kind of social support necessary if they are to maintain any programs in the community. Helping professionals need to assist them with all these matters if they are to be of any real service to these individuals.

Finally, counselors should consider their role as advocates for this population. The school counselor might remind school officials of their legal obligation to make a variety of accommodations for homeless students. In other settings, the counselor may need to advocate for exceptions to agency policies to allow those experiencing homelessness to participate in various programs. Most important, as programs and services (e.g., shelters) are considered, counselors might attempt to combat the NIMBY (not in my backyard) syndrome and persuade communities to provide services to this population.

A NOTE TO SCHOOL COUNSELORS

School counselors provide essential and invaluable services to youth experiencing homelessness. School may be the only predictable element in the lives of children experiencing homelessness, and it is important that the school counselor make certain that these children are able to participate fully in their educational experience, and to see that barriers and obstacles are removed. Walsh and Buckley (1994) described the dilemma, saying "on the one hand, school can serve as a haven for these children, providing them with stability and security in an otherwise chaotic world . . . . On the other hand, school can be a source of frustration and pain as a result of academic and social struggles as well as the stigma of being homeless" (p. 6).

The ASCA (2018) has a position statement that is worth restating here and with which every school counselor should be familiar:

School counselors recognize that homelessness/displacement may greatly affect the whole child, encompassing mental, physical, social/emotional and academic development. School counselors help to identify students who are experiencing homelessness. As social justice advocates, it is school counselors' duty to recognize and work with students around their specific strengths. School counselors collaborate with community stakeholders to connect students and their families who are experiencing homelessness to community supports, work to remove barriers to academic success and implement responsive prevention and intervention programs for children experiencing homelessness. (para. 1)

The statement reiterates that "The McKinney-Vento Act, as amended by the *Every Student Succeeds Act* (*ESSA*), outlines the rights of homeless students and creates directives for schools to ensure students are able to enroll and succeed in school (U.S. Department of Education, 2017). This charge includes removal of institutional barriers within schools, such as transportation, immunization and physical examination requirements, fees, residency and birth certificate requirements and lack of school records impeding homeless families' ability to enroll their children in schools" (ASCA, 2018, para. 4). This document includes additional content about the role of the school counselor with respect for students experiencing homelessness, and we recommend all school counselors review that document carefully.

Unlike the definitions of *homelessness* used by other agencies to determine eligibility for services, the McKinney-Vento Act includes youth who are staying in shared housing (staying with relatives, couch surfing) or living in hotels or campgrounds, cars, or in unsafe housing (squatting). The requirements of this law include enrolling students experiencing homelessness even when the necessary paperwork is not available, providing transportation to the school they attended prior to experiencing homelessness, and assigning persons responsible for overseeing the implementation of the legislation.

Although teachers have the most frequent direct contact with students, they rarely have any preparation for working with youth experiencing homelessness. Those students may exhibit behavior difficulties, may have academic struggles and uneven attendance, and may be targets of victimization by peers due to unavailability of basic hygiene facilities and suitable clothing. The school counselor can serve as a consultant to teachers, helping them identify children who are homeless, suggest strategies to engage them in classroom activities, and so on. Identification can be challenging as children are aware of the stigma of homelessness and may be reluctant to disclose that status. The school counselor can meet with each student who enrolls at times other than the start of the year and will find clues in the paperwork and/or may have contact with the parent and gather information. They can also work with the school or agency social workers to connect students and parents to available resources and services. The counselor can meet the child when they first enroll to begin building a relationship and can monitor progress both by checking in briefly every day with the child and/or helping them find a buddy—a student volunteer who helps acculturate the new student (homeless or not) to the school's norms and informal culture. The counselor collaborates with other school personnel (e.g., nurse, social worker) to develop a team approach to assisting the child. The school counselor can serve as a liaison to the parent/guardian whenever possible.

The limited research on school counselors' work with students experiencing homelessness revealed that they had limited or no preparation for working with this population. In one study 23 school counselors interviewed by researchers emphasized two main themes: feeling that they were the "first line of support" and feeling helpless to provide the help the children needed (Havlik et al., 2017–2018). They saw themselves as the primary conduit to services to meet students' basic needs for reliable transportation to and from school clothing, school supplies, and costs for incidentals such as field trips. As mental health professionals, school counselors can provide individual and group counseling services to help students with social-emotional needs. Several participants expressed frustration that after working with a child and seeing initial progress, the student moved again, and the counselor could not continue to work with the youth or receive updates. It can be helpful to share stories like that of Richard Jenkins, who lived in homeless shelters for most of his childhood. Determined to lift himself and his family out of homelessness, he early on decided he wanted to obtain a quality education. Fortunately, he benefitted from an after-school program in middle school to improve his skills. His academic potential secured a place in a boarding high school. Mr. Jenkins graduated in 2022 (debt free) from Harvard with a bachelor's degree in computer science (Hess, 2018).

Children experiencing homelessness need assistance from school counselors because their circumstances negatively impact their development, and they come to school with fewer skills and internal resources than their peers (Baggerly & Borowski, 2004). Children experiencing homelessness are frequently embarrassed by their homelessness and seek to hide that fact from peers and teachers, which serves to isolate them socially. In addition, frequent family relocation and uncertain living conditions have kept many children from developing age-appropriate social skills, which adds to the challenge of making friends in a new school. They often bring behavioral problems, such as aggressive behavior, and/or emotional problems, such as depression and anxiety. Academically, they are more likely to have learning disabilities and to struggle academically (Strawser et al., 2000; Walsh & Buckley, 1994). Children experiencing homelessness often miss a considerable number of days of school and may find that the academic curriculum and expectations at a new school are different from those of their last school, amplifying academic challenges. When students change schools, records might not be immediately available, so important services (e.g., speech therapy) may not be provided right away. Living conditions may make doing homework quite difficult, making it hard for children to keep up with assignments.

Baggerly and Borowski (2004) suggested that school counselors provide services in the four components of the ASCA national model: prevention, individual planning, responsive services, and system support. For the prevention component, various age-appropriate social skills programs can be delivered to all students as part of the classroom guidance curriculum. Classroom management systems, including token economies, will also benefit all students, particularly those who may struggle with self-regulation (e.g., those experiencing homelessness). The individual

(Continued)

planning component of services includes assessment, and the school counselor can select appropriate measures to gain a complete picture of the child's academic, social, and emotional functioning. When necessary, referrals can be made for further testing to determine eligibility for special education services. It is beyond the scope of this chapter to list assessment tools the counselor might want to use, but they will have guidance in that regard from their own districts. Responsive services are based on a developmental approach, so the strategies selected will depend on the child's needs and developmental level. Other strategies might include individual and group counseling, to be described in more detail next. System support can include working with teachers to develop strategies for the classroom that can be used to enable children experiencing homelessness to be successful. Further, the school counselor can design a system for collecting needed data so that each child's needs can be quickly understood and appropriate interventions implemented (Strawser et al., 2000).

The school counselor will also want to ensure that children experiencing homelessness have access to available services, such as tutoring, after-school programs, and summer programs (Strawser et al., 2000). Programs that offer school supplies and clothing are also needed for these children, who are unlikely to be able to afford them. Arrangements to use school showers may be helpful to students who are unable to attend to personal hygiene in overcrowded shelters or makeshift living situations. One significant role that school counselors must play is that of advocate who knows the requirements of the McKinney-Vento Act (reauthorized in 2015 as part of Title IX, Part A of the Every Student Succeeds Act) and can insist that they be applied.

Establishing a collaborative relationship with the parents or guardians of children experiencing homelessness is an important but daunting task for the school counselor. Keep in mind that the parent may be wary of school personnel, fearing that they may report them to protective services. A good relationship with local shelters and homeless service providers can facilitate a child's transition to a new school, with school counselors serving as a liaison.

Strawser et al. (2000) make many other suggestions for the school counselor, which will be helpful to all students but particularly to students experiencing homelessness. An organized orientation program for new students alleviates many anxieties for new students, and a student buddy can be a helpful adjunct to other strategies. Short-term groups for new students can assist all children in acclimating to the new setting and would be very helpful for children experiencing homelessness. Classroom activities that increase awareness and appreciation of diversity among students, in addition to lessons designed to learn social skills and stress management, are additional activities that school counselors deliver. Whenever possible, services to parents can have a big effect on student success in school, so offering parenting workshops at times when parents experiencing homelessness might attend is a wonderful contribution. In addition, having material available for parents on local resources for food and medical services in the area is important.

Per the KcKinney-Vento Act, school districts are required to have a person designated to be the liaison for children experiencing homelessness, and it would be useful for the school counselor to establish a line of communication with that person. Finally, providing training to teachers and other school staff about homelessness is essential. In order to ensure such training is current, school counselors need to keep abreast of current literature and attend conferences on the educational needs of children experiencing homelessness.

A qualitative study conducted in 1997 utilized interviews with 21 students experiencing homelessness who were residing in shelters and who attended six public schools in Hawai'i (Daniels et al., 1997). Although 14 participants said they knew who their counselor was, seven (33%) said they did not know the counselor at all or very well. If school counselors are to have an impact on students experiencing homelessness, they must make themselves both visible and available to them. Although the participants seemed to understand the school counselor's role, only two said they would go to the counselor for help. Students said they would like assistance with school-related concerns, their living situations, and interpersonal challenges. In order for counselors to provide this help, Daniels et al. suggest that school counselors reach out to the students without drawing attention to their homelessness. They also recommend that school counselors work to create a positive and welcoming school climate in which all students are respected and that they consider peer counseling programs, which might offer help to students who are uncomfortable approaching adults.

Small group counseling interventions can be helpful for many students, including those experiencing homelessness. Daniels et al. (1999) provided a group intervention for eight students and their mothers, with the goal of reducing family conflict by improving problem-solving skills. The intervention received positive evaluation from participants. Another school-based group intervention was delivered to low-income students and students experiencing homelessness in conjunction with a summer school program. Parent groups were also included in the program. The program was delivered by trained clinicians, but school personnel attended. Manuals were produced so the program could be available in other settings. Researchers found statistically significant positive changes in functioning as rated by teachers and parents. No control group was used. On the survey completed by parents before and at the end of the program, the parents of homeless children rated their children's grades higher than did parents of other children in the program. While these reports are encouraging, more rigorous research remains to be conducted to confirm positive findings.

To summarize, the school counselor has a crucial role to play with students experiencing homelessness. In addition to supporting the children's achievement in school, I hope that by helping the children (and the parents), these children will not become the next generation of adults who experience homelessness.

Ethical Concerns

While there are no specific ethical guidelines for working with the homeless, counselors must be mindful of their primary duty to do no harm and to treat clients with dignity and respect. Counselors working with those experiencing homelessness or other difficult clientele should obtain supervision and consultation as needed with other professionals. Counselors must closely monitor their own reactions and discuss negative transference with supervisors.

A major dilemma for school personnel, including school counselors, as mandatory reporters, is whether being homeless is something that must be reported. That varies by jurisdiction, so it is imperative that school counselors know the legal requirements of their state and school district. In many places, it is not homelessness itself but the inability to provide for the basic needs of children (food, medical care, safety, and security) that precipitates removal of the child. According to Youth.gov (n.d.), 21%–53% of youth experiencing homelessness have been placed in foster care or an institutional setting. Parents and children have a vested interest in concealing their status in a desire to remain together. Children experiencing homelessness often have ACEs, including experiencing trauma, and children experiencing homelessness have high rates of becoming homeless as young adults.

Summary

- Children and young people experiencing homelessness face difficult obstacles to health development because of their lack of housing stability.
- These youth are also likely to have experienced other traumas and may struggle academically and socially at school.
- Theories of development help frame the perspective of helping professionals who work with this population.
- Programs do exist to help move people experiencing homelessness into permanent housing, employment, and mental and physical health care.
- Counselors are pivotal resources for these people, and they need to reconsider how they go about providing effective services in this context.

Additional Resources

On the Web for Counselors

- http://www.nationalhomeless.org/ is the website for the National Coalition for the Homeless; it has a wealth of information on all aspects of homelessness and is highly recommended.
- http://www.familyhomelessness.org is the National Center on Family Homelessness website, another goldmine of information you will want to visit.
- http://www.nlchp.org/ is the National Law Center of Homelessness and Poverty's website.
- http://www.endhomelessness.org/ is the National Alliance to End Homelessness's website, which has additional information and is an excellent resource.
- http://state.ia.us/educate/ecese/is/homeless/doc/scr.html is for school counselors; this is a one-stop website that has everything imaginable, including lesson plans and guidance curricula, community activities, educational materials that can be reproduced, links, reading lists for children, and so on. In fact, anyone working with children will want to bookmark this website.
- https://store.samhsa.gov/product/TIP-55-Behavioral-Health-Services-for-People-Who-Are-Homeless/SMA15-4734 is is an extremely comprehensive resource that mental health professionals who work with this population will find invaluable. It can be downloaded from this site or ordered in print version.
- https://www.nytimes.com/2023/05/13/us/san-diego-homelessness.html is a very moving story about a man who is homeless and a counselor who worked with him. It is too long to include in this book, but we strongly recommend reading it.
- For those who work with children and families experiencing homelessness, this downloadable book is extremely thorough and practical: https://www.researchgate.net/publication/335738850_Responsive_Early_Education_for_Young_Children_and_Families_Experiencing_Homelessness.
- A detailed review of the current legislation regarding the McKinney-Vento Homeless Assistance Act can be retrieved from https://www2.ed.gov/policy/elsec/leg/essa/160240e-hcyguidance072716updated0317.pdf.

In Print for Counselors

A number of recent nonfiction books examining various aspects of homelessness include the following:

- Colburn, G., & Aldern, C. P. (2022). *Homelessness is a housing problem: How structural factors explain U.S. patterns.* University of California Press.
- Shinn, M., & Khadduri, J. (2020). *In the midst of plenty: Homelessness and what to do about it.* Wiley-Blackwell.
- Gibbs, L., Bainbridge, J., Rosenblatt, M., & Mammo, T. (2021). *How ten global cities take on homelessness: Innovations that work.* University of California Press.
- Winegarden, W., Tartakovsky, J., Jackson, K., & Rufo, C. F. (2021). *No way home: The crisis of homelessness and how to fix it.* Encounter Books.
- *Grand Central Winter: Stories From the Street* by Lee Stringer is a touching first-person account of life as a homeless person, which helps the reader understand this situation on a more personal level.
- *Street Crazy* by Stephen Seager is an excellent account of the mentally ill homeless population in a highly readable format and should be on the reading list of anyone who works with this population.

- *Tell Them Who I Am by* Elliot Liebow's is a moving portrait of women experiencing homelessness and is another enlightening and highly readable perspective.
- *The Street Lawyer* by John Grisham is a novel. The protagonist is an attorney who has lived a life of privilege with little real concern for those less fortunate. A series of events compels him to become familiar with those experiencing homelessness, and because of his need to learn about this population, the reader learns as well.

Film and Television

- A good list and descriptions of movies featuring homeless themes is available here: https://www.springsrescuemission.org/top-10-movies-about-homelessness/.
- Best social justice documentaries on Netflix: https://movieweb.com/social-justice-documentaries-netflix/.
- *Homeless to Harvard* is a film based on a true account of a homeless high school student and is helpful in balancing the viewer's perspective on those experiencing homelessness. The protagonist, Liz, is remarkably resilient, and her efforts to change her life are inspiring.
- *Dark Days* is a documentary that will open the viewer's eyes to the homeless experience. The film takes the viewer to a community of those experiencing homelessness in the tunnels of New York's subways, and we have the opportunity to see them through their eyes. The language is raw, but the film awakens the viewer to the reality of the lives of these people.

Exercises

1. Assume a person experiencing homelessness has been mandated (as a result of a legal violation) to come to you for substance abuse counseling on an outpatient basis. Discuss how you would work differently with this person than you would with a housed individual with a similar problem.

2. Volunteer in a homeless shelter or soup kitchen. As part of that experience, have at least one extended conversation with a person experiencing homelessness and find out what happened to make them homeless. Write a brief case study about the person you interviewed and what a mental health professional would need to know to be effective with this person.

3. Volunteer in a children's program in a homeless shelter as a tutor or daycare provider. Write a reflection paper about your experience.

4. Watch *Homeless to Harvard* and discuss what you think enabled Liz to be so resilient.

5. Imagine that you are going to do outreach to the people in the film *Dark Days*. What would be the role of a counselor in that community? What kinds of services would you want to obtain for them? What keeps them in the homeless life?

6. Prepare a presentation for school counselors and/or teachers to help them work more effectively with students experiencing homelessness.

7. Investigate the resources available for people experiencing homelessness in your community and compile an annotated resource list.

8. Interview a mental health professional who works with clients experiencing homelessness and write a reflection that includes what you learned and your reaction to the interaction.

Credits

CHAPTER 5

Grief and Bereavement

In the 21st century, only about a third of Americans die at home; most deaths take place in hospitals, and hospice

Introduction

Facilities or nursing homes are the third most common place of death (Olaisen, 2020). A hundred years ago, death at home was a common event. Bodies were not embalmed and were viewed at home before burial. Now, funeral preparations take place out of sight of the family, and funerals are typically held away from the home. By the time the body is viewed, it has generally been embalmed and otherwise treated so it appears lifelike (in repose, sleeping), protecting viewers from the reality of death. In the work setting, bereavement leave is often limited to 3 days, suggesting that is enough time to grieve and is only for death in the immediate family. These factors all contribute to the difficulty some people experience managing grief.

During the pandemic, the number of deaths was staggering—3,464,231, of which COVID-19 was the cause of death for 416,893. Some families experienced multiple losses, and because of concerns about contagion, there were numerous cases when families were unable to visit their dying loved ones or even hold a funeral. This has left many with prolonged grief. (See Chapter 2 for a full discussion of this issue.)

This topic is different from all of the others covered in this book in that grief is the one experience that mental health professionals are sure to experience personally at some time in their lives. Death and loss are inevitable and painful aspects of the human experience. Because counselors dealing with grieving clients know that this issue is one they have faced or will face personally, self-awareness is particularly important to ensure that it is the client's, rather than the counselor's, needs that are the focus of counseling. Grieving is not a mental disorder, and individuals who are grieving don't always need counseling. In fact, most people manage this experience without complications and with available support in their environment. However, there are cases when a counselor, grief specialist or not, will encounter a grieving client for whom environmental support is absent or insufficient for their needs. There are also some individuals for whom grief becomes complicated, and these people may seek counseling or be referred for counseling to assist them in returning to an adaptive level of functioning.

Terminology

Although these terms are not technical jargon, they nevertheless should be defined clearly. Grief refers to the emotional aspect of loss, the painful feelings experienced when a person faces a loss (Dershimer, 1990). Grief is a normal response to loss. Losses other than death can cause the experience of grief, although in this chapter we will focus on the grief experience following death. Mourning refers to the actions and behaviors that accompany the feeling of grief in an attempt to adapt to the loss. Mourning is the public expression of grief and is strongly influenced by cultural and societal rituals and expectations. Bereavement is a broader concept, referring to the time period during which the person is in the process of recovering from the death of a significant person in their life. Complicated grief refers to a condition in which symptoms are more intense and of longer duration than is usual in the culture. In the DSM-V (2013), a diagnosis of persistent complex bereavement disorder is indicated when the grief is severe and symptoms are present for at least 12 months and accompanied by a "significant distress of impairment in psychosocial functioning" (p. 791). The DSM-V-TR includes a diagnosis of prolonged grief disorder. This will be discussed in more detail later in the chapter.

CASE STUDY

James was a 21-year-old college senior when his mother died by suicide. She was 50 years old, a professional nurse, in good health. A year or so before her death, her husband of 25 years announced his intention to divorce her. Her husband accepted a new job and was living in the new city, visiting home on occasion. In addition to James, she had two other sons, one 2 years older than James, and another who was 10 years old at the time of her death.

The summer prior to his junior year, James was working in another state when his father called, asking him to come home because his mother was "not well." When he landed, his mother met him at the airport, and James was confused. Later, James's father told him that she had attempted suicide by taking an overdose of medication, but James had difficulty absorbing that information since she appeared to be fine. He stayed with them for a week, and in an effort to be helpful, arranged for couples' therapy for his parents. He believes they went a few times.

James returned to his summer job, and a month later, his father called to say his mother had "done it again." James left his job and returned home, where he stayed at his mother's hospital bedside for several days. James felt burdened, and then relieved when arrangements were made for her to enter a psychiatric hospital. After a month-long hospital stay, his mother was discharged, and arrangements made for her to live with a married sister in another city. James drove his mother to her sister's home and recalls that on the long trip his mother was obviously sad, and said she wanted to drink. During the drive, James felt trapped and again burdened with responsibility for his mother.

James eventually returned to college, and his mother remained with her sister. She found a good job, enrolled her younger son in school, and even received a promotion. James came home for Thanksgiving and Christmas, and his father also visited on those holidays. James had a sense that things were tenuous, but his father was there, and he was somewhat reassured. He visited again on his college spring break. At that time, James and his mother discussed plans for James's upcoming graduation in May, and she showed him the dress she had chosen to wear for the occasion. She was concerned about James's plans after graduation, and he told her he was considering either an international position or teaching in the United States. His mother said that if he decided to teach, he could do so in the city where she was now living, and they could live together. James, ready to begin his independent adult life, said he did not want to do that. James returned to college to complete his senior semester. That conversation haunted him for years after her death; he felt guilty for telling her that he did not want to live with her after graduation and felt that he had contributed to her decision to end her life.

Shortly after James's visit, James's aunt and uncle wanted to go out of town to visit their own adult children but were concerned about leaving James's mother alone. She urged them to go, saying her husband would be visiting and they needed privacy. James's father did indeed visit. Just a few weeks after James's visit with his mother, his father called to say his mother had taken another overdose of medication and urged James to come home again. One of his college roommates drove James to the hospital and provided emotional support on the long drive.

James saw his mother in the hospital. His aunt told James that she was not going to make it this time, but he was numb and did not react. James's mother remained in a coma for a week, and then they received the phone call from the hospital telling them of her death. James's father told him that his mother had died of a stroke, and he clung to that explanation, which was easier to accept than suicide. James accompanied his father and uncle to the hospital, returned home, and went to bed, all without crying or really feeling the impact of the loss. The next morning when he awoke, however, he experienced a crushing feeling when he realized she was not there and would never be. The tears and sadness overwhelmed him. When James's father saw him crying, he said "Let me give you this" (a pill, probably Valium) and the tears stopped; they did not return for many years.

James's father eventually gave this account of events: He and James's mother were talking and drinking when his mother announced that she felt tired and cold and wanted to lie down. She went to her upstairs bedroom. When it seemed to his father that she was gone a long time, he went upstairs and found her unconscious and called for an ambulance. When the emergency personnel were taking his mother to the ambulance, they bumped into a grandfather clock, which stopped. After her death, the police came to investigate the death, and the time on the clock turned out to be discrepant with James's father's account of events. The police wondered about foul play and wanted to exhume the body, but James's aunt denied permission to do so. When James learned of the police request about 6 weeks later, he focused on that situation, believing he would have given permission. He also experienced a shock when he saw the death certificate, with the cause of death given as "suicide." He had chosen to believe his father's explanation of a stroke and seeing "suicide" on an official document forced him to confront reality. He was embarrassed to tell anyone that his mother died of suicide, and that feeling continued well into adulthood.

James was a cosignatory on a bank account with his mother, so he knew that she had been saving money for the future, and he believed she had goals and was thinking of the future. This added to his confusion about her death.

Many relatives and friends came to the funeral. James viewed his mother's body but did not touch it. He remained unemotional throughout the funeral and burial rites. He stayed at home for a week after the funeral and then returned to school and dedicated himself to finishing his courses. He saw a counselor on campus two or three times and found it helpful to talk to someone about his feelings. He chose not to attend his graduation ceremony.

Another blow came when James's father telephoned him at school 2 weeks after his mother's death to announce that he had remarried. James was shocked and angry. When he told his concerned roommates what his father had done, one of the roommates reacted, saying how terrible it was for his father to do such a thing. James turned on his roommate, releasing his anger, and the friendship never recovered.

James's emotions focused on his anger at his father's quick remarriage rather than on his feelings about his mother's death. He thought of his father as selfish and inconsiderate but did not think much about what his mother's role was in the tragedy. James has kept some reminders of his mother: a vase that she loved, a sweater she knitted for him when he was in junior high school, letters she had written to him, and family pictures.

After graduation, James gladly accepted a position that would take him overseas for 4 years. He was immersed in learning another language and culture, loved his work, and did it well. During his first year abroad, he had recurrent nightmares about his mother. He came home for a visit after being gone for a year and had an honest talk with his father, telling him how hard it was to see him remarried and to see his father's new wife using his mother's things. His father listened and told James to always remember that his mother was a wonderful woman. That comment meant a great deal to James, and the nightmares did not return. When James returned to the U.S. 4 years later, he sought psychotherapy to deal with the confusion he felt about his mother's death and his anger toward his father.

(Continued)

James's aunt and uncle were also angry with his father, and James himself eventually withdrew from most of his mother's side of the family. He did not feel welcome in their midst, and he thought he was somehow tainted by his relationship to his father, whom his mother's side of the family, in their grief, hated. It took many years, and several courses of therapy, for him to accept that he was not responsible for his mother's death, and to construct a more balanced and realistic view of both his mother and father.

The inability to say goodbye and have closure with his mother resurfaced decades later when his younger brother died suddenly. The brother's doctor had diagnosed heart problems and advised the brother to lose weight, stop smoking, stop drinking, and change his diet. He did none of those things and told no one about the doctor's diagnosis. James enjoyed Christmas dinner with family, including his brother, and was shocked to get a call the next day saying he had died of heart failure. Again, he felt anger at his brother for ignoring the doctor's advice, felt sad and heavy, and felt incomplete because of the absence of closure. James is now very concerned that this will happen again with other people to whom he is close.

Kübler-Ross's Stages of Grief

- Denial: There is some mistake. I am not dying.

- Anger: How can this happen to me?

- Bargaining: I promise I will … if I get better.

- Depression: I don't care anymore.

- Acceptance: I am ready now.

Many readers will be familiar with the stages of grief described by Elisabeth Kübler-Ross, whose 1969 book *On Death and Dying* described this theory. Readers should be aware that the stages she described were those experienced by dying patients; these were later applied to grief experienced by survivors after a death. Kübler-Ross's stages were denial, anger, bargaining, depression, and finally acceptance. By now, it is clear that individuals do not progress through such stages in a linear fashion and that the grief experience is highly individual and difficult to fit into a neat series of stages. In addition, research has not found empirical evidence to support this theory, despite its wide popular acceptance. Nevertheless, her work brought attention to the topic of death and dying and was the impetus for the development of hospice programs around the country.

Theoretical Perspectives

Parkes (1998) drew on the attachment work of John Bowlby and proposed phases of the grief experience. Bowlby's (1969) attachment theory described the strong emotional bonds between infants and caregivers, which ensures the safety and survival of the infant. These attachments are formed very early and persist over time. Bowlby believed that a child's strong attachments are with only a few individuals. The child with a healthy attachment to a parent feels secure enough to explore the environment and move away from the parent, knowing that they may return to the parent for safety when needed. If these attachments are disrupted, the infant tries to regain them by crying and clinging and displays of anger. If those behaviors are not successful in restoring the lost object of attachment, the child experiences despair (Fast, 2003). This is the model for the grief process for all humans. Parkes suggested that individuals first experience numb disbelief, then yearning for the deceased person, disorganization and despair, and finally reorganization, when a new life without the deceased is structured.

Depending on whether the death was anticipated (as in someone who was terminally ill) or sudden and unexpected, there are difficult formalities that need to occur. Depending on the cause of death, it might be necessary for a relative to identify the body. In some cases, that helps accept the reality of the loss. For others, it is a traumatic event that might be challenging to overcome. If the deceased person has a living will or some other legal directive regarding their wishes for end-of-life care, survivors are relieved of having to make that decision. When such information has not been provided, someone has the responsibility to do so on their behalf. That choice might be the degree of heroic medical procedures to permit. There will also be decisions about the disposition of the body (burial or cremation), the type of funeral to arrange, and overseeing the enactment of the will, or in the absence of one, to investigate state laws that apply to the situation (hopefully with the assistance of a lawyer).

Worden (2018) conceives of mourning as a set of tasks after a death that need to be accomplished in order to restore functioning: accepting the reality of the loss, working through the pain and grief, adjusting to an environment in which the deceased is missing, and emotionally relocating the deceased and moving on with life. Worden's influential work will be the foundation for much of the discussions in this chapter.

The reader should note that there is some disagreement about these theories of grieving, in which adjustment is measured by how well the individual has broken the bonds with the deceased and returned to normal functioning (see Lindström, 2002; Stroebe et al., 1992). Stroebe and Schut (1999) outline a model that acknowledges the work of Worden (1991) and other theorists. We mention this model here because it adds something to the discussion that appears absent from other approaches in that it postulates a dual process that has *loss-oriented* and *restoration-oriented* tasks. The loss-oriented tasks are primarily emotional while restoration-oriented tasks are more cognitive and behavioral. Both tasks are necessary for the bereaved person to adjust to the changed world that is the result of the death. They include the difficult and essential task of forging a new identity (e.g., wife to widow, child to orphan, partner to single person, etc.). What is new in this model is the idea of *oscillation*, moving back and forth between the two sets of tasks. These authors propose that oscillation allows the person to take a break from the draining emotional tasks and that this process helps individuals restore a balance between emotional and cognitive aspects of self. Oscillation is conceived of as necessary for future adjustment and recognizes that denial is at times purposeful and helpful, as long as it is not extreme or persistent.

Oscillation: Alternating between the loss-oriented emotional tasks and the restoration-oriented cognitive tasks of grieving.

Thus, the helping professional should avoid a rigid idea of what is the "right" way to grieve and instead appreciate the wide range of ways in which bereavement is experienced. When some form of counseling is indicated, careful listening will alert the compassionate therapist to the individual needs of the client (Stroebe, et al., 1992).

What Is Normal Grief?

With wide variability among individuals, there are common elements of a grief response that are often present, which include physical, emotional, cognitive, and behavioral elements. Emotional responses to a death include sadness, although the way this is expressed (e.g., crying) differs markedly from one person to another. Less often recognized but commonly experienced is a feeling of anger, which can be anger that there was nothing that could be done, anger at God for allowing this to happen, or anger at the deceased for leaving (which is a common reaction in children when an attachment figure leaves them).

While anger is normal, there is the potential for problems when the anger is misdirected or displaced to someone else or to oneself. Also normal is the feeling of guilt, which may be realistic but is often irrational. The guilt may focus on what the survivor did or did not do to prevent the death or how the deceased was treated when alive. This usually dissipates relatively quickly, and if so, does not bode future problems. Many survivors (spouses in particular) may become anxious about how they will survive without the lost person. Existential anxiety about one's own mortality may also be heightened at a time of loss and is also part of a normal reaction. Loneliness is felt most often when the person was part of the survivor's day-to-day experience, and the absence is acutely noticed. In some cases, relief is a part of the experience, particularly when the deceased was in pain and suffering prior to the death. Others may feel a sense of liberation, as when the perpetrator of abuse dies.

Physical components of grief often include fatigue, tightness in the chest and throat, feeling short of breath, feeling weak, and lacking energy. In addition to all of these feelings, it is not uncommon for people to report the absence of feeling or numbness. This is similar to the shock experienced when one has a physical injury and pain is not felt. This typically is a short-term initial response to the loss.

Thinking patterns that emerge in bereavement may frighten the bereaved because they are so unlike one's ordinary cognitive style. People may find they initially cannot take in the information about the death, especially an unexpected one. They may convince themselves there is a mistake, for example. This typically is short-lived and is prominent when the news is first received. Confusion and distractibility are also typical of newly bereaved people, and for those who are typically very efficient and organized, the frequent forgetting or confusion may be alarming. It is quite common for survivors to think obsessively about the deceased person, and even to have the sense that the person is nearby. This experience usually diminishes over time. In grieving people, hallucinations, which are usually considered symptoms of serious mental disorders, may occur. These are not problematic unless they persist beyond the first few weeks after the death.

Behaviorally there are also common patterns, which include sleep difficulty, loss of appetite, dreaming of the deceased, and frequent crying. Some people may avoid reminders of the deceased while others may cling to objects that remind them of the deceased. For an overview of the factors that affect the grieving process, see the information below.

FACTORS AFFECTING THE PROCESS OF GRIEVING

Factors relating to the relationship between the deceased and the survivor:

- *The nature of relationship to the deceased.* The death of a distant relative is different from that of a member of one's immediate family. The losses of different people in one's life are experienced differently because the nature of the relationships differed.
- *The degree of emotional closeness to the deceased.* The intensity of the attachment is related to the intensity of the grief.
- *The importance of the deceased to the well-being of the survivor.* If one's self-esteem and security needs were satisfied primarily by the deceased, the loss will be experienced more acutely.
- *The degree of ambivalence in the relationship.* If there was a high level of ambivalence (love-hate) in the relationship, or a high degree of conflict (particularly unresolved conflict), the grief is usually more difficult.
- *The way the person died.* Deaths have been categorized as natural, accidental, suicidal, and homicidal (Worden, 1991). The death of a young person may be more difficult that the death of an elderly person who has had a long and full life. Whether the death was expected or unexpected (sudden) affects the bereavement.

Factors relating to the survivor:

- *Experience of an earlier loss.* Whether people have experienced the death of someone close before, and how they managed these earlier losses, will affect how they grieve the current death.
- *Other life changes.* The number of life changes in the year prior to the death also seems to affect mourning, with more changes portending a more difficult grieving process.
- *Dealing with intense feelings.* How people deal with intense feelings, how they cope with stress, and how they manage anxiety are individual personality factors that will be reflected in the grief and mourning process.
- *Culture and religion.* For those who have strong affiliations with religious or cultural groups, following the prescribed practices can facilitate a better adjustment to the loss.
- *The level of social support.* Family and friends can reduce stress by taking on many of the tasks following a death, by providing emotional support and companionship, and by serving as a buffer against environmental pressure.
- *Level of stress.* If the death comes at a time when there are economic or other stressors already affecting the survivor, it will be more difficult for the person to negotiate the bereavement.

Patterns of Grieving

Martin and Doka (2000) described patterns of grieving, which are influenced by (but not determined by) such factors as gender and culture. The patterns reflect differences in how grief is experienced internally, how it is expressed, and in coping strategies preferred. The two primary patterns are intuitive and instrumental. These patterns exist along a continuum, with most people favoring one pattern rather than being exclusively one or the other:

- *Intuitive*: Grievers who are primarily intuitive will feel the loss deeply and intensely and will experience extremely painful feelings. Their outward expression of grief reflects the intensity of the emotional pain—crying and emotional displays are frequent and open. This type of griever is comforted by sharing their feelings with others. The emotional component of grief is prominent in this pattern, which is often thought of as a female pattern, although many men are intuitive grievers. Intuitive grievers may experience periods of confusion, have difficulty with concentration, and feel disorganized and disoriented at times. They often feel physically exhausted.
- *Instrumental*: Instrumental grievers are less attentive to emotion and focus on cognition. They try not to become emotional and prefer not to talk about feelings. If any feeling is expressed, it is most likely to be anger. Quiet contemplation is common. Instrumental grievers prefer to direct their energies into problem-solving activities such as planning services and memorials, staying busy, returning to work or school, taking charge of loss-related tasks (working with insurance companies), and so on. This pattern is typically thought of as the male approach, although it is seen in both genders. Instrumental grievers also experience periods of confusion and difficulty concentrating.
- *Blended*: This pattern is a combination of the intuitive and instrumental styles, usually with a preference for one style.
- *Dissonant:* The dissonant pattern is one in which the individual's way of coping with grief does not match their internal preferred style. Dissonant grievers suppress emotions, which

takes considerable energy. They may be concerned with how others will view their grieving and strive to demonstrate control and mastery, despite their inner pain. Other dissonant grievers may feel guilty because they do not have the intense emotional reaction they perceive to be "normal." The danger is that this type of dissonant griever will seek unhealthy ways to release emotions (e.g., substance use).

Prevalence

In 2021, there were 3,464,231 deaths in the United States, which means that there are many more grieving a loss (Xu et al., 2022). Although grief and loss are universal human experiences, complicated grief is estimated to occur in 10%–20% of bereaved individuals (Shear et al., 2005).

Special Cases of Grief

Grief is painful in all cases, but there are some specific types of death that may make bereavement more challenging.

Suicide

Although there are more similarities than differences between survivors of a death by suicide (SOS) and other bereaved individuals, the differences are important and merit attention. In 2021, 48,183 people died by suicide (American Foundation for Suicide Prevention [AFSP], 2023). Death by suicide is usually unexpected and may be violent, amplifying the shock and dismay of survivors. If the survivor either witnessed the event or found the body, PTSD may develop. Suicide survivors may have some of the same reactions as other mourners but may experience them more intensely or for longer duration. The differences most often identified are a persistent struggle to make sense of the death, increased levels of guilt and feelings of responsibility for the death, and greater feelings of rejection and abandonment along with anger toward the deceased. In addition, there is a perceived stigma associated with suicide that extends to SOS, so their social support may be disrupted. Finally, there is an increased risk of suicide among this group of mourners. Van Dongen (1990) noted that there were differences among the SOS according to their perceptions of the risk of suicide. In several of her subjects, the deceased had prior attempts and the survivors were aware of the psychological difficulties. This seemed to lessen the struggle to find meaning in the death.

Some experts note that SOS are more likely to lie about the cause of death in an effort to avoid the negative associations with suicide. In such cases, the family may create a secret that can ultimately be disruptive to family functioning.

The dynamics of grief after a suicide have several clinical implications (Jordan, 2001). One is that group support services are best provided specifically for this group of survivors, who may feel increased isolation in a general bereavement group. Others may be uncertain about how to respond to the survivor and may even avoid contact out of fear of saying or doing something that would exacerbate their suffering. Second, since the risk for suicide is greater in this group, this risk should be closely monitored. Third, educational information about suicide and about suicide bereavement should be provided. Next, interventions should target the social network, both from the perspective of teaching skills for dealing with the perceived stigma and from the position of directly involving the support network in the intervention. Finally, because of the potential for disruption of family processes, intervention should target the entire family system and work toward increasing cohesion.

Worden (2004) advises that helping the survivors test the reality of their guilt may reduce their feelings of responsibility. They may realize they had made more efforts to be helpful than they acknowledged earlier. Survivors may need help avoiding blame as well, since blaming others (particularly other family members) can increase stress on an already burdened family system. Worden also believes it is important to confront the reality of the suicide by avoiding vague or imprecise terms to describe the death. SOS may need assistance in accessing a balanced view of the deceased rather than a black-or-white view based solely on this final act. Finally, Worden believes that due to exacerbated feelings of abandonment by the deceased, a mental health professional who has an existing relationship with the survivors should initiate contact and offer support.

Sudden Death

Some experts believe that sudden or unexpected death is, like suicide, more difficult for the survivors than expected deaths. Also similar to suicide is the sense of unbelief and shock that comes with an unanticipated announcement of the death and the decision of how much to share when notifying others. It is frequently the case that the survivor must contact people to inform them of the death and to provide information about funeral services. Having to repeat this over and over can be emotionally overwhelming. Guilt also is a common reaction, with thoughts such as "If only I had …" predominating. For those who may have had angry words with the deceased prior to the death, the unresolved conflict may influence the grieving process, and the unfinished business may linger for years. Some may obsess about the wish they had apologized or to put differences aside, for example.

For death by accident or homicide (and to some extent suicide as well) there may be frequent contact with authorities and interactions with the system at a time when the survivors are just learning of the death and attempting to accept the reality of it. Determining the cause of death and the identity of the deceased usually requires that a relative identify the body. This can be traumatic. For some, the grieving process may be delayed while these matters are the focus. Sometimes the bereavement process cannot really begin until there is some resolution to the legal matters (e.g., lawsuit settled, murderer convicted). An additional feeling that is common among survivors of a sudden death is helplessness. Such things are not in anyone's plans, and the sense that there is no order or justice can become overwhelming for mourners. Sometimes these feelings lead to anger and sometimes misdirected blaming of others (e.g., doctors, witnesses).

SIDS and Stillbirth

There were 1,389 deaths in 2020 attributed to sudden infant death syndrome (SIDS), which is the leading cause of infant mortality in the United States (CDC, 2023). These deaths occur in apparently healthy babies, and although the deaths are called SIDS, there is no explanation that clearly points to a specific cause of death. Exciting new research by the Paterson group discovered an underlying developmental disorder involving certain brain neurons that puts infants at risk. When this vulnerability is present, the infant in the face-down or side-sleeping position appears to lack the protective reflexes for arousal and head turning when they are not getting sufficient air. The authors point to three factors, which, when coupled with this vulnerability, increase risk for SIDS: prone or side sleeping, face-down sleeping, and bed sharing. Mental health professionals who work with new parents might want to be sure they are aware of this new research and take measures to avoid putting their child at risk.

For survivors (parents, siblings, grandparents), the shock of the death is intense and difficult to absorb. In addition, there is often considerable guilt on the part of parents, who believe they could have somehow prevented the death by being more attentive. One client of mine described playing cards with friends in the living room after putting the baby to sleep. When he checked on her later, she was dead. He berated himself for many years, believing he must have waited too long to check on the sleeping baby.

Like other unanticipated deaths, there may be police involvement, questions regarding autopsies, and so forth that elevate feelings of guilt. Parents may have to explain to surviving siblings an event that they themselves do not understand. Different grieving styles in the marriage partners may increase tensions between them at a time when they most need support.

SIDS survivors may benefit from group support with other families who have lost a baby to SIDS. Accurate information should be provided about what is known and not known about SIDS, and an arena to discuss whether to have another baby right away can be helpful.

The experience of having a stillbirth is similar in many ways to SIDS death, in that it is often completely unexpected. Parents may feel responsible for the death and feel confused when there is no medical explanation. Fears about future pregnancies are common, and returning home to a newly equipped nursery without a baby can trigger overwhelming sorrow. If there was ambivalence about the pregnancy, parents may feel they were somehow punished for their feelings, and stress between the couple may increase. Couples therapy may be helpful to assist the pair with coming to terms with the tragedy and attending to their relationship.

One thing SIDS deaths and stillbirths share is the opportunity for a funeral or farewell ritual. Parents may wonder about naming the baby, how to dispose of the body, and how to tell other family members. Many parents choose to spend time with the baby, take photos, and have a service of some kind to acknowledge the death. Support groups may be useful for these mourners, who can talk about their experience with others who understand the impact of such a loss.

An additional complication with a stillbirth is poignantly described by Alison Gardy (2005), who was distressed at the quantity of promotional material for baby products that continued to arrive even after she had notified all possible sources of her information that the baby had died. The onslaught of mail and products was an impediment to this woman's process of grieving, with a great deal of anger directed toward the inconsiderate vendors who continued to send unwanted mail that served only to remind the parents of their loss.

Miscarriage/Abortion

Those who experience a miscarriage may not receive the social support that is so critical for good adjustment. It has been our experience that the well-intentioned comments of others often increase the distress of the aggrieved parent. For example, they may be told that miscarriage is nature's way of taking care of a problem. Many women who miscarry are already worried about their ability to have a healthy baby, and hearing that the baby was likely "damaged" in some way is not a comfort. One young woman I (SB) worked with became pregnant with a second child by her abusive husband. When she miscarried, others told her it was a blessing that she would not have any more ties to this man. However, she was excited about the pregnancy, eagerly anticipating the birth, and already imagining how her older child would respond to being the "big brother." The intended reassurance of others was extremely hurtful.

An additional challenge with miscarriages is that there is usually no body to see or bury and no formalized rituals for marking the loss. To the extent that funerals and memorial services assist the survivors in the bereavement process, miscarriage does not have rituals that accompany other deaths. In fact, it is often treated as a medical procedure (e.g., appendicitis) rather than a profound loss. Mental health professionals can be helpful by listening and accepting the loss of the mourner, and sometimes by helping them create a personal memorial or ritual that acknowledges the loss.

Abortion is not always accompanied by grief, but it may occur, and may occur many years later. One client I (SB) worked with was a graduate student who had an abortion as a young teenager at her parents' insistence. When she eventually married and began to plan a family with her husband (who knew of the abortion), she was overcome with guilt and feelings of loss. She sought counseling because she became agitated and depressed and was unable to think about having a child with her husband without becoming overcome with grief. Interestingly, she discovered a solution to her pain: She volunteered at a neonatal intensive care unit, where she provided contact and holding for very high-risk newborns. She decided that perhaps this work would save lives and then she could forgive herself for having the earlier abortion.

If an abortion is chosen as a way to manage an unplanned pregnancy, the woman is often deprived of social support. Currently, access to providers of abortions is severely restricted or illegal in some states. Although legal in some places under certain conditions, abortion still has a negative stigma in many social contexts, so the woman may not feel able to discuss this with family or friends. Others (parents, partner) may be angry with her for becoming pregnant, so she receives negative input from others rather than support. One danger in these cases, when guilt may linger, is that the woman will choose to become pregnant again as a way to assuage their guilt. This may not be effective and may increase her problems. Mental health professionals must understand that despite the reason for the abortion, many women feel a sense of loss and grief and need a nonjudgmental person to allow them to process their feelings.

Death of a Child

Although we have discussed the impacts of a death due to SIDS, miscarriage, stillbirth, and abortion, there are other causes of a child's death. Accidents are the most common cause of death in children up to age 14. In children up to age 4, congenital causes are next, with homicide following. For children ages 5 to 9, the second leading cause is cancer, with homicide in third place. For children 10–14, the leading causes are accidents, suicide, and cancer (CDC, 2023). Many believe that the death of a child is the most devastating experience, causing intense suffering and roiled emotions for long periods after the death. The death of a child contradicts the natural order: Parents die before their children do. Parents and other close family members must accept that the child is gone, and their dreams and hopes for the future must be revised.

In a family, members may each grieve differently, which may add tension to an inherently painful situation. There are different issues to address for death by illness that may be anticipated and unexpected death by accident or homicide. Clinicians must determine the best approach: Meet with individuals separately, provide couples therapy to parents, do some work with the entire family (including extended family such as grandparents). Mental health professionals must help the surviving loved ones manage their guilt, blame, fear, and depression and assist them with important decisions (or refer them to a local source of advice, often a funeral home). Experts recommend that a therapist focus on encouraging the bereaved to remember the child and the time they had together. An organization that is devoted to family members who have lost a child for any reason is Compassionate Friends, Inc., which has over 600 chapters offering support and many resources for survivors. Therapists should familiarize themselves with this organization and make referrals as indicated.

Military Deaths

As American troops, including women, are engaged in combat, the need for understanding of this type of loss is essential for mental health professionals. There are several unique aspects of the death of a soldier that are important to note (Carroll, 1998). Although the military has well-established procedures and rituals for the death of military personnel, the impact on survivors may not be as well prepared for. First, some family members may be at odds with the notion of a "glorious death" and may feel uncomfortable expressing their anger and frustration. In addition, if the family was living in military housing, they will be forced to relocate after the death, when the supports they have created among friends are most needed. The many changes in lifestyle that are imposed on military families increase the stress of the death. Carroll is a strong advocate of support groups for military families who have experienced the death of a soldier, as their unique experience can be shared. In fact, she is the founder of Tragedy Assistance Program for Survivors to provide support and events for families. See the resource list at the end of the chapter for information about this organization.

Pets

The last special case to be discussed is the death of a pet. The 2023–2024 National Pet Owner's Survey reports that 66%, or 86.9 million, of American households own a pet (American Pet Products Association, n.d.). Animals have shorter life spans than humans, so it is likely that many pet owners will experience the death of at least one pet in their lifetime. There is no doubt that for most pet owners the attachment to pets is strong and important. Pets provide unconditional love and affection and give many people a sense of being needed. When a beloved pet dies, people experience many of the same grief reactions as have been described for other losses: sadness, guilt, anger, disruption of daily functioning. However, there are no socially sanctioned rituals for grieving the loss of a pet: no funeral, no bereavement leave from work, and few expressions of condolences. People may feel friends and family do not understand the significance of the loss and that others treat the loss casually, so pet owners may stifle their outward expression of grief. Further, in cases when the pet was euthanized, the pet owner had to make a painful decision. Pet owners are often torn between relieving the animal's suffering and the desire to keep the pet with them. These aspects of the death of the pet may make the bereavement difficult.

For people living alone and for children, the loss of a pet can be particularly devastating. The pet may have been the only companion of the person living alone, so the void experienced after the death can be especially large. This is especially likely in the elderly, who may already feel isolated and lonely. The loss of a pet has been found to trigger feelings of grief over previous losses in some individuals, so the feelings experienced may be magnified. For children, the loss of a pet is often the first experience with death. Children often have close bonds with their pets, and it is not unusual to hear a child describe a pet as their "best friend." Children grieve according to their developmental stages. It should be noted that children's tolerance for strong affect is not as high as that of adults, so they may alternate between periods of sadness and return to usual functioning. Depending on the age, the child may wish to be involved in decisions about the disposal or burial of the remains, and parents will need to decide whether this is appropriate in any given case.

Parents may need assistance in how to help a child with grief when a pet dies. Parents need to know that such euphemisms as "put to sleep" can be frightening for the child, who can then fear that they will die when asleep. Parents can encourage the child to talk about their pet, make a memorial, or whatever seems to acknowledge the importance of the pet in the child's life. Therapists who work with children might want to communicate in their offices their own interest in pets, with posters or photos of animals and thoughtful questions about pets and their importance in initial interviews with children. The Grief Support Center (www.rainbowsbridge.com/grief_support_center/grief_support_home.htm) has resources and tips that might be a worthwhile resource for clients.

Developmental Factors

The experience of grief doesn't just vary among individuals; there are developmental influences as well. People at different times in the life span have different levels of understanding of death, different prior experiences with death and loss, and different needs in the bereavement process.

Children

When a loved one dies, parents may struggle to assist their children because they are grieving themselves. They may become emotionally distant to avoid situations that will trigger emotional outbursts and frighten the child. In doing so, the child may feel deprived of closeness with the parent while also grieving the loss themselves. Children's understanding of death is related to their cognitive and emotional development. Despite their lack of accurate understanding, children may nevertheless have their own ideas about death that need to be taken into account when responding to the death of a loved one in the child's world.

Infants do not have any conception of death, but they do form attachments to the primary caregiver (usually the mother) and will react to the absence of that person. Separation anxiety is common among children in the latter part of the first year of life, and those responses are typical of what these children will exhibit when the loss is of the caregiver: They may cry more than usual, show changes in sleeping and/or eating habits, and be less active and somewhat withdrawn from contact. Infants are sensitive to changes in others and will often respond to changes in routines with distress and irritability. As infants approach the end of the 1st year, their emotional repertoires expand, and they also begin to develop language and symbolic thinking. Like younger infants, they will notice the emotional reactions of others and be sensitive to changes in their routines. The loss of the primary caregiver will usually result in sadness and distress in the baby.

Toddlers and children up to age 5, with their emerging language, are quite literal. They may confuse death and sleep and often believe death is temporary. A client reported that he explained carefully to his 4-year-old son that great-grandma (who was an important figure in the life of the family) had died and gone to heaven. The child listened very carefully and then asked how she got to heaven because he wanted to be sure that she knew the way back so she could come to his birthday party. This is a typical response of children at this age. Children who are exposed to television, where death is often temporary (the actor or character appears later in another episode, movie, etc.), may be quite certain of the temporary status of death. In some cases, children of this age who learn that the deceased is buried may become quite distressed and concerned that the deceased will be unable to breathe or eat. In addition, children of this age may believe their thoughts are powerful enough to cause the death. If they were angry with the deceased, they may believe they caused the death and grief they see in others. Regression to early behaviors (problems with bowel or bladder control, thumb-sucking, etc.) is not unusual in this age group.

Children at this age are very literal in their understanding of language. Adults may say things like "It is hard to lose a parent," while a child may think that means if they look hard enough they can find the "lost" parent. Young children are likely to ask many difficult questions, and answering them carefully and directly will help them adjust.

Children aged 6 to 9 have developed cognitively, so they generally understand that death is permanent. They may be curious about the mechanical aspects of death (what happens to the body) and may think of the deceased as having another form (an angel or a ghost). Because children now understand that death is permanent, they may worry about dying themselves and may become anxious that others close to them will die. One client, whose primary caretaker (a grandparent) died suddenly and accidentally when the child was 3 years old, developed what appeared to be an extreme case of school phobia years later. She believed that if she stayed at home, she could be sure no one else in the family would die. Children of this age may not have the verbal skills to express their feelings of grief and may act out or become clingy with survivors. Their themes in play may reveal their concerns following a death.

Children aged 10 through 12 generally have an accurate cognitive appreciation of death. In this period, they may want more information about rituals observed by families and may be most concerned with how this death will affect their own lives. Their emotional, physical, cognitive, and behavioral manifestations of grief are more adult-like, but they may be particularly concerned about being different from other children and how their friends will react to the loss. I (SB) worked with a 10-year-old child who was convinced that the reason she did not have friends at school was that she was the only one without a mother. Her mother had died several years earlier. Her strong belief about the reason for her rejection prevented her from focusing on her deficient social skills.

Despite their cognitive advances, preteens may experience excessive guilt about past misbehaviors toward the deceased and may still express themselves more behaviorally than verbally. They may be especially sensitive to grieving parents and resist burdening them with their own concerns. Some children, particularly if the deceased was a parent, may feel they must assume the role of the person who died (e.g., become the "man of the house"), which can feel overwhelming and arouse resentment.

Mental health professionals need to be aware that children (and adolescents) who have experienced the death of a parent may seem to have accepted the loss and gone on with their lives may have a resurgence of grief at significant moments in their lives (religious rites—confirmation, bar mitzvah—birthdays, graduations, marriage, having children). This is not a symptom of complicated bereavement, but a common experience that nevertheless calls for compassion and understanding.

Adolescents

Although adolescents have the cognitive skills to understand death, their emotional development is not yet adult like, and grief may be especially disturbing, given their propensity to feel invulnerable. They are also engaged in developing an identity, so depending on the relationship to the deceased (e.g., a parent), they will be concerned with how the death will influence their own lives. Emotional displays can be flamboyant at this stage, and withdrawal from social interaction is not unusual for some teens.

Although they may understand the finality of death, when someone their age dies (a friend, classmate, cousin), they become aware of their own mortality and may experience fear about that. Sometimes, an adolescent has never attended a funeral and needs to be prepared for what to expect. Will there be an open casket? What religious rituals will be observed? How are they expected to behave? Having this information in advance of the funeral can reduce the discomfort to an extent.

Because of the discrepancy between the cognitive and emotional development of an adolescent, it is important for mental health professionals to remember that an adolescent understands and processes death and loss through their developmental lens at the time of the loss. Cognitively, they understand the finality of death, as an adult would. However, they likely experience it much differently emotionally (more childlike). If they aren't able to emotionally understand the loss in a different way as time passes, the grief may remain in the context of the time in which the loss occurred. For example, a 30-year-old who experienced the loss of a parent when they were 13 may still have remnants of the emotions regarding the loss that they had when they were 13 (the same thoughts, feelings, and beliefs). What may have been developmentally appropriate at 13 is no longer appropriate at 30. A mental health clinician may need to spend some time with an adult client revisiting and reexamining the thoughts and feelings that the client had at the time of the loss—and attempt to facilitate or reframe a different (more mature) perspective regarding the loss (e.g., discuss the irrationality of the anger or guilt of past behavior toward the deceased, discuss the rationality of why they may have felt overwhelmed, see if they still have a fear of mortality, etc.).

Adults

In adulthood, death is understood to be an unavoidable experience, and while the loss of elderly relatives causes grief and sadness, it is usually accepted as part of life. For adults, the difficult losses are those that are unexpected (accidents, murder, suicide) or off-time (death of a young person). For those in middle adulthood, awareness of one's own mortality may increase, and it is not unusual to hear that people check the obituaries of strangers to see how old they are at death. In adulthood, many will have to confront the death of parents, and even among secure adults, the change in status ("Now I am an orphan") can be unsettling. The first years after the death may be particularly difficult around special occasions and holidays, and clinicians can help by normalizing this reaction and reassuring clients that this typically becomes less painful over time.

The Elderly

Among the elderly, bereavement is more frequent than at other life stages. According to Ball (2022), 58% of women over age 75 had ever been widowed, with 54% currently widowed. For men, 28% had ever been widowed, and 20% were currently widowers. Many of these elders have also lost friends and various family members. Although not unanticipated, the loss of a spouse at this age can be extremely disorganizing. Consider the loss of a partner of many decades, with whom one carried out daily activities as a unit. Doing those same activities alone can be overwhelming for the elderly person. In marriages of long duration, it is not unusual for partners to assume certain roles (financial manager, home manager, correspondent, etc.), and when the spouse is gone, the remaining partner may not know how to function solo. If the couple socialized as a unit, the survivor may feel unwelcome among the familiar social group and may even fear that children or old friends will also abandon them. If the death necessitates relocation of the surviving spouse, this means the loss of familiar surroundings and personal objects, which may further add to the emotional distress. Unfortunately, some elderly people attempt to cope with the painful feelings by increasing their use of alcohol, sedatives, or tobacco, and thoughts of suicide may emerge. There is also an increased risk for death in the surviving spouse, which peaks from 7–12 months following the loss.

Elderly individuals with various forms of *dementia* may need special assistance when experiencing a loss. One of the troubling features of individuals with dementia is that the memory problems result in their forgetting the death. This means that they experience the shock of learning about the death repeatedly; family members may find this quite disturbing. Those in the advanced stages of the disorder may not understand death

Dementia: A mental disorder characterized by loss of intellectual abilities (thinking, reasoning, memory) of sufficient degree to interfere with daily functioning.

at all. To assist these individuals, Lewis and Trzinski (2006) applied two techniques that are reported by staff in nursing homes to be beneficial. The first is a spaced retrieval (SR) learning strategy used with people to help them remember that their loved one has died. Research had found the techniques to be helpful in the short-term, but long-term improvement has been disappointing (Small & Cochrane, 2020). The second technique is a form of play therapy, "group buddies" (puppets or stuffed animals) who attend group treatment sessions with the patient. The group buddy's job is to attend all group session and, watch and learn in the group. Staff members reported that in addition to being useful within group sessions, patients were observed using their buddies as confidantes, supports, and comfort objects. Mental health professionals in a consulting role might consider suggesting these techniques, although there is no research evidence to support their effectiveness.

Assessment

How does the clinician determine whether the client's grief is within the normal range, or whether it qualifies as complicated grief, which may require treatment? There are several conditions that can be used to identify those at risk for complicated grief, and the counselor would be wise to pay attention to these. As social support is so important to the bereaved person, those clients who either have no social support or perceive a high level of nonsupport from their relationships are more likely to have complicated grieving. If the death occurs under traumatic circumstances, there is a greater risk for difficulties with the grieving process. Finally, if the client is already in crisis at the time of the death, their coping resources may be depleted to the extent that they are unable to cope with the loss.

There are several clues that the grieving process has developed into complicated grief. Complicated grief is likely when the grief is prolonged. Although experts vary in their opinion of what constitutes "prolonged" grief, periods of from 1 to 4 years are mentioned in the literature. Complicated grief may reveal itself as behavioral symptoms or somatic complaints, often noticed when the bereaved person visits a physician frequently for vague complaints for which no medical explanation can be found. These symptoms sometimes persist for 1 to 3 years (Rosenzweig et al., 1997). When the grieving appears to be excessive or exaggerated beyond what is usual, as noted in the severity and frequency of symptoms and the disruption of life tasks, complicated grief should be considered.

Shear et al. (2005) observed that complicated grief is different from depression and in fact is similar in many respects to PTSD. Complicated grief causes significant impairment in functioning and is related to negative physical health. One of the characteristics of complicated grief is that it does not respond to standard treatment approaches for depression. Assessment of complicated grief is facilitated by the use of the Inventory of Complicated Grief (Prigerson et al., 1995), which is a 19-item scale on which clients rate how often they have experienced the symptoms described in the statements. A score equal to or above 25 indicates complicated grief. Shear et al. believe this should be administered no earlier than 6 months following the death. A recent tool, the Traumatic Grief Inventory Self-Report Version (TGI-SR), has 18 items and good psychometric properties linked to the symptoms that are persistent (Boelen & Smid, 2017).

Treatment Options

The first question to consider is whether and for whom treatment for uncomplicated grief should be provided. Worden (2004) believes bereavement counseling should be offered to anyone who has experienced a loss, particularly if the deceased is a parent or child. Certainly, individuals who seek counseling at such a time should receive services.

Researchers have investigated the effectiveness of treatment for grief in a systematic review. Many of the studies located did not meet criteria for rigorous experimental design, but Neimeyer (2000) found 23 studies that met his criteria and were published between 1975 and 1998. The mean number of sessions in the treatments examined was 7, and treatment was initiated from 6 months to several years after the loss. This study revealed that for people experiencing normal grief, counseling did not show any positive effect, while those experiencing traumatic (complicated) grief did show positive effects. In addition, in one of two persons with normal grief, counseling had a negative effect, while this was true for only 17% of the mourners with traumatic grief. Neimeyer concluded that counseling for normal bereavement is "difficult to justify," while for "protracted, traumatic, or complicated grief reactions" (p. 546) such services are appropriate.

When assistance is sought for a normal grief reaction, it is frequently the case that either the individual does not have sufficient social support or that they believe it would be unfair to burden others (particularly those who are also mourning) with their own pain. What does a grieving client need? Worden (2004) recommends a number of tasks with which the mourner may need help. The first task is to help them talk about the loss. We have noticed that some clients need to tell the story more than once—many times in fact—as though they want to be sure it actually occurred.

They may believe that others in their life get tired of hearing them recount the story over and over, whereas the therapist can allow the necessary repetition.

Allowing the mourner to express feelings is also helpful. The mourner may feel that others close to the deceased will not understand their anger, for example, but are relieved to unburden themselves to a nonjudgmental and compassionate professional. When guilt is expressed, the clinician may help the client determine if the guilt is really justified. Sometimes, grief reactions include unrealistic guilt (e.g., "If I were there, I could have prevented the accident") and the counselor can help the client test the accuracy of such beliefs. If the grief is not unrealistic (e.g., "I chose not to go to the hospital although I knew he was dying"), the client can sometimes be helped by verbalizing what might have been said to the deceased if they had the opportunity.

Some people need help figuring out how to manage tasks that the deceased handled before. For example, if the deceased took care of financial matters, the survivor may need a referral to money management resources. Deciding what changes will be necessary and which can wait is a task that a counselor can support. Worden (2004) and others typically advise the mourner not to make major decisions (e.g., relocating) until a year or so after the loss, but circumstances do not always allow the mourner that opportunity. Ensuring that the bereaved person has sufficient unbiased guidance (e.g., an attorney) in any necessary decisions is a role the counselor can fill.

In other cases, the survivor may have spent years caring for a chronically ill family member. For those caregivers, the loss they experience involves not only the loss of a beloved person, but also the loss of a major role in their lives. Filling that time and energy can be challenging and frightening for one whose life has been consumed by caring for another. The clinician can recognize that the mourner may feel adrift and may need assistance reshaping their identity when their major life role is concluded.

Finally, Worden believes that the mourner needs to struggle to find a "place" for the deceased so that they can move forward. He notes that some people feel that forming new relationships will dishonor the deceased, while others feel that no one can replace the person they lost. Even returning to normal routines such as work or school may be difficult if the person makes the deceased the sole focus of their energy. Counselors can help clients sort out these common feelings and help them anticipate and prepare for times that are often difficult (anniversaries of the death, holidays, and other special occasions). In addition, the counselor may reassure clients that their experience is normal for those grieving a loss, as it is not unusual for mourners to feel as though they are going crazy. They also need to hear that they will improve and that support is available as needed.

Therapy for complicated grief is more specialized. Shear et al. (2005) note that treating bereavement-related depression has not had significant benefits for complicated grief. These researchers studied the effectiveness of an integrated interpersonal therapy (IPT) and CBT approach to complicated grief. The treatment was administered in 16 sessions held over 16–20 weeks. The study was carefully controlled and involved 102 bereaved individuals who were randomized to this treatment approach or IPT alone. Fifty-one percent of the treatment group was improved at the end of treatment, compared to 28% of the control (IPT) group. Improvement was also more rapid for the specialized approach.

In another randomized controlled study, the effectiveness of an interpretive group therapy was compared with that of supportive group therapy. Interpretive group therapy had a goal of increasing the mourners' understanding of conflicts and trauma that interfered with the grieving process, while the supportive group therapy worked to improve the members' adjustment to their new life situations. Improvement was greater for the group receiving interpretive therapy (Ogrodniczuk et al., 2003).

For clients with complicated grief, Iglewicz et al. (2020) have developed a structured approach (complicated grief therapy [CGT]) that has empirical support and a protocol that can be implemented by a grief therapist or generalist practitioner whose client has been diagnosed with this disorder.

Their protocol includes seven steps. Their approach reminds clinicians of the importance of show-ing compassion (both verbally and nonverbally) and avoiding cliches ("time heals all wounds") and using the name of the person who died rather than a relational description (Suzie, rather than your sister, etc.). The 2020 article referenced here and listed in the References is rich with specific recommendations and would be well worth reading. It includes a brief grief questionnaire (five items) to help the clinician decide if complicated grief is a possible diagnosis. Figure 5.1 presents a useful framework showing how acute grief may be adaptive or integrative that is helpful to con-ceptualize the process.

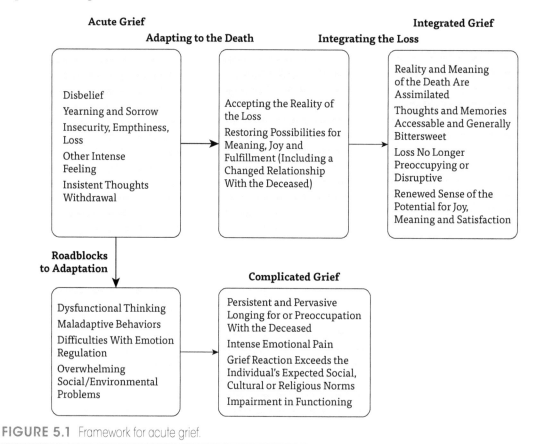

FIGURE 5.1 Framework for acute grief.

The treatment protocol involves seven themes:

- Understanding and accepting grief
- Managing emotional pain
- Thinking about the future
- Strengthening ongoing relationships
- Telling the story of the death
- Living with reminders
- Connecting to memories (Iglewicz et al., 2020, p. 94)

CGT includes specific techniques therapists and has an excellent website (https://prolongedgrief. columbia.edu/) with manuals, tools, training courses, and links to their research that provides clinicians with a complete toolkit. Note that there is a cost for the materials, but there are also many useful resources available at no cost.

Companioning Model

Alan Wolfelt, who directs the Center for Loss & Life Transition, has written a number of books on the concept of "companioning." Companioning focuses on being totally present to a person who is mourning. A mental health professional working with someone experiencing grief need not always worry about fixing or resolving their client's grief. For those clients who have very recently suffered a loss, it is normal for them to feel grief. The clinician may only need to spend time listening. Wolfelt has described this approach in a set of principles:

- Being present to another person's pain; it is not about taking away the pain.
- Going to the wilderness of the soul with another human being; it is not about thinking you are responsible for finding the way out.
- Honoring the spirit; it is not about focusing on the intellect.
- Listening with the heart; it is not about analyzing with the head.
- Bearing witness to the struggles of others; it is not about judging or directing these struggles.
- Walking alongside; it is not about leading.
- Discovering the gifts of sacred silence; it is not about filling up every moment with words.
- Being still; it is not about frantic movement forward.
- Respecting disorder and confusion; it is not about imposing order and logic.
- Learning from others; it is not about teaching them.
- Compassionate curiosity; it is not about expertise. (Center for Loss & Life Transition, n.d.)

Those interested in learning more about companioning may wish to start by visiting the website for the Center for Loss and Life Transition at www.centerforloss.com/.

Group Therapy

Many communities have self-help groups to assist with bereavement issues. These groups assume that the support and understanding of others with similar experiences can normalize the experience and provide support. Counselors may choose to lead such groups and/or refer clients to those groups for additional support. Keep in mind, however, that while such programs are often recommended, there is little research evaluating their effectiveness. Schut et al. (2001) reviewed the existing literature and concluded that despite the widespread use of grief counseling, the results have been "disappointing, sometimes even negative" (p. 705). In examining the studies closely, these researchers observed that while primary prevention counseling is beneficial for children, it is not helpful for other age groups. Secondary prevention was somewhat helpful, but the effects were quite temporary. For tertiary prevention (complicated grief), the outcomes were more positive. It is important to note that the participants in these studies were recruited to participate in research, and Schut et al. believe that this may have affected the outcome. They recommend that organizations or counselors not contact the bereaved to offer counseling immediately after the loss. Interventions that were administered after time had passed had better outcomes, so it may be the case that counseling is helpful for complicated grief that does not resolve on its own but not so helpful in the early stages or normal grief. Mental health professionals should keep this in mind and avoid routinely advising people who have experienced the death of a loved one to seek counseling.

Levels of Prevention

Primary Prevention: Activities to prevent a problem before it occurs. Death education and interventions targeted at all who experience a death would be primary prevention.

Secondary Prevention: Activities for those at risk for developing a problem; counseling for those whose loss is known to be difficult (e.g., survivors of suicide or unexpected death).

Tertiary Prevention: Activities designed to reduce the harmful consequences of a problem. Treating complicated bereavement is tertiary prevention.

These results suggest that those providing treatment for complicated grief should have specific training in delivering specialized treatment designed for this group of bereaved individuals, while counselors with knowledge of the grieving process who are interested in working with normal grief and loss might be able to provide this service with minimal additional training. CGT offers very specific guidelines and additional materials that can be a resource for clinicians. Workshops and professional training on grief and loss are often available, and clinicians who expect to do this work would benefit from attending such professional development programs. In many areas, hospice programs offer training to community members, and these tend to be extremely useful for professionals when they are available. Hospice organizations also may have support groups available for the bereaved, including some for specific types of loss (e.g., suicide), and these can be helpful adjuncts to individual therapy. Mental health professionals would be wise to have information about these resources so that they can make accurate referrals.

Issues of Diversity

Funeral practices and mourning rituals vary by culture and religious perspective, but it is important to note that there is more variation within groups than between groups. This means the treatment provider must be careful not to make any assumptions about the client's needs solely based on cultural group membership. However, it can be very helpful to have some basic knowledge of various practices in order to fine-tune one's listening and understanding. The information we provide next refers to Americans of various ethic/racial/religious affiliations; practices in heritage cultures might be more traditional or prescriptive. Keep in mind that some communities have significant populations of some groups (e.g., Chinatown in San Francisco, etc.), which means more people and services are likely to be available for those groups. For deaths in locations that do not have such communities, it may be difficult for the bereaved to observe expected rituals, making grieving more stressful and perhaps guilt inducing.

Japanese Americans

There are many different cultural groups among Asian Americans, and discussing each is beyond the scope of this book. However, two examples may illuminate some of the ways practices might differ from those more commonly seen in European American traditions. Among Japanese Americans, some will observe Christian practices, but many will observe Buddhist rituals. The funeral consists of a wake, cremation, burial, and memorials (Asakawa, 2016).

At the wake, the body lies in the casket with the head facing north. The priest, holding a *juzu* (prayer beads) will chant a *sutra* while mourners offer incense in an urn at the front of the body, and a *koden* (envelope) with money to help with funeral expenses. Guests will bow to the family as a sign of respect. The cremation is held the next day, and the remains are transferred to an urn by family members. Ashes are sometimes scattered but may be buried in an urn in a family grave; attendees leave flowers, water, and incense at the site. The traditional attire in Japan at funerals is white, but in the United States black is more commonly worn.

The first 49 days involve many observances because the soul only enters heaven on the 49th day after the death. Memorial services are held on every 7th day until the 49th day following the death, and then on the first, third, fifth, seventh, and 13th year anniversaries of the death. At these events, mourners will typically place flowers and incense at the burial site. The rituals are intended to tell the person they are dead and to go away. A formalized expression said to the survivor at the funeral is "Now you are experiencing how the end of life is."

There are beliefs among the Japanese that newly dead spirits can cause harm to the living if the proper rituals are not observed. Thus, some people will perform rituals for those deceased who have no one to care for them. The Japanese mourner will often experience regret for unmet obligations toward the deceased. It is common for the 49 days to include a resolution of "unfinished business," often in the form of a dream that the deceased has forgiven the survivor for any slight. When the survivor is able to relinquish any ambivalent feelings about the dead, the spirit is free to go on with the purification process.

Traditional Japanese households will have an altar containing memorial tablets for the dead ancestors, who still have a presence in the family. The altar also contains "transitional objects" that evoke the dead person, as well as offerings of flowers or foods that were preferred by the deceased. The altar is visited by survivors and is a link to the deceased. There is also a summer festival, in which the dead return for 3 days to visit the living. Thus, the dead maintain an important role in the family, and the survivors receive continuing support from the community.

Chinese Americans

Chinese American practices stress the importance of performing burial rites appropriately since bad luck is believed to come to the family if all rituals are not observed. In America, funerals are often held in funeral homes, but in China they would be held in a Buddhist temple or family home.

Music is important in Chinese funerals. In some cases, a procession to the home of the deceased will be led by musicians playing loud music, which is believed to keep evil spirits away. Numerous floral arrangements are common and are moved to the cemetery for the burial; white or yellow chrysanthemums are appropriate. Mourners wear dark monochromatic attire, although the traditional color would be white. Red is particularly inappropriate. The process begins with a wake with the casket present, held in the home if the deceased died there, or outside the home otherwise. The casket includes clothes and personal items and special blankets (*pei*) that are placed over the body in a ceremonial rite. The wake lasts for 3 days, and the casket is open. The day of the week for the funeral is guided by numerology: Saturdays and Sundays are the luckiest.

Attendees will bow in front of the casket to show respect. Gifts such as candles, fruits, and flowers are placed on an altar surrounding the casket. Friends of the family will come to the home of the deceased as soon as they learn of the death. Pregnant or engaged couples do not attend, as there is a belief that doing so invites bad luck. Wakes can continue for 5 to 7 days or longer depending on the prestige of the deceased, followed by the funeral, which can last up to 49 days, the first 7 days being crucial. The length of the funeral depends on what the family can afford. Bringing food to the bereaved is customary.

Women are expected to wail in grief, with the volume commensurate with the wealth of the deceased. Sometimes professional wailers are employed to ensure this important element is observed. Visitors bring money (odd-numbered amounts only) in white envelopes to assist with the cost of the funeral. Family members pray continually and burn joss paper to ensure the deceased has a comfortable afterlife. When the wake concludes, the casket is covered in holy paper of white and yellow color, symbolizing protection.

Among most Chinese Americans, white is the color of grief. If the deceased had a long life, bright colors may be worn in celebration of the deceased's longevity (80 years or more). At the funeral, symbolic items are burned to promote the welfare of the deceased's soul. Following the funeral, a procession to the gravesite ensues, which begins with loud noises and music, including firecrackers to scare off harmful ghosts. Family members will throw a handful of dirt into the grave, and a procession away from the gravesite symbolizes the return to life of the mourners. As people leave, the family gives guests a red envelope containing money and a white one with candy. A banquet follows the funerals, with the size of the feast commensurate with the degree of success of the deceased.

Postfuneral rituals begin 3 days later when the spirit of the dead person visits the family. The bereaved should not engage in any entertainment for 100 days; the period of mourning is 3 years for a parent or child and 1 year for a spouse. On significant days (deceased's birthday or anniversary of the death) memorial services may be held. The Chinese American customs may include a *Qingming festival*, similar to the Day of the Dead in the Mexican tradition, at which time the family will clean the grave, pay respects, and leave offerings (Coriell, 2022).

Muslim (Islamic) Americans

For Muslims, the purpose of this life is to prepare for the next, and this belief is taught to children from an early age (Raad, 1998). Despite the strong belief that there is a better life to follow, survivors still grieve the death of loved ones. As with Jewish Americans, the burial takes place as soon as possible; there is no viewing or visitation, and caskets are usually closed. Traditional Muslim practice would have someone reading the Koran over the dying person (who would be facing Mecca), and at the moment of death the eyes are closed and the jaw bound shut. The washing of the body is an important ritual and may be done by a professional washer or by family members. All items used in the washing must be brand new, and the water used must be disposed of in accordance with prescribed ritual. The body is wrapped in a shroud. Cremation is prohibited. The funeral takes place outside the mosque where community members gather, facing Mecca, during which the imam leads prayers, after which the deceased is taken to the burial place in a silent procession. The burial is usually attended only by men. The communal mourning period lasts 3 days, and modern practice advises mourners not to hurt themselves physically, although in some places self-harm still occurs among mourning women. Community members bring food to the bereaved family for the first 3 days. During the period of 40 days following the death, most female mourners wear black and cover their heads, although Indian Muslim women wear white.

Jewish Americans

Traditional Jewish rituals around death include burial as soon after death as possible (Grollman, 1998). Embalming, public viewing, and "cosmetization" of the body is against Jewish law, as mourners are urged to remember the dead as they were when alive. Autopsies are also prohibited, so in the case of a death by homicide when the law may require an autopsy, there may be considerable additional distress for the family. The deceased may be buried in regular clothes but is often buried in a shroud. Male attendees at a funeral generally wear a skullcap (yarmulke) at the funeral as a sign of respect. Flowers are not generally used in modern Jewish funerals (their ancient purpose was to disguise the smell of the decaying body), but a contribution to a charity in the name of the deceased is appreciated. Cremation is not customary, although some modern Jews will choose this method of disposition of the body. In that case, the funeral is still held with the body present, and cremation takes place afterward.

The casket is to be made completely of wood, to hasten the natural process of returning to dust. Family members traditionally would tear their clothing to demonstrate their suffering, but many now cut and wear a black ribbon instead. This is usually worn for between 7 to 30 days following the funeral.

The period of mourning immediately after the funeral lasts for 7 days and is known as *shiva*. Family members remain home and do not pursue ordinary activities. They will light a shiva candle upon returning from the cemetery, which burns for 7 days. Some Jews cover mirrors during this period to discourage mourners from thinking of themselves rather than the deceased. Friends and family members visit and offer condolences during this period, with the first meal consisting of bread (the staff of life) and hardboiled eggs (the cycle of life and death). During shiva, the bereaved recite a prayer called the *Kaddish*.

Following this 7-day period, mourners gradually assume their normal activities but observe a bereavement period of 30 days. When the deceased is a parent, the bereavement period lasts for a full year. On the anniversary of the death, the Kaddish is recited in the synagogue, and a candle is lit. The ritual that symbolizes the end of the mourning period is the unveiling of the tombstone or memorial plaque, which is usually held at the end of the first year.

African Americans

Barrett (1998) pointed out that the practices of Blacks Americans will vary according to the religious and cultural affiliation but suggested that there are some generalizations that apply fairly widely. He also advised that this group often experiences untimely deaths (those of younger individuals) due to poor access to health care and increased likelihood of dying before their time. In 1990, Blacks' average life span was 7 years shorter than Whites; in 2018, the gap was reduced to 3.6 years (Huber, 2021). In general, Blacks share an acceptance that death is a part of life and show great reverence toward both the process and the deceased. Funerals are considered very important rituals, and attending a funeral is considered a social obligation of members of the community. The dead are typically buried rather than cremated, and ancestors are considered present in the spirit world. Honoring the dead is important and can be demonstrated by naming a newborn after someone who has died, passing babies over the casket, and pouring libations on the ground.

Libation: A liquid used in a religious ritual.

Friends and families will gather at the home of the deceased immediately upon learning of the death in order to provide support to survivors. It is customary to give food, money, or resources to survivors, but personal attendance at the time of loss is highly valued.

Mexican Americans

Most Mexican Americans observe Catholic traditions of death and mourning. One author (Moore, 1976) described Mexican American funerals as "more emotional" and more participatory variations of the standard Catholic traditions. She observed that the immediate family of the deceased is visible in the service, usually at the front of the congregation. Children were more likely to be present than in other cultures. Among Mexican Americans, there may be a velorio, which is a watch over the body before burial. The rosary is generally said in Spanish the day before the funeral. Some Latinx groups say the rosary for 9 nights after the death, and some families say it every month for a year and on the anniversary of the death thereafter. After the rosary, there is viewing of the body, with touching and kissing not uncommon. Friends and extended family may move to the family's home at that time to provide support. The funeral is a traditional Catholic Mass, with pallbearers chosen to be representative of important ties to the community. Following the funeral, there is often a meal (comida) at which mourners will gather and express condolences to the family. In many cases, money to help defray funeral costs is given to the family. In the postburial period, the family will typically offer special prayers and visit the grave regularly for several months. The family will return to usual activities but limit social activities.

In many communities with large Mexican American populations, the Day of the Dead (*Dia de los Muertos*) is an annual celebration of the lives of the deceased held on November 1 and 2. The deceased's favorite meal may be brought to the gravesite, where family members gather to pray and sing and tend the gravesite. It is a festive occasion that may include confections in the shape of skulls or skeletons and *pan de muerto* (bread of the dead). Altars are created to commemorate the lives of the deceased, with special mementoes on display in order to attract the deceased to participate in the festivities. Families will socialize with other families with nearby gravesites (Salvador, 2003).

Native Americans

There are hundreds of different tribal groups among the Native American population in the United States, and differences in grief and mourning practices vary among tribes. Generalizations are hard to make, but several concepts are relevant. The focus on harmony with the natural world is widespread, and many tribes believe the deceased rejoins the natural world. Traditional spiritual leaders may lead ceremonies for the dead, but some communities observe Christian practices instead of, or in addition to, traditional rituals. Preservation of the body is not central, so embalming is not often practiced. In some tribes, gifts and particular objects are buried with the body to accompany the spirit to the next world. Many Native Americans want to be buried in traditional homelands (Spungen & Piccicuto, 2002).

The Navajo are one of the largest tribes in the United States. Among Navajos, the body of the dead is never touched—this is a very strong cultural taboo. In fact, the word *death* should not be uttered. Navajos believe that when a person is born, the Holy People give it breath or wind. When a person dies, the evil part of the person stays with the body and becomes a *chi'indi*, or an evil spirit. Only infants or elderly who have lived a long life do not produce *ch'iindi*. The most dangerous of the *ch'iindi* is the Skinwalker, who is greatly feared. Contact with a *ch'iindi* is the cause of "ghost sickness," which can be cured only by a long and expensive ceremony called the Enemy Way. When a person dies in a *hogan*, the hogan is destroyed. In fact, some families will take the dying relative to a hospital to avoid losing their home (Alvord & Van Pelt, 1999). Consequently, hospitals are seen as places to be avoided. Before mortuaries were readily available, Navajos would ask non-Navajos to bury their dead.

The part of a person's spirit that is good may take a 4-day journey to the afterworld (*ciditah*) guided by deceased relatives and friends. The afterworld is an underworld, which is very much like the earth and in which the spirits continue with the same activities they were involved in on earth.

It is essential that mental health professionals communicate and demonstrate respect for the varying cultural and religious practices and to acknowledge the importance of these rituals in the lives of many mourners. Encouraging and supporting clients in participating in these practices is ethical and appropriate.

Persons With Disabilities

There are several forms of disability that need special attention when a death occurs. People with intellectual disabilities are reported to frequently experience unusual grief reactions, which are then ignored or unrecognized as grief by family and professional caregivers (Clements et al., 2004; Dowling, et al., 2006; Hollins, 1995). Often, well-intentioned adults and family members believe they need to protect the disabled person from the loss, so they withhold information or exclude the person from mourning rituals. Because many individuals with cognitive challenges have limited verbal skills, they may be unable to describe their experiences or needs. Caregivers may erroneously assume that the person with intellectual disabilities is incapable of understanding the concept of death, a belief that justifies withholding information. This protective behavior deprives the individual of experiences that increase awareness about death and grief. Lavin (1998) stresses what must be understood by mental health professionals working with persons with learning or intellectual disabilities:

> By definition, they have impairments; this does not mean they are without any cognitive ability. They can reason, comprehend, and remember, although they may do so in unique ways. Helping individuals with developmental disabilities cope with loss requires that intervention and support be based on their cognitive strengths. (p. 171)

Particularly when the individual has lived a sheltered existence, the death of a parent or caregiver can be very frightening. The person is likely to have crucial questions about how this death will affect their life, and the lack of involvement of the person in decisions affecting them is commonplace, however hurtful. Lavin (1998) offers some practical suggestions that can assist persons with cognitive disabilities in dealing with the death of a significant person. These tips are useful for caregivers, and mental health professionals can either assist caregivers with these tasks or provide information to facilitate their support of the disabled person:

- Use concrete examples to explain the essential concepts about death: irreversibility, universality, and cessation of functioning. The death of a plant or pet can be an opportunity to explain this. Movies and books can be used to create a structured program of death education.
- Prepare the person to attend the funeral or other mourning rituals. Advance discussion may not be sufficient; arranging a private visit with a sensitive person from a funeral home can demystify the event and give the person firsthand experience prior to the funeral event.
- Attend carefully to the terms used to describe the death. Euphemisms may be confusing and can create misunderstanding.
- Many individuals with intellectual impairments think egocentrically and may believe they caused the death. Be certain to dispel this notion, explaining the cause of death in simple and direct terms.
- Locate a support network. If the parent has died and the person must relocate, this may be challenging, but advance arrangements can ease the process.
- If the person has a religious affiliation, encourage contact with clergy.
- Normalize grief reactions. If the individual has no prior experience with death and grieving, they may not realize that their strong feelings and distress are experienced by everyone who experiences the death of someone they cared about.

A team of researchers (Dowling et al., 2006) tested two interventions for bereaved adults with intellectual disabilities. Although their study was carefully designed, the intervention that involved both family members and care staff at day treatment centers was only actually implemented fully with one individual. The researchers learned that this format was likely too demanding of time from nonclinical persons.

The positive findings for the intervention using bereavement counselors, who took a 2-day training on working with individuals with intellectual disabilities, are very encouraging. The individual sessions were provided at the location chosen by the client (usually home or treatment center) for 15 weekly sessions of approximately 1 hour duration. Counselors used a variety of strategies to communicate with the clients, including drawing, using books and pictures, and making memorial items. The researchers found significant gains in those who received the individual counseling intervention, while the others who had originally given consent to participate but did not receive any services either made no gains or actually deteriorated. Both outcome measures assessed changes in behavior and were completed by family members or caregivers at treatment centers. This seems to be a very promising intervention and demonstrates that individuals with such disabilities do in fact have grief responses to a death that need attention.

Deaf persons may also have unique difficulties when a death occurs, although the difficulty is more likely to be caused by their treatment by the hearing population than by the death itself (Zieziula, 1998). Although the emotional impact of a death is similar in Deaf[1] and hearing people, it is more difficult for the Deaf person to communicate their experience to others, especially if

---

1 When Deaf is capitalized, it refers to the Deaf community or people who are part of the Deaf culture. The lower ase deaf refers to the inability to hear or hard-of-hearing people. This distinction is very important to many Deaf individuals.

most other mourners are not Deaf. The difficulty communicating with the hearing population extends to getting accurate information. For the Deaf person who loses a Deaf spouse, the loss can be particularly devastating, as the spouse may have been a "cultural and communication partner" (p. 191). Ziuziula notes that most Deaf people have partners or spouses who are also Deaf but may have hearing children. The grief process involves coming to terms with the loss and continuing one's life, changed as it will necessarily be. For a Deaf person whose childhood is likely to have involved considerable dependence on others, and the death of a partner may cause those dependency issues to resurface. Practitioners should emphasize the client's strengths and assist them in learning skills to accomplish tasks that they have not done before. Although it is possible (via an American Sign Language interpreter) for a hearing clinician to counsel a Deaf person, a Deaf practitioner is much preferable. Most communities have agencies that provide services to the Deaf community; referral to those resources may be best for the clients.

Counselor Issues

Working with bereaved clients inevitably brings up one's own losses, feelings, and fears about death and heightens our awareness of our mortality. It is essential that counselors clarify their own beliefs and address their own fears prior to engaging with clients. Dersheimer's (1990) Personal Grieving Style Inventory is a very useful vehicle for exploring thoughts and experiences about grief and loss. It is recommended that this inventory be completed individually but shared and processed with others. Often training workshops and professional development programs will invite participants to engage in this type of self-exploration, and doing so will raise the counselor's awareness of the kinds of situations and individuals that may present personal challenges for the client. Because the nonjudgmental aspect of grief counseling is so critical, counselors need to pay close attention to their own reactions and be willing to refer those clients with whom they cannot provide that supportive stance.

Bill Moyer's 2000 PBS series *On Our Own Terms: Moyers on Dying* is a moving account of the death and grief experience. We show this to students, who consistently say it is difficult to watch but necessary. This series can be a stimulus for further discussion with peers about how each counselor copes with loss and responds to grief in others.

Counselors who work with bereaved clients, as a specialty or occasionally, need to be prepared and tolerant of high levels of emotionality. It is important that clients have a safe place to express their feelings, which may be of high intensity.

NOTE TO SCHOOL COUNSELORS

School counselors have a number of important roles related to death and grief in schools. One of those roles is delivering guidance curriculum. Although some degree of death education would be helpful, some schools will not allow the topic to be presented (Samide & Stockton, 2002). For those school counselors interested in using literature to teach about death, Bologna (2020) provides a list of books that would be very useful in today's classrooms. Several other internet sources of children's book titles will be provided in the Resources section later in this chapter. When there has been a death that affects children in school, visiting classes and providing age-appropriate lessons on death can be helpful to students and a relief to teachers who might be uncomfortable doing such lessons themselves.

There are several situations in which the counselor is likely to have a major responsibility: the death of a student or staff member and the death of a child's parent or sibling. The death of a student can be quite challenging to manage. In a school in which one of my students was doing an internship, a third-grade student died of leukemia only weeks after diagnosis. Several of the children in the class were fearful that they would catch the disease and die as well. Most children were sad and were shocked to know that someone their age could die. The school counselor was able to visit the child's class and provide information in a sensitive and age-appropriate manner and to allow for children to express their feelings and ask questions. Some children received additional individual counseling as needed. Another situation occurred at the high school where SB worked as a school counselor. A teacher died in a car accident on a weekend. She received the information prior to school convening on Monday morning and met with teachers before students arrived. As the deceased teacher had been at the school for many years, colleagues were deeply saddened, and several did not feel able to help students. SB delivered the information to students in classroom groups. Students varied in their responses to the news, with those who felt closest to the teacher experiencing the more intense emotional reactions. In addition, several students who had acted out in his class recently felt extremely guilty about their behavior and the loss of an opportunity to apologize. Another phenomenon that is quite common is that even those students who did not know the deceased are affected by the memory of losses of their own and may need support revisiting those events and understanding that such delayed reactions are normal.

Swihart et al. (1992) described their experience in a small school when a popular 16-year-old died of leukemia. They point out that although high school students have the cognitive skills to understand death, few had had any direct experience with death, and had also not previously discussed the topic with adults who could provide information. These school counselors found themselves intervening with individuals, providing small groups, and serving the entire system as it coped with this loss. They surveyed the student body 18 months after the death and gathered data about the students' recalled initial experience and their ongoing responses. They learned that teachers were unable to provide meaningful assistance to students because they were struggling with their own grief. They also discovered that many students believed they needed more opportunity to talk about the death, while many others wanted school to proceed as usual and not dwell on the death. These opposite opinions are understandable, given what we know about patterns of grief responses.

Approximately 6 million youth will experience the death of a parent before they are 18 years old. (Judi's House, n.d.). In some cases, school counselors are involved when an individual student is first notified about a death; the school counselor is the best prepared person on the school staff to be present, and some experts recommend that this task be officially assigned to the school counselor to ensure sensitive and appropriate treatment of the child (Servaty-Seib et al., 2003). If the school counselor is present when a student learns of a parental death (from a surviving parent, a relative, a clergyperson), they can assist by giving the child choices about who they want to be notified of the death and what information they wish to be given. They also should be allowed to decide from whom and how to get their belongings and be invited to return to talk with the school counselor as needed. The companioning model of counseling the bereaved may be especially helpful.

Usually, the school will receive notification of a death from the family, and the school counselor is likely to be the primary liaison between the family and school. It is not unusual for family members to be consumed with their own grief to the extent that the child's needs go unrecognized. The school counselor can be available to listen to the child and to normalize the grief process. The school counselor also should be an advocate for the student, arranging for appropriate accommodations following the death: allowing time to see the counselor, excusing absences related to the death, making academic allowances for the expected reduced academic performance after the death, and so on (Costa & Holliday, 1994; Samide & Stockton, 2002; Servaty-Seib et al., 2003).

Gray (1988) interviewed 50 students who had experienced the death of a parent while in secondary school. Students had mixed reactions regarding how helpful the surviving parent had been, with equal numbers finding them very helpful and not at all helpful. Gray suggests that the school counselor could be helpful in those cases when the relationship is strained by the loss. For most teens, the most helpful person was a friend or peers in a

(Continued)

support group. Many reported that other friends and acquaintances seemed to pull away, which made them feel isolated. Those students who participated in a school support group were much more likely to say that peers understood them than those who did not participate in a group. One of the disturbing findings from these interviews was that 42% of students said teachers were not helpful. Students appreciated expressions of condolences from teachers when they were given privately and were appreciative of those who adjusted academic expectations during the bereavement period. Several students reported having been told by teachers to "buckle down and focus on their schoolwork" (p. 188), which was quite unhelpful. School counselors need to educate teachers about the grief process and provide suggestions for how they might respond to students who have experienced a death of a loved one. Students in support groups found the school counselor more helpful than those not in groups, suggesting that the planned, regular contact that occurs with a group was an effective way for students to access their counselors.

Another difficult loss for students is that of a sibling. Balk (1983) observed that much of the literature on grief focuses on the death of a spouse or parent, with far less available on this other difficult loss. In order to understand the impact of the death of a sibling, Balk interviewed 33 teenagers who lost a sibling and discovered that for many of them the emotional responses continued as long as 2 years or more after the death. Schoolwork and school motivation deteriorated, at least temporarily, for most of his participants. Like Gray's (1988) participants, students in this study found that peers were most helpful, but some peers withdrew, often as a result of their own discomfort and uncertainty about how to respond. Balk suggested that one role school counselors might take is to meet with friends of the bereaved study to give them suggestions about how they might interact with their bereaved classmate. One comment was made by several participants that would be useful for classmates to know: Students emphatically resented being told "I know how you feel" by anyone other than someone else who had lost a sibling. Thus, Balk found that helping the grieving student reestablish social support and helping other students learn how to respond to a peer at a time of grief a very useful contribution by the school counselor.

It is clear that some students benefit from bereavement groups in the school setting. The groups in Gray's (1988) study were for those who had lost a parent. Participants believed that those who had lost a loved one who was not a parent would be welcome, but 90% opposed including students who lost a parent through divorce. Samide and Stockton (2002) provide an outline for offering school bereavement groups. They recommend the group be at least 8 weeks in duration and that screening interviews include both the student and their parent if possible. These experts recommend that students not participate in school counseling groups for 2 to 4 months after the death. Students who have experienced a death, especially younger children, cannot tolerate lengthy sessions with intense effect, so it is important to plan the group so that there are a variety of activities to relieve the intensity. These authors provide an outline of activities for an eight-session group that is flexible and can be adapted to different levels. Gray also offers helpful guidelines for conducting bereavement groups in the schools.

Ethical Concerns

When working with clients experiencing grief, counselors must be sure to adhere to all ethical guidelines of their profession, including boundaries of competence. If counselors find that grief counseling becomes a focus of the work, it is important that they obtain current information by attending professional training and reading the professional literature.

Counselors must be aware of cultural differences and observe ethical codes for working with multicultural clients. It may be appropriate to attend the funeral or pay a condolence call if a client experiences the death of a loved one. If a counselor is uncertain about the propriety of such a gesture, consultation with a colleague, preferably of the client's cultural background, is strongly recommended.

Perhaps the most important ethical concern regarding grief is the necessity of self-awareness. As grief is a universal experience, counselors must ensure (via consultation and supervision) that they are able to separate their own needs from those of clients. It is strongly recommended that counselors engage in some type of personal growth experience related to grief prior to working with any clients. Most professional conferences have sessions on this topic, and there are numerous professional training opportunities specifically focused on grief. There are several online courses on grief that the interested counselor may take if no other training is available.

Summary

- Normal grief involves physical, emotional, cognitive, behavioral, and spiritual components. Most people do not need professional services to deal with grief, but in some cases lack of environmental support will bring mourners to counseling.
- Although the stage theory of Kübler-Ross is best known, it does not accurately describe the individual variations of the grief and mourning experience.
- Worden proposes a task model suggesting that individuals need to accomplish four tasks in order to move forward: accepting the reality of the loss, working through the pain and grief, adjusting to an environment in which the deceased is missing, and emotionally relocating the deceased and moving on with life.
- In addition to normal grief, some individuals experience complicated grief, with longer duration and additional symptoms. There are specialized assessment tools to help the counselor distinguish between normal and complicated grief. These individuals are more likely to receive professional help and require a different approach to treatment. CGT is an evidence-based approach that is accessible to clinicians.
- The experience of grief changes over the life span as cognitive and emotional development affects people's understanding of death and their ability to recognize and express feelings associated with the loss. Different strategies are indicated for individuals at different developmental levels. The elderly are at risk for complicated grief, and professionals who work with this population should be alert to difficulties and losses.
- Some special cases of grief may require more understanding. Survivors of death by suicide, families of babies who die of SIDS, those who experience miscarriages and abortions, and military deaths are among those special cases. In addition, sudden death presents particular challenges, and survivors may need more support and information to manage the grieving process. The death of a pet is sometimes discounted and trivialized but can be a very painful loss to pet owners. The loss of a pet may be a child's first experience with death and grief.
- Sensitivity to the cultural influences in grieving is important so that the helping professional does not offend when they intend to be helpful. Because cultural practices vary so widely (and because individuals within a culture vary in how closely they follow those practices), the professional would do well to respectfully inquire about relevant practices and beliefs.
- Persons with disabilities may have unique needs when they experience a death, and counselors can help ensure that those needs are met.
- Counselors must be self-aware so that their own grief issues do not interfere with those of clients. Counselors must be aware of ethical issues in dealing with any client, and with grief counseling, sensitivity to issues of diversity is particularly critical.

Additional Resources

On the Web

- http://www.adec.org/ is the site for the Association for Death Education and Counseling. It has training modules available from the organization by well-known experts as well as publications and other resources.
- https://www.centerforloss.com/ is the site of Dr. Alan Wolfelt, who directs the Center for Loss and Life Transition. SB has attended his workshops and found them to be very beneficial.
- http://www.programsforelderly.com/endoflifecare-national-center-for-death-education.php is the National Center for Death Education's website, which offers online and residential training.
- http://www.taps.org/ or http://www.military.com/benefits/survivor-benefits/tragedy-assistance-program-for-survivors are links to Tragedy Assistance Program for Survivors (TAPS). This is an organization a clinician will want to recommend to families who have experience the death of someone in the military.
- http://www.nlm.nih.gov/medlineplus/suddeninfantdeathsyndrome.html is an excellent site on SIDS that includes information and links to other sites that have the most current research.
- http://www.sids.org/ is another good website with factual information about SIDS.
- https://whatsyourgrief.com/childrens-books-about-death/ and http://www.santaclaracountylib.org/kids/lists/death_dying_grieving.html have good lists of children's books on death and dying, coded for age level.
- http://childrensbooks.about.com/od/themesubjectbooksby/tp/petdeath.htm has a list of useful books for the death of a pet.
- http://www.compassionatefriends.org/ is a website for parents and siblings of a deceased child and is a wonderful resource. The website of the national organization has much helpful information and can assist in locating local chapters.
- http://www.dougy.org/ is the website for the Dougy Center, which is dedicated to helping grieving children and teens and has useful links for kids, teens, and adults. There is information about their programs for training professionals interested in providing services for grieving children and adolescents.
- http://www.helpguide.org/mental/grief_loss.htm is a well-designed website with good information for clients about grief.
- http://www.nci.nih.gov/cancertopics/pdq/supportivecare/bereavement/patient/allpages is the National Cancer Institute's website.
- https://elunanetwork.org/resources/developmental-grief-responses and https://childmind.org/guide/helping-children-cope-with-grief/ are good sites for parents who need information about developmental aspects of grief.

In Print for Counselors

- *On Death and Dying* by Elisabeth Kübler-Ross is the best-known book on death and grieving, and despite the criticism of the book from more modern experts, it is definitely an important one for a counselor to have read.
- *Grief Counseling and Grief Therapy: A Handbook for the Mental Health Practitioner* (fourth edition) by J. William Worden is a classic reference in this field. It is also highly readable and

offers specific suggestions for counseling. His book on *Children and Grief: When a Parent Dies* is another valuable reference by Worden.

- *A Grief Observed* by C. S. Lewis is the famous author's personal account of his grief upon the death of his wife and is a window into the intimate experience of one man. The film *Shadowlands* is based on this story.

- *The Loss That Is Forever: The Lifelong Impact of the Early Death of a Mother or Father* by Maxine Harris will be helpful for those counselors who may work with children who lose a parent and may be appropriate for some adult clients for whom this loss continues to be an issue.

- *Children and Grief: When a Parent Dies* by J. William Worden is another important and useful reference for working with children.

In Print for Clients

- *Living When a Loved One Has Died, Straight Talk About Death for Teenagers: How to Cope With Losing Someone You Love, What Helped Me When My Loved One Died, Living With Loss, Healing With Hope*, and for children, *A Child's Book About Death* are all by Earl Grollman, who is a master of speaking to those who are grieving. I often recommend these books to clients who have experienced the death of someone important in their lives. Readers might want to explore the long list of books he has written on this subject.

- *The Fall of Freddie the Leaf: A Story of Life for All Ages* by Leo Buscaglia is a classic book for children about death that can help prepare them for a loss. This story is also available in Spanish.

- *Talking With Children About Loss* by Maria Trozzi is an excellent book for parents, but counselors who work with grieving children will find it helpful as well.

Film and Television

- An excellent list of films on grief and loss, organized by age group and specific kind of loss (e.g., of spouse, sibling, parent, friend) and those focusing on healing can be found here: https://www.mygriefassist.com.au/inspiration-resources/movies/.

- *On Our Own Terms*, a PBS series about death and dying (http://www.pbs.org/wnet/onourownterms/about/index.html). Ideally, this series would be the focus of a study group where one could discuss and process the videos. There is a discussion guide available to assist in that process. A follow-up series, *With Eyes Open*, includes an episode that focuses on grief and loss (http://www.pbs.org/witheyesopen/about_the_series.html).

- *In America* (2002), is great film about the impact of the death of a child on the parents and surviving children.

- *P.S. I Love You* (2007).

- *Extremely Loud and Incredibly Close* (2011).

- *Marley and Me* (2008).

- *The Sweet Hereafter* (1997) examines the impact of a sudden tragic loss of many children on the survivors in a small town.

- *Moonlight Mile* is a good film that focuses on impact of the death of a woman on her boyfriend and her parents.

- *Corina, Corina* (1994) is about the impact of the death of a wife and mother on the survivors and the positive effects on the grieving father and daughter of the nanny dad hires.

Exercises

1. Apply the concepts in this chapter to the case study at the beginning of the chapter. List the aspects of the situation that contributed to the complications. In what ways did James's experience illustrate Worden's tasks of grief? Imagine you were the counselor James met with right after his mother's death. What are some strategies or interventions you might have used to assist him? What books might you have recommended he read?

2. Watch any of the films mentioned and discuss your own responses. What does the film teach you about grief? How would you have worked with the protagonist if you were their counselor?

3. Complete individually, and then discuss as a group, the Personal Grieving Style Inventory in Appendix A of Derhseimer's book.

4. Investigate resources in your own community to which you might refer clients who are struggling with grief issues. Check for local branches of organizations such as Compassionate Friends.

5. Find out whether the local hospice offers training for professionals and attend the training.

6. Visit a funeral home and find out if they have a person who assists with bereavement (often a bereavement counselor or director). Find out about what services are available and how clients can access them. Some funeral homes provide support groups and other services for up to a year after a death.

7. Assume you are a school counselor. One of the teachers in your school was killed in an automobile accident over the weekend. You will be going into her class on Monday morning to work with the students. Plan how you will tell them of the loss, how you will answer their predictable questions, and what other services you might offer. Do this exercise as if you were an elementary counselor, middle school counselor, and a high school counselor.

8. Assume you are a counselor in an agency and one of your adult clients experiences the death of a parent while in treatment with you. How and when will you determine whether the client is experiencing normal grief or complicated grief? What would be some indicators that a complicated grief is likely?

9. How will you respond to your friend whose 13-year-old dog has died?

10. Go http://www.amazon.com/exec/obidos/tg/listmania/list-browse/-/KC8JRF33CG21/qid%3D1119815136/sr%3D5-1/ref%3Dsr%5F5%5F1/103-3538514-4167807. Locate copies of as many of these books as possible and decide if you would recommend them for a grieving child. Note the ages for which the book is appropriate and any special circumstances for which the book would be particularly useful.

11. Review the section of diversity and examine the practices of each cultural group from the perspective of Worden's tasks of grief. How do each group's rituals help survivors accomplish each of the tasks?

Credits

---- PART III ----

SERIOUS
DISORDERS

CHAPTER 6

Trauma

As I do every morning, I began my day today by reading the news online, and then had breakfast while reading the local print newspaper. During that brief time, I read survivor accounts of escaping the horrific wildfire on Maui, a gut-wrenching story about injured soldiers in Ukraine suffering from severe PTSD, another recounting the victims' statements at the sentencing of the Goon Squad (their sadistic, unrestrained torturers), a narrative of the dramatic rescue of a teenager who fell more than 100 feet in the Grand Canyon (who has no memory of the 2 hours between the fall and being in a helicopter to a hospital), and a moving piece describing the experience of a murder victim's 15-year-old son who was present in the car when his father was shot to death. He spoke at the sentencing (life in prison) of a local man for murder; his story describes a classic case of PTSD.

Sadly, these are just one day's news stories. There are undoubtedly many other cases of trauma and violence that did not make the news. Mass shootings, natural disasters, accidents, the COVID–19 pandemic, and other tragedies are not rare events. *Trauma* has become a buzzword because of its common occurrence. There are numerous self-help books, YouTube videos by experts in the field, webinars, and seminars available. Interestingly, it was only in 1980 that the condition PTSD received a place in the DSM; mental health professionals finally recognized that there was an identifiable cluster of symptoms in some people who had been exposed to all manner of traumatic events, and the inclusion of this diagnosis was an important acknowledgement of the long-term psychological consequences such events can initiate.

Helping professionals must understand the nature of trauma and the ways in which people react and recover from traumatic experiences. Even the clinician who does not become a trauma specialist will encounter trauma in their career. Whether or not you will work with trauma survivors as a specialist, this chapter is important to read. A client you are treating for a seemingly unrelated problem may eventually disclose a history of trauma. A current client may have a traumatic experience during treatment. In both of those situations, the clinician should be prepared to respond appropriately. When a strong therapeutic alliance has been established, it may be prudent and ethical to address the trauma, albeit with consultation and supervision. Even if a referral is necessary, making appropriate referrals requires considerable knowledge about the effects of trauma, how to assess whether a person is experiencing trauma-related symptoms, and which treatments have been shown to be effective.

CASE STUDY

At 30 years old, Jane had been driving for 14 years. She had been a passenger in two minor fender-benders in her lifetime, neither of which involved injuries. During high school, she had been treated for bulimia but had been symptom free for many years.

Jane was starting out on a road trip to introduce a foreign friend to the American desert when the excursion was abruptly terminated. On this day, she and her friend, both wearing seat belts, were about an hour and a half into the 8-hour planned journey on a divided interstate highway. There were two lanes in each direction, and Jane had set the car's cruise control to travel a mile or two above the posted speed limit. She passed some cars traveling slowly in the right-hand lane when she suddenly had to apply the brakes behind a semi-trailer traveling below the speed limit in the left lane. She was uncomfortable traveling for any distance in the left lane and returned to the right lane, where she gradually increased speed to the previous rate. She was slightly ahead of the semi when she heard a loud noise and lost control of the vehicle.

Jane realized that the semi had hit her car on the rear driver's side. "Oh God" and "I could die" were her thoughts as the accident seemed to happen in slow motion. She was watching out the windshield, terrified and helpless, as the vehicle spun and flipped and somersaulted along an embankment. She felt as though they were in a clothes dryer being tossed about. At impact, she watched the windshield cracking as the car finally came to a stop, on its roof, with both Jane and her friend hanging upside down by their seat belts. She was completely disoriented and could not free herself from the seatbelt. She felt the weight of her body on her neck. She heard her friend's voice saying, "Are you okay?" and saw that her friend had managed to free herself from the seat belt. At the same time, she heard voices outside the car and saw feet and heard someone say, "Don't move, the car is unstable." She saw blood dripping and knew it was her own. She was also shaking uncontrollably and felt desperate to get out of the vehicle. She asked people to clear a space so she could see out the window.

An off-duty fireperson was among those who stopped to help, and he was able to enter the vehicle through the missing rear window. He thought Jane's neck was broken, and carefully reclined her seat to reduce the pressure on her neck. Jane later learned that her friend was imagining the gas leaking out of the damaged car and the car exploding in flames, but Jane was most aware of feeling trapped and wanted to get out of the vehicle. Before the ambulance arrived, a policeperson came up to the window and asked for her driver's license and registration. She later learned that the truck driver was cited for improper lane change.

When the ambulance arrived, she was removed from the vehicle and strapped to a gurney. Her friend was transported to the hospital in the same ambulance. The attendant asked Jane why she was shaking, saying, "Are you cold?" At the hospital, the friends were separated, and Jane's clothes were cut from her body. She was poked and prodded, and a catheter inserted. She felt like an object rather than a human being, as attendants ignored her during these procedures and spoke over her about what they would order for lunch.

Jane was left in a room alone while she was waiting to be taken for X-rays. At this point, she felt overwhelmed and panicky and felt her thoughts "catching up." She was worried about her friend and thought she had heard someone saying her friend's heartbeat was irregular. She eventually got the attention of a nurse and asked the nurse to stay with her while she waited. After X-rays determined her neck was not broken, she was given a cervical brace and paper scrubs to replace her clothes. She and her friend met with a hospital liaison who attempted to provide assistance. They now had no clothes, all their belongings, including wallets, were in the crashed vehicle or strewn about the crash site, and they did not know anyone locally. Jane felt she could not think straight to figure out what to do. The nurse who attended her friend was kind enough to allow both women to stay in her home for a few days, giving them time to retrieve their belongings and contact support. Jane was petrified riding in the nurse's car.

Seeing the crashed vehicle was not nearly as disturbing as seeing the site of the accident, where Jane found her warped and smashed sunglasses. Jane did not want to be alone and was comfortable only around her friend because they had shared this experience. Particularly since the hospital personnel appeared so detached and insensitive, it was difficult for Jane to believe anyone could understand how she was feeling. Following the trauma, she found that previously routine activities became frightening and overwhelming. She was extremely sensitive to crowds, sounds, and lights in such places as grocery stores. She wanted to be in a quiet, controlled environment.

She had several nightmares shortly after the accident: in one she was sledding on a course that became more and more complicated, and she was going faster and faster, knowing she was about to crash, feeling powerless, hopeless, and terrified. In the other, she was being hung (executed) and awoke, terrified at the instant her neck was about to snap.

Jane became extremely distressed and hypervigilant in cars as a passenger, feeling as though she had to be watching for other drivers to make a mistake or unsafe maneuver. She did not drive a car herself for more than 8 months—at which time she borrowed a car and drove at no more than 25 mph around residential areas for 10 minutes. She drove rarely after that and avoided interstate highways or any roads where traffic was fast. She became extremely defensive in a car, and on one occasion 2 years after the accident, when she attempted driving with a friend in the car, her heart rate increased, she became short of breath, sweated with clenched muscles, and became so dizzy she thought she would pass out and had to pull over.

Jane was unable to afford intensive treatment and had never heard that PTSD occurred outside of combat situations. She did not feel that anyone could understand what she was experiencing and did not want to burden others with her concerns. Her friend's visa expired 2 months after the accident, and Jane found herself isolating from others and becoming more and more reclusive. She did have one session of EMDR, with no noticeable benefit. She saw a psychologist for two sessions, who provided a workbook on anxiety and suggested gradual exposure to driving, which Jane did on her own, beginning with very low-speed driving on residential areas, then progressing to busier streets with traffic, and eventually to multilane thoroughfares with increasing speed, which was extremely difficult for her.

Jane also developed intense social anxiety following the accident, which became extreme when she enrolled in school and needed to speak in class. She would have intense physiological reactivity in social situations, feeling as though she would either throw up or pass out. These symptoms led her to consult a neurologist, who prescribed an SSRI to manage those symptoms. About 7 years postaccident, Jane got a job that required the use of an interstate highway to commute, and she did manage to do so with minimal symptoms. She now sees herself as a very cautious driver and passenger who would prefer not to drive on high-speed interstate highways but does so when necessary. The social anxiety that seemed to be precipitated by the trauma has diminished.

Reflecting on her experience, Jane felt that she was revictimized by her callous treatment in the ambulance and at the hospital. The attendant did not appear to recognize that Jane's shaking was symptomatic of shock, and the hospital personnel did not make any effort to reassure or comfort her. Being left alone while waiting for X-rays was psychologically harmful and also led her to believe that if professionals did not understand how difficult and disturbing this experience was, friends and others surely would be unable to do so. This belief led to the increased social withdrawal. Jane's only source of comfort was her friend, who could say, "Yes, I feel that way too" and help to dispel the sense of going crazy.

Jane felt that some awareness that PTSD was not confined to combat or rape victims might have encouraged her to feel less alone and perhaps to seek help sooner. The lack of awareness that trauma of all types can result in PTSD made the effects of the event seem bizarre and incomprehensible, when in fact many who are in traffic accidents experience symptoms of PTSD. Decades later, she still avoids driving on busy highways and is an annoyingly vigilant backseat driver.

Definitions and Description of the Problem

The first DSM to include PTSD defined *trauma* as events "outside the range of human experience" (American Psychiatric Association, 1980, p. 236). However, the frequency with which trauma occurs belied that definition, and PTSD is now defined as "exposed to: death, threatened death, actual or threatened serious injury, or actual or threatened sexual violence in the following ways: direct exposure, witnessing the trauma, learning that the trauma happened to a close relative or close friend, indirect exposure to aversive details of the trauma, usually in the course of professional duties (e.g., first responders, medics)" (U.S. Department of Veterans Affairs, n.d.a.) The Substance Abuse and Mental Health Services Administration (SAMHSA, 2014) has a more expansive view: "Individual trauma results from an event, series of events, or set of circumstances that is experienced by an individual as physically or emotionally harmful or life threatening and that has lasting adverse effects on the individual's functioning and mental, physical, social, emotional, or spiritual well-being" (p. 6). Exposure to trauma can be through directly experiencing the traumatic event, witnessing the event as it occurred to others, learning that the event occurred to a family member or a close friend, or indirect exposure in the course of occupational duties. War, physical and sexual assault, terrorist attacks, and natural disasters are all examples of traumatic events. (See Appendix A for the complete DSM-V diagnostic criteria for PTSD.) Trauma is not restricted to any age, gender, sexual orientation, race, or ethnicity and is not limited by geography. However, we must acknowledge that some communities (of low socioeconomic status) are more vulnerable due to proximity to sources of toxic environments, high levels of violence, and the absence of effective preventive and protective resources.

Readers should be aware that when DSM-V was released, the changes from DSM-IV caused consternation among some professionals. These changes meant that some people who would meet criteria for a diagnosis under one version would not on the other. Having an accurate diagnosis has implications for treatment eligibility, eligibility for insurance coverage, forensic matters such as detection of malingering (Levin et al., 2014), eligibility for compensation for disability, and potential legal disputes (McFarlane, 2014; North et al., 2022). The DMS-V-TR was released in 2022, but the changes were minor and do not alter diagnostic criteria.

Since the diagnostic criteria for PTSD require a duration of symptoms for at least 1 month post-traumatic event, an additional diagnosis of acute stress disorder (ASD) applies to a condition of extreme distress during the 1st month after the traumatic event. Bryant (2019) argued that although ASD may appear to be a precursor of PTSD, about half of trauma victims who develop PTSD would not qualify for an ASD diagnosis, which requires the presence of nine acute stress reactions in the 1st month. An important reason for including this category is that often an individual must have a diagnosis for insurance to cover treatment.

The International Classification of Diseases (ICD) is a diagnostic system used worldwide that covers medical diagnoses in addition to mental health (Curic, 2022; World Health Organization, 2024.). The current version is the ICD-11, released in 2018. The DSM is primarily used in the United States and covers mental disorders only, as the name implies. The ICD lists codes for each diagnosis as required by most insurance companies, but the DSM-V-TR uses codes from ICD-10-CM (ICD-10 Clinical Modification). The ICD-11 also includes a diagnosis that is not in the DSM: complex PTSD. The three main symptoms of PTSD (reexperiencing, avoidance, and hypervigilance) are required, with the addition of difficulties with emotional regulation, shame and guilt, and interpersonal conflict to an extent that the individual's life and functioning are disrupted (disturbances in self-organization; Fernández-Fillol et al., 2021). Using ICD-11 criteria, the relative prevalence of Complex Post Traumatic Stress Disorder (CPTSD) and PTSD female victims of IPV were determined (Fernández-Fillol et al., 2021). CPTSD was detected in 39.5% of the sample compared to 17.9% for PTSD. Although many symptoms were present in both cases, the presence of maladaptive emotion regulation strategies were present in the CPTSD subsample.

According to Herman (1997), a pioneer in the field of traumatology, traumatic events are those that overwhelm our adaptive abilities and result in "intense fear, helplessness, loss of control, and threat of annihilation" (p. 33). A *disaster* is a "sudden event that has the potential to terrify, horrify, or engender substantial losses for many people simultaneously" (Norris, 2002, p. 1). *Natural disasters* are those caused by weather or geophysical events (e.g., severe flooding in Ft. Lauderdale, Florida, in April 2003; massive wildfires in California, Canada, and Maui in 2023) and have more severe consequences in that housing and warning systems may be inadequate and few resources for recovery are available. *Human-caused disasters* include mass shootings, gang violence, arson, chemical or hazardous material spills, oil spills, train derailing, explosions, acts of terrorism, and so on. It is obvious that individuals, families, communities, and nations do not lack settings that cause traumatic responses in those affected.

Bessel van der Kolk, another authority on trauma and author of popular book *The Body Keeps the Score,* explained that trauma "temporarily or permanently alter their capacity to cope, their biological threat perception, and their concepts of themselves ... [, and] the memory of the traumatic event comes to dominate the victims' consciousness, depleting their lives of meaning and pleasure" (van der Kolk, 2000, p. 1). We find this description captures the essential elements of PTSD.

Prevalence

Most people who have had traumatic experiences recover without intervention. About 70% of Americans experience a traumatic event during their lifetime, but only about 20% of those will develop PTSD. In a given year, about 5% of Americans has PTSD. Women are more likely to be diagnosed with PTSD than men. Rates of PTSD vary by type of trauma, with sexual assault (49%) and severe physical assault (32%) having the highest rates of subsequent PTSD. Among veterans, about 14% who served in Iraq, and 30% who served in Vietnam, have had PTSD at some point in their lives. PTSD often co-occurs with other disorders such as anxiety, depression, and substance abuse (Carmona, 2023; SingleCare Team, 2023). We wish to make it clear that we believe that people can heal from trauma, although some will need appropriate intervention and treatment.

Theory

Judith Herman's ground-breaking book *Trauma and Recovery*, first published in 1992, was based on her many years of treating clients who had experienced trauma. She emphasized the importance of context because the way a person responds to a traumatic experience is shaped by their culture and environment. More recently a research group provided neurobiological support for her theory of recovery from trauma (Zaleski et al., 2016). They note that responses to trauma have a biological basis, which diminishes the sense of self-blame that often accompanies trauma. She proposed that the symptoms commonly experienced with trauma are the result of the person's ineffective attempts to protect themselves. Those are *hyperarousal* (perceiving danger where none exists), inability to handle frustration, having a "short fuse," being easy to startle, *intrusion* (reliving the events, not just remembering), and *constriction* (avoidance strategies such as dissociation, and numbing).

An important tenet of the theory is that insight alone is insufficient to recover from a traumatic experience because the prefrontal cortex does not diminish the emotional arousal and sensations that disturb the client's functioning:

> What most people do not realize is that trauma is not the story of something awful that happened in the past, but the residue of imprints left behind in people's sensory and hormonal systems. Traumatized people often are terrified of the sensations in their own bodies (van der Kolk, 2009, as cited in Zaleski et al., 2016.).

Herman's theory posits that there are three phases to recovery from trauma: *safety, remembrance and mourning,* and *reconnection.* Herman stressed that the relationship with the therapist is of paramount importance to this process. Zaleski et al. connect those stages to the brain areas and functions. During the safety phase, in which the nervous system is agitated or in a state of hyperarousal, the client must be taught strategies to manage the sympathetic nervous system's reaction to perceived danger (fight, flight, or freeze), or the parasympathetic system's initiating dissociation and numbing. This may include practice with breathing and relaxation techniques, mindfulness practices, and activities (e.g., yoga) that encourage relaxation and calmness. This phase should not be rushed, and the client's ability to regulate affect must be certain. Before moving to the next phase, the client should have restored healthy sleeping and eating patterns, improved concentration, and experienced fewer panic attacks.

The remembrance and mourning phase involves processing and assimilation of the trauma in the hippocampus and the neocortex. As the client recounts the traumatic memories, they are coached by the clinician to enact calming strategies as they emerge. The purpose of this stage is to empower the client to trust themself to ensure their own safety. Since traumatic memory includes physical, sensory, and emotional memories, gaining control of the narrative is the goal. That is, the activity in the amygdala is moved to the frontal cortex (executive functions) to consolidate and make meaning of the experience. Note that this phase is similar to exposure treatment, to be discussed later in the chapter. The reconnecting phase involves consolidating the gains, using the skills to control agitation so that the individual is able to reestablish social connections. SAMSHA (2023) also provides a helpful guide to trauma-informed care.

Special Populations

Although trauma is widespread, there are groups who are uniquely vulnerable to traumatic experiences. In the interest of space, we focus briefly on three of those populations to provide an overview of each.

Military

Although U.S. military forces withdrew from Afghanistan on August 30, 2021, many military personnel, whether veterans or active-duty personnel, have experienced trauma related to their military service. Of those, some develop PTSD. Prevalence rates vary widely depending on the source of data, but it is safe to assume that the disorder is more prevalent in people with a military history. Armenta et al. (2018) analyzed data from three waves of the millennium cohort study of 2,409 U.S. service members and veterans who screened positive for PTSD at baseline. Of those, 47% still had PTSD at the first follow-up 3 years later, and 71% of those were still positive for PTSD at the second follow-up 6 years after baseline. These findings illustrate the persistence of PTSD in some cases. Predictors of continued PTSD were intensity of combat exposure, PTSD severity at baseline, having additional diagnoses including depression and/or physical symptoms, and sleeping less than 4 hours per night. Two additional factors associated with persistent PTSD were being upset by not having social support and retiring or separating from the miliary. Social support was also important in a meta-analysis (Blais et al., 2021) that found that social support from civilians received in the home environment was more protective against persistent PTSD than support from military sources.

Another study followed 9,566 military veterans for 3 years after separation from the service (Copeland et al., 2023). Their findings showed that 30% of their sample endorsed symptoms consistent with PTSD, with 4% exhibiting those symptoms later rather than immediately. Females and African American participants were found to have higher scores on a measure of PTSD symptoms. Females also exhibited symptoms after a period of time rather than immediately following discharge. Sexual assault while in the military and more combat exposure were associated with increased symptoms; current stressors were additional risk factors. Protective factors were identified: psychological resilience and social support.

Several of the symptoms of PTSD are survival mechanisms in combat zones: elevated cortisol levels associated with the fight-or-flight reaction that provide the biological fuel that ready the body and brain to respond: increased heart rate and blood pressure, tensed muscles, increased focus, and shorter reaction time. In most circumstances, when the danger is over, the body calms and is restored to normal levels. In a combat situation, in which danger is often the norm, the need to be hypervigilant and ready to react is frequent and may be maintained for long periods of time. The body then adjusts to this activated state, and for some, this will be the new normal, and the individual is no longer able to calm the bodily systems that maintain this status. This is one ingredient for developing PTSD. Although often the case in combat situations, many examples of repetitive, ongoing abuse achieve the same effect.

Although beyond the scope of this chapter, it is important to note that families of people with trauma are indirectly affected by the person with PTSD. Miliary families in general have numerous stressors: frequent relocation and absences due to deployment and adjustment upon return. These all affect the family's ability to provide support and compassion for the traumatized member.

Interpersonal Violence

Interpersonal violence (IPV) is defined by the CDC (2015):

> Intimate partner violence includes physical violence, sexual violence, stalking and psychological aggression (including coercive tactics) by a current or former intimate partner (i.e., spouse, boyfriend/girlfriend, dating partner, or ongoing sexual partner). *They further define an intimate partner as* a person with whom one has a close personal relationship that may be characterized by the partners' emotional connectedness, regular contact, ongoing physical contact and sexual behavior, identity as a couple, and familiarity and knowledge about each other's lives. The relationship need not involve all of these dimensions. (Breiling et al., 2015, p. 11)

Complex PTSD is a relatively new diagnosis and a mental health disorder that is diagnosed according to a number of symptoms in the ICD-11. (CPTSD is not found in the DSM-5.) About 31%–84% of victims of IPV in the United States experience symptoms of PTSD (Fernández-Fillol et al., 2021; Klostermann, 2015; Woods, 2005). Haselschwerdt (2014) indicated that between 7 and 15 million children are exposed to IPV each year. Exposure to IPV was associated with decreased IQ scores in children in a longitudinal study of children from birth to 5 years old. Moreover, this effect was more pronounced and more persistent in children younger than 2 years old (Bosquet Enlow et al., 2012).

Types of IPV

Several classification systems of trauma have been proposed. For example, Terr (1991, as cited by Birkeland et al., 2022) distinguished type I trauma (a single, life-threatening traumatic incident) and type II (a trauma that occurs over a long period of time). IPV is an example of a type II trauma. Later, Solomon and Heide (1999) proposed that type II should be separated into type II and type III, characterized by multiple violent ongoing events that began at an early age.

Haselschwerdt (2014) reviewed four types of IPV proposed by Johnson. Those are *intimate terrorism*, characterized by the use of coercive control by the perpetrator. *Coercive control* includes demands and credible threats, stalking and monitoring communications outside the couple, and using psychological tactics to weaken any resolve the victim might have. Generally, males are more likely to engage in this type of IPV. The *violent resistance* and *mutual violent control* categories are less common. *Situational couple violence* is the final type and along with *intimate terrorism* is the most common in this schema. Regardless of which system one subscribes to, it is clear that treatment approaches need to take these differences into account.

According to Dokkedahl et al. (2022), there are several types of IPV: *physical*, *sexual*, and *psychological*, with psychological violence the most common form and arguably the most harmful (also see Pico-Alfonso, 2005). As with many terms used in this book, definitions of psychological violence vary by agency or group providing the definition (e.g., European Institute for Gender Equality, 2023; WHO, 2012). Trauma can be acute, chronic, or complex. Dokkedahl et al. suggest that there are distinct subtypes of psychological IPV: emotional/verbal, dominance/isolation, and coercive controls, each of which independently predicts PTSD and depression, with emotional/verbal having the strongest association with those disorders. PTSD can persist long after the woman has left the abusive relations, with two studies reporting PTSD systems in women 6 to 9 years following the end of the relationship (Pico-Alfonso, 2005). The duration of the traumatic experience increases the likelihood of developing complex PTSD.

Adolescents and young adults also may be engaged in IPVs. Analyses of data from 3,279 respondents in the UK revealed that by the age of 21, 29% of males and 41% of females had been victimized by IPVA (IPV + abuse), and 20% of males and 25% of females acknowledge having been perpetrators. Types of violence were (in order of frequency) emotional, physical, and sexual. Risk factors for both genders were past anxiety, self-harm, antisocial behavior, cannabis or other drug use, or risky sexual behavior. Males with a history of depression, sexual abuse (not by a partner), observing IPV, and parental separation were also more likely to be victimized by IPVA, while those whose parents monitored extremely closely, who were academic high-achievers in adolescence, and those who were unemployed or uninvolved in education or training had lower risks (Herbert et al., 2021).

Women victims of IPV in the Prosman et al. (2014) study appreciated support from friends and family and were more likely to seek services if their networks dispelled misinformation and provided encouragement. For many, the most immediate needs were for basic survival: a place to stay, financial assistance, help with transportation and childcare. They also commented that their physicians in general did not broach the subject of IPV, even when the victim had repeated visits for similar injuries.

A review of research determined that women are as aggressive as male partners. A common assumption is that IPV toward women is motivated by the male partner's drive to establish and maintain their power and dominance in the relationship and that if women are violent toward a partner it is only for the purpose of defending herself. In reality, many men restrain themselves from violence toward women due to the social norms against hurting women. Motives for much IPV, whether perpetrated by male or female partners, include getting the partner's attention, jealousy, releasing negative emotions (anger, etc.), and difficulties in communication (Powney & Graham-Kevan, 2019). In the UK in 2016, 4.4% of men were victimized in IPV, and it was estimated that the lifetime prevalence of IPV in men was about 17%. Unsurprisingly, men are less likely to report victimization, perhaps due to embarrassment of assumptions that help is only available for women. Women perpetrators did not believe that their victimized partners were afraid of them (or momentarily at best), which is in contrast to female victims. It is the case that women are more likely to be injured in physical IPV, whether perpetrator or victims. This is likely due to the advantages in size and strength of men compared to women.

IPV also occurs in transgendered and same-sex relationships, although this has generated a sparse body of literature. A concern is that the existing literature on this topic has generally omitted racial/ethnic minorities and people of low socioeconomic status from their research (Li et al., 2022). A recent systematic review and meta-analysis by Peitzmeier et al. (2020) found that transgender individuals experience significantly more IPV that cisgender people. They were more than twice as likely to suffer physical IPV and two and a half times as likely to be a victim of sexual IPV than cisgender people. They also had worse outcomes, including problems with sexual health, mental health, and substance abuse. Similar findings were reported by Rollè et al. (2018), who indicated that 61% of bisexual women, 43.8% of lesbian women, 37% of bisexual men, and 26% of homosexual men had experienced IPV, all significantly higher than rates in heterosexual subjects (Kar et al., 2023). Although many risk factors for IPV in same-sex couples are present in heterosexual couples, specific stressors (discrimination, internalized homophobia) play a role in the same-sex IPV dynamic (Li et al., 2022). Those stressors may be different for each partner, perhaps increasing the likelihood of IPV. When a trauma has occurred, the reactions from others in their social circle can reduce or exacerbate symptoms (Solomon et al., 2021). Clinicians need to consider these additional stressors when working with same-sex couples.

IPV has been investigated among military servicepersons and veterans with PTSD (Misca & Forgey, 2017). IPV is highly prevalent in this population. Researchers have demonstrated that the relationship between PTSD and IPV in military personnel is bidirectional: Both partners engage in perpetration and victimization by IPV. PTSD is both a risk factor for perpetration of IPV and a risk factor for victimization. Misca and Forgey reviewed published studies of IPV and PTSD in veterans and current military personnel. They point out the methodological weaknesses of many of those studies and urged future research to consider bidirectionality in their designs. The two studies that examined this line of inquiry reported interesting findings: Half of the sample of couples reported physical IPV. Half of that subsample reported mutual IPV, and of those reporting one-way aggression, females were more often the aggressor than males. More male veterans acknowledged perpetrating sexual IPV, and females in couples were more likely to perpetrate physical aggression.

Most of the research of victims on IPV and PTSD have recruited participants from clients of various services (e.g., shelters), and those may not reflect the experiences of the many victims who do not seek help. Barriers to seeking help are important for clinicians to understand, especially when IPV is suspected but not the focus of treatment. The following obstacles are often present (Prosman et al., 2014; Voth Schrag et al., 2021):

- fear of partner (jealousy, intimidation, threats to victim and family members)
- unwillingness to think of self as victim
- fear of losing custody of children
- lack of understanding of impact on children of witnessing IPV
- fear of negative reaction of friends and family
- shame
- misunderstandings about services (e.g., they will be required to leave the relationship to receive services, take legal action, or to attend religious services)
- lack of awareness of availability of services
- logistical concerns (e.g., transportation, cost, childcare)
- cultural differences (language, sexual orientation, disability)
- fear they will be blamed, ignored, or dismissed
- turnover in mental health agencies

It is impossible to discuss this topic without mentioning Lenore Walker's (1980, 1984) influential work. This psychologist proposed a specific battered women's syndrome, based on her own research. The original volume was published just before the diagnosis of PTSD was added to the DSM-III. Although she has made a significant contribution to understanding this population, the syndrome has never reached the status of a diagnosis, is not in the DSM-IV-TR, and is not always accepted in courts of law. As a result, we recommend that counselors determine whether the client qualifies for a diagnosis of PTSD and consider other disorders (e.g., depression) when appropriate.

Bullying

Being victimized by bullying can be traumatic (Švecová et al., 2023). Bullying is not just a problem in childhood and adolescence; bullying occurs in the workplace, in organizations, in relationships, and among the elderly. Childhood bullying and victimization are associated with negative mental health outcomes in early adulthood and later (Arseneault, 2017; Copeland et al., 2013; McDougall & Vaillancourt, 2015). We submit that bullying be viewed in a trauma-informed framework; treatment implications are discussed later in this chapter.

In a study of posttraumatic stress symptomatology in a large sample of children and adolescents in Norway, participants were asked to indicate their worst traumatic experience. Results showed that sexual trauma victims reported the highest level of symptoms of all trauma types. Respondents who reported severe bullying (50.6% with probable PTSD) and IPV (49% probable PTSD) had higher levels of symptoms than other types. There was no significant difference between victims of severe bullying and IPV on the number of symptoms endorsed, and the profile of symptoms was similar in both groups. Victims of severe bullying and sexual trauma presented more negative beliefs and emotions than other symptoms (Birkeland et al., 2022). These researchers argue that bullying needs to be examined from a trauma framework because being victimized by bullying can negatively affect aspects of healthy development if there is no intervention.

Bullying was found to be a moderator between experience of trauma, resilience, and psychopathy in a population-based sample of 1,018 adults from age 18 to 85 in Slovakia (Švecová et al., 2023). About 13% of the sample indicated they had been bullied. The researchers discovered that resilience was associated with lower scores on the indicators of psychopathology, but when participants had been bullied, they had higher rates of psychopathology than participants with the same level of resilience who had not been bullied.

Refugees and Migrants

The global population of people forced to escape from their homes at the end of 2021 included 27.1 million refugees, 4.6 million people seeking asylum, and 53.2 million people living in camps for displaced persons within their country. The war in Ukraine is expected to add to those numbers, given that 6.9 million people have already become refugees from that country. The recent hostilities in Israel and Gaza are also likely to cause more people to become refugees. These people are not seeking economic advantages or improved opportunities. They were forced to leave their homes due to war, armed conflicts, persecution, and other forms of violence (Jou & Pace-Schott, 2022).

The traumatic experiences typically began prior to the escape, were prevalent during transit, and encountered in the new country. Prior to leaving, refugees may have witnessed the death or murder of a loved one and experienced torture and/or physical trauma. They also may have struggled to meet basic needs for food, water, and shelter and lacked the financial resources to meet those needs (Vukčević Marković et al., 2023). The travel to hoped-for safety is also fraught with danger, including possible exploitation or extortion by smugglers, abandonment by smugglers, illness or accidental injuries, separation of family members, and more. Vukčević Marković et al., (2023) reported that 80% of refugees in Serbia experienced a life-threatening incident on their travel, with an average of 10 traumatic incidents. When they reach their destination, they often must spend time waiting for a chance to enter processing centers and are relegated to primitive conditions.

Andermann et al. (2021) argues that PTSD may be misunderstood in the refugee and migrant population. This population has about 10 times the rate of PTSD as is found in the general population, and comorbid depression and anxiety are also prevalent. Factors such as stable housing, paid employment, age, rate of language acquisition in new country, complicated bereavement, and perceived discrimination can exacerbate or ameliorate mental health conditions. Obstacles to achieving mental health postmigration are detention, inability to obtain work, dispersal, lack of access to health care, poverty, uncertain immigration status, and discrimination. These authors contend that an emphasis on premigration and relocation trauma is less helpful than attending to these postmigration challenges that can alleviate some of the social isolation, hopelessness, and distress, which can be traumatic. On the other hand, many migrants and refugees have developed resilience, which can be enhanced by compassionate treatment.

Refugees may be denied entry into the destination country and risk being forcibly returned to their place of origin. Some refugees also experience violent mistreatment at the point at which they are being returned. Thus, it is not a surprise that depression, anxiety, and PTSD are prevalent as a result of their experience. The challenge is that most do not have the knowledge of resources to seek mental health treatment and are focused on meeting basic needs. If they are successful in finding residence or asylum in the new country, they have to contend with acculturation and language barriers. In the United States, waves of refugees have come from places such as Latin America, Vietnam, Laos, Syria, Somalia, Iraq, and Ukraine. Unfortunately, the odds are this will be an ongoing challenge, and the issue is worldwide, with European countries struggling to manage the problem.

Mental health professionals are likely to encounter refugees in one of two ways: via children's school or in a refugee service center. School counselors and other professional educators should be alert to the likelihood of trauma history in refugee children and use a trauma-informed approach to ensure a safe environment. It is also an opportunity to make contact with parents and inform them of local resources available to them. When schools have a significant number of refugee children from a country, it is advisable to have a community liaison who knows the culture and speaks the language who can be a bridge to the refugee community and translator when needed.

The second circumstance in which mental health professionals may encounter refugees with mental health needs is in churches or community centers that serve as temporary shelters while refugees are being relocated to a more permanent residence. Such places are usually staffed by volunteers, but mental health workers can serve as consultants and/or on-call crisis responders.

An example of the far-reaching and complex effects of being a refugee is in the case of Juan, a 16-year-old boy, born in the United States to illegal immigrant parents. They fled their home because gang violence was rampant and they had witnessed neighbors being murdered. They feared for their lives. The parents had never obtained legal status but had managed to live undisturbed for many years. Juan had four younger siblings and an older brother, who were also born in the United States. His father had worked in the construction industry for the past 15 years and made a good living, and his mother was a homemaker. One day Juan came home from the charter high school he attended to learn that his father had been apprehended and deported. His mother decided it would be best if she and the younger children joined the father, but that the older boys should stay and finish their education. Juan and his brother had to find a place to live (with the assistance of a local agency) and manage a household with no experience or money. Juan and his brother found part-time jobs, and Juan continued to attend school (with poor attendance), while his brother dropped out. Adding to the challenge, Juan and his brother had an extremely conflictual relationship, and there was constant tension between the two. Fortunately, Juan's school soon realized what he was facing and stepped up to provide trauma-informed emotional, social, and tangible support. Juan graduated from high school at age 18.

Developmental Influences

A recent report by the CDC found that 64% of adults in the United States had experienced an ACE (defined as a preventable, traumatic event experienced prior to age 18), and 17% reported four or more such incidents (Swedo, 2023). The data revealed an unequal distribution across various demographic groups and noted the intergenerational aspect of ACEs. These rates confirm that trauma in children and adolescents is not a rare occurrence. Furthermore, a report by SAMHSA (2023) revealed that about 66% of children had experienced one or more traumatic event by age 16, and Haselschwerdt (2014) indicated that between 7 and 15 million children are exposed to IPV each year.

It is important to keep in mind that most people who experience a traumatic event will not develop PTSD, and of those who develop it, most will recover without treatment. However, given the potential for the negative impact that PTSD (especially chronic PTSD) can have on someone's life, it is essential that clinicians are prepared to recognize and treat this disorder. Trauma affects people differently depending on a number of factors, one of which is the developmental stage of the traumatized individual. In this section, we discuss how the experience of trauma interacts with development across the life span.

Infants and Young Children

In this age group (0–5), the most common traumatic event is the unexpected death of a loved one, but natural disasters, IPV, accidents, family disruption, hospitalization, and so forth may also occur. The DSM-IV did not have separate criteria for children under 6, but that was changed in the DSM-V. In the interest of space, we have included the new criteria for children under 6 in Appendix B. The DSM-V diagnostic criteria are provided in Appendix A. Note that for criterion A, the clinician must distinguish between the way the trauma was experienced (directly, indirectly, or witnessed). Witnessing an event via media no longer qualifies as a symptom, although many children exhibit symptoms after viewing (often repeatedly) such incidents as terrorist attacks in the media. The individual's subjective reaction to the trauma is also no longer a relevant criterion. An additional category was added, so the four symptom categories are now intrusion, negative alterations in mood and cognition, avoidance, and arousal. Finally, the criteria for E have been expanded to include marked alterations in arousal and reactivity in response to the trauma, which might be expressed as irritability, angry outbursts, and self-destructive behaviors (McLaughlin, 2022). It is important to learn whether symptoms have emerged after the trauma rather than continuing prior behavior.

It may seem that because young children with immature thinking may not understand the extent of the danger, they are not as upset by traumatic experiences as they are older children. In fact, during infancy up to about age 2, children are sensitive to reactions and difficulties of parents or caregiver, and when caregivers are upset, unhappy, or very stressed, the child senses that, and their sense of safety and security is disrupted (Blank, 2007). If a parent is hospitalized or deceased, a child may exhibit symptoms of trauma. Very early in life, infants recognize basic emotions from tone of voice and facial expressions and are sensitive to change in the disturbances in the family, including relocation, IPV, and new routines.

PTSD is possible in preverbal or early verbal years. Prior to about 9 months of age, infants may display a response to fear but cannot be diagnosed with PTSD. Although infants and toddlers do not have the cognitive skills to make an independent appraisal of a threat, they observe attachment figures in circumstances in which there is some uncertainty about safety.

Behaviors that may be seen in young children who have been exposed to trauma include extreme distress when separated from caregiver, absence of playful behaviors (smiling, vocalizing), regressed eating skills, being difficult to soothe when upset, and regression in mobility skills. They also may have decreased verbal output, exhibit memory problems, cry excessively, have diminished appetite, and have nightmares. Some young children who do not meet the full criteria for PTSD may still be significantly upset and need attention. Most interventions with infants and toddlers involve caregivers on how to respond to the traumatized child. This can be a delicate situation if the caregiver is the perpetrator. Furthermore, difficult attachments are often present when the caregiver has unresolved trauma and losses of their own. The first 2 years of life are critical to developing healthy attachments, and when that is not a successful process, the child is more likely to develop chronic PTSD. If there is chronic IPV, and/or abuse of the child by their caregivers, disturbances in all areas of functioning are more likely.

Until about 18 months, the right brain is dominant, and memories and accompanying feelings are not verbal but are stored in somatic and sensory areas of the brain in the form of images. These implicit memories can be activated in the limbic system by sensory stimuli. By about age 3, children may have a verbal memory of the trauma (Blank, 2007). Blank explains that once toddlers and preschool children become mobile, they may respond to perceived danger by employing the fight-or-flight reaction and become reckless in their activities. They begin to use language and play in attempts to understand the traumatic event. Although their cognitive development is progressing, the do not yet have the ability to comprehend cause and effect and may blame themselves. This is consistent with their age-appropriate egocentric perspective. As in older children and adults, the core system clusters of PTSD appear at a young age. They may reexperience the trauma via repetitive play, repeated telling of the story of the event, and being triggered by sensory exposure to sounds, smells, and sights associated with the event. They may also reexperience the event in nightmares.

Trauma affects the brain, and this is especially important in infants and young children when brain development is substantial. The child's brain has reached 90% of its adult size by age 3, although the body is only 20% of adult size. The brain organizes to develop coping pathways during critical periods in infancy (Schore, 2002). From birth, white matter in the brain increases, facilitating communication between hemispheres, and gray matter increases until age 10 and then decreases. These effects are due to myelination and pruning (Thomason & Marusak, 2017). Researchers have discovered that children who have been traumatized by abuse and neglect have smaller brains than children of the same age without exposure to trauma; the longer the duration of the abuse, the greater the difference is brain size. This effect is more pronounced in males. Specifically, the amygdala, hippocampus, and prefrontal cortex are affected by traumatic experience (Bremner, 2006; Putnam, 2006).

Blank (2007) indicated that *states* (a temporary condition) sometimes become *traits*, an enduring part of one's personality. Infants and young children respond to perceived threats (trauma) in one of two ways. Using the fight-or-flight response, the *arousal continuum* causes an increase in cortisol. When this happens repeatedly, a child with trauma may behave in ways similar to youth with ADHD. The other option is the *dissociative continuum*, which is associated with the "freeze and surrender" pattern, with decreased movement and attention in response to endogenous opiates and activation of the parasympathetic nervous system. Children with repeated activation of this system may display problems with attention, learning disabilities, memory, and behavior.

When an infant or child perceives a threat, the brain has instinctive ways to respond. We often hear of the fight-or-flight response that increases heart rate and respiration when a threat is perceived. But fighting or fleeing would not be in the best survival interest of an infant or small child, who could neither attack the source of the threat nor escape. The more useful (from a survival perspective) response is to freeze and surrender. If this response in the brain is activated often, sensitivity will develop, and various neuronal changes will occur. These changes are responsible for observed cognitive, behavioral, and socioemotional effects in traumatized children.

Infants and toddlers will respond to trauma initially by searching for protective figures. They will exhibit "alarm reactions" (crying, reaching) to gain the attention of caregivers. Preschool children who do not find the expected protection

Dissociation: The separation of some aspects of mental functioning from conscious awareness. This is not always pathological. Most of us experience it when daydreaming and being unaware of present surroundings, or when driving a familiar route and being surprised when arriving because you do not remember much of the drive. Victims of sexual assault or abuse may disconnect conscious awareness of the experience in order to manage an otherwise uncontrollable situation.

often react with intense fear, rage, or shame and exaggerated motor behavior or extreme passivity. In some situations, when the preschool child perceives the danger, the child may use "dissociative" responses to protect themself from the overwhelming anxiety (Peterson, 2018). That is, since the child cannot physically escape the traumatic event, they may escape mentally, using dissociation (Guérin-Marion et al., 2020).

Neuron: Specialized cells in the nervous system (brain and spinal cord and nerves) that conduct impulses that allow the brain and body to communicate.

The most harmful aspect of trauma to infants is the effect on the developing brain. Perry et al. (1995; Perry, 2006) provided a description of how trauma affects this development. The human brain is an enormously complicated organ containing billions of *neurons* that are organized into systems that control different functions to ensure survival. Different areas of the brain control thinking, motor activity, and emotional response, for example. One important property of neurons is that they change in response to various signals. This is, in a very simplified version, how learning and memory take place. The kind of information that is stored depends on the type, intensity, and frequency with which the same pattern of neurons is stimulated. More frequent and intense activity makes a stronger impact, and then this pattern filters new activity in the brain. When a particular pattern of neuronal activity is repeated, *sensitization* occurs. That means that the pattern will now be activated by less intense stimulation. This explains how children who are traumatized (repeatedly or very intensely) will exhibit what seem to be exaggerated responses to minor stressors (Thomason & Marusak, 2017).

Another important feature of brain development is that it develops in a predictable sequence from the most primitive functions (e.g., breathing) to the most complex (planning, making decisions). There are critical periods for the development of the brain during which the different systems are most sensitive to input from the environment. If disruption (trauma) occurs when more basic systems are developing, those systems will be less able to contribute to the development of the more complex systems. Infancy is a critical period for brain development, including coping mechanisms for perceived danger. On the one hand, detrimental patterns can become embedded in the structure and neurophysiology of the brain, but the plasticity of the brain at this stage also means that corrective experiences can alter the long-term impact (Schore, 2002).

To summarize, although infants and toddlers are unable to verbalize their experiences, traumatized children at this age may be more irritable, cry more than usual, and want to be held a great deal. Preschool children may display fearfulness and insecurity and may regress behaviorally (return to thumb sucking, bed wetting, disrupted sleep, separation anxiety). They are very sensitive to their parents' reactions and will exhibit more anxiety if the parents are anxious. It is common for children at this age to re-create the trauma in their play and to do so repeatedly. This is their way of attempting to gain mastery of the situation. Because cause-and-effect thinking has not yet developed, young children may believe their misbehavior caused the trauma.

Children

Children exposed to disasters and other trauma have high rates of PTSD (Goldmann & Galea, 2014). Overall, about 25% of children are exposed to trauma by age 18, with higher rates in children displaced by, or present at, war or armed conflict. Children who have direct exposure to IPV are at the highest risk of psychological disorders; those diagnosed with PTSD are more likely to have comorbid disorders, including internalizing and externalizing problems. Because this population is at such high risk for serious outcomes, and PTSD or PTSS is often undiagnosed (Danese et al., 2020), it is essential to examine the dynamics of trauma in children.

During the traumatic event, children also automatically use the fight-or-flight response, or the freeze-and-surrender responses. When in either of those states, brain functioning decreases in two essential areas of the brain: Broca's area (speech) and Wernicke's area (language comprehension; Baggerly, 2005). As a result, children may have difficulty finding words to describe their traumatic experiences but may instead have encoded a very clear visual image. Some children may focus their attention on a seemingly small image (e.g., an item of clothing), which becomes a disturbing mental picture that can elicit fear responses. They may also have difficulty with the time sequence when trying to recall the event, and some children will develop a belief in "omens" in an attempt to avoid future trauma This means that they believe there were warning signs they just did not notice, but if they are vigilant, they will notice such signs before another trauma can occur (Hamblen & Barnett, n.d.).

Research on trauma and the brain determined that trauma exposure in early life is related to PTSD and that the underlying neurological structures are most sensitive to trauma at about age 10, or middle childhood. Deprivation in infancy, exposure to trauma and abuse during middle childhood, and hormonal changes during puberty all increase risk for PTSD via changes in the brain. Interestingly, maternal availability in childhood is necessary for the positive aspects of social support in adulthood to be beneficial. Protective factors include maternal availability and social support; there is some evidence that enriched environments may decrease the negative effects. The period between early and middle childhood seems to be critical for the positive impact of environmental factors (Stevens et al., 2018).

Mass shootings, particularly school shootings, may elicit trauma and other mental health symptoms. Although these events are rare, the media attention and focus on such incidents can affect vulnerable people at a distance from the incident (Cimolai et al., 2021). Immediately following a mass shooting, children often engage in denial, experience shock and disbelief, and feel vulnerable and unsafe. "Is this going to happen at my school?" In mass shootings, when the motive is often unknown, and the perpetrator targets people randomly, children may feel unsafe at school or other locations (e.g., grocery stores) that have been the site of such events because of their unpredictability. As noted earlier, most children will resolve the symptoms of stress in time and without intervention. However, some with chronic symptoms do not fare well. In the months after the Stoneman Douglas school shooting, a student was taken to the emergency room three times in 3 months. McLaughlin and Kar (2019) studied this case. The girl was having nightmares, avoiding public places (including school) because they triggered panic attacks, and having suicidal ideation and thoughts of self-harm because images in the media triggered symptoms. They concluded that the media exposure interacted with low sympathetic brain activity to cause the symptoms. She had inpatient treatment followed by an intensive outpatient program upon discharge.

In their review of school shootings, Shultz et al. (2014) found that features of the event that were likely to induce mental health problems were the intensity and severity of the exposure (hearing gunfire, seeing the gunman shoot someone, being close to the site of the shooting, and the fear of being killed). Exacerbating these effects is the loss of a close friend or family member (or the inability to ascertain their status) in an event. Prior trauma exposure, particularly sexual trauma, was associated with poorer mental health following a shooting, as was the level of psychological functioning and attachment style. Social and family support tended to reduce symptoms while loss of resources for support were likely to increase symptoms. Individuals who experienced a mass shooting, directly or indirectly, were impacted by overall community response and available mental health services. In general, children are likely to exhibit acute stress responses immediately after the event, but most will not develop PTSD. Being younger (younger than 9 years old) and from an impoverished community appears to increase the likelihood of PTSD, whereas older children are likely to develop symptoms when there are multiple exposures.

"Every single day ... we had to walk past the building where the shooting happened. And people were just so unwell, mentally unwell, including myself," she said. "Stoneman Douglas was such a toxic, toxic place after what happened.... There were almost 5,000 students that went through an extremely traumatizing event and didn't get the mental health resources we needed" (Lauren Hogg, freshman at time of shooting, statement made 3 years later; Shapiro, 2018, para. 7).

Five years later: survivors and families have engaged in charitable activities and keeping public awareness of the tragedy, according to the mayor of Parkland at the time of the shooting. "Still," she said, "it is really important to remember that no matter how many 'good things' have come out of the aftermath, no one is ever the same again. No one loses that pain" (Spencer, 2023, para. 4).

Like younger children, anxiety is often experienced by school-aged children who experience trauma. They may worry about a re-occurrence of the trauma and exhibit physical symptoms (e.g., frequent headaches and stomachaches). Their school performance may change, and they may ask many questions about death and dying (Gurwitch et al., 2002). They may be preoccupied by the traumatic event, talking about it constantly, infusing their writing, and drawing and playing with themes of the event. Some young trauma victims will be extremely sensitive to certain sounds (loud noises, thunder, etc.). While such reactions and behaviors are normal responses to trauma, there are children in whom the intensity or duration of those symptoms signals a serious problem. For example, a personal injury can be a traumatic event for a child, and rates of PTSD diagnosis among injured children range from 13% to 45% (Winston et al., 2003).

Because children are dependent on adults, they are very sensitive to trauma reactions in adults (Pine & Cohen, 2002). The COVID-19 pandemic affected everyone in some way, and children were impacted not only by the event but by the ways in which adults and others responded. Thus, when traumas disrupt the family, children are at higher risk for trauma-related psychopathology. And when trauma is inflicted upon children by adults (as in physical or sexual abuse), the child may feel extremely vulnerable. To reduce their anxiety over being so vulnerable, children may engage in fantasies in which they are the powerful aggressor. Some may act out these fantasies, and others may do so when they are older. Some children tend to be *anxiety sensitive,* which means they experience (or imagine) symptoms that are much more severe than they are in reality and have such fears as "I am going crazy." Children with this cognitive pattern are more likely to develop PTSD.

Parental psychopathology was found to be the best predictor of psychological problems in children posttrauma (Norris et al., 2002). In their systematic review of the literature on traumatized children, Alisic et al. (2014) found that the presence of PTSD was much greater when the trauma was interpersonal (25%) compared to noninterpersonal (10%) and that girls were more likely (21%) than boys to be diagnosed with PTSD. The highest rate of PTSD was in girls experiencing interpersonal trauma (33%), and the lowest was in boys experiencing noninterpersonal trauma (8%).

Adolescents

Adolescents generally react to trauma as do adults. Common responses include flashbacks, nightmares, emotional numbing, and avoidance of reminders of the trauma, depression, and increased substance use or abuse. In addition, adolescents may exhibit an increase in problems with peers and some antisocial acting out. Not unusual are withdrawal and isolation from others, suicidal ideation, poor school attendance and decreased academic performance, sleep disturbances, and physical complaints. Some adolescents experience guilt because they were unable to prevent the trauma, and others create fantasies of revenge toward perceived responsible parties.

Like adults, not all adolescents who experience a traumatic event respond in the same way. Previous exposure to trauma, existing mental health problems, and the absence of family support increase the risk for problematic reactions. Research points to high rates of exposure to violence among many adolescents. A national sample of adolescents reported that a third had been the victim of a physical assault (by peers and siblings, predominantly), and 9.3% of those resulted in an injury. Adults perpetrated the assault in 5.1% of cases in this past year. More assaults were directed at boys, including assault by adults, nonsibling peer assault, and nonsexual assault to the genitals (Finkelhor et al., 2015). Helping professionals need to inquire about this in adolescent clients and explore their reaction to the trauma. Recall that some believe that chronic exposure may desensitize adolescents, while others believe exposure to prior trauma interferes with a person's ability to recover from later trauma. Despite possible desensitization to violence, adolescents may experience anxiety, depression, substance abuse, and suicidal ideation even if they do not meet full criteria for PTSD.

A final comment on the experience of trauma in children and adolescents is based on the theory that trauma shatters one's basic assumptions about the world (Janoff-Bulman, 1992). This will be discussed in more detail in the section on adults. What is important here is that children and adolescents are still forming these basic assumptions or worldviews, and the relative flexibility of assumptions is both good news and bad news. For many traumatic events, the reactions of parents and other close adults strongly influence the child's interpretation of what occurred. Even when the event separates the child from parents, as in kidnapping, the response and reassurance provided by parents provides protection from damage. It is precisely because primary caregivers have such an influence on the developing worldview of the child that when the trauma is deliberately inflicted by those individuals (as in sexual abuse by a family member) that the damage is so severe. The child's sense of safety and protection is destroyed, and the sense of self is disturbed. In fact, there is evidence that the origin of many personality disorders, particularly borderline personality, is in this type of trauma and the effects it has on one's understanding of the world and oneself in the world. Table 6.1 summarizes common reactions to trauma by age group.

Although most trauma survivors do not develop PTSD, research over the years has identified factors that increase risk:

- being female
- being aged 40–60
- little prior experience or training for coping with such an event
- being a member of an ethnic minority group
- low SES
- having children at home
- for women, having a distressed spouse
- prior psychiatric history
- severe exposure to the disaster (e.g., injury, threat of loss of life)
- living in a highly disrupted or traumatized community
- loss of resources

Although these characteristics were identified for victims of disasters (floods, tornados, terrorist attacks, etc.), it is clear that many of these would elevate risk of complications in adults who experience a wide range of traumatic events.

There are several opinions on how previous experience with stress and trauma impacts one's ability to cope with a current trauma. One view is that prior experiences make people more resistant to effects of current trauma; perhaps they have developed coping strategies that can be employed in current situations. On the other hand, it is possible that previous experience may deplete the

TABLE 6.1. Age-Specific Reactions to Disasters/Traumatic Events

---

Preschoolers (Ages 2–5)

Somatic: Sleep disturbances (e.g., recurring nightmares, night terrors, sleepwalking, refusing to sleep alone), eating problems, dizziness

Cognitive: Magical explanations for the event, repeated retelling of the event, unpleasant memories of trauma, persistent fears

Emotional: Crying, difficulty in identifying feelings, emotional upsets, excessive clinging, irritability, sadness, separation anxiety, stranger anxiety, trauma-related and generalized fears

Behavioral: Anxious behaviors (e.g., fingernail biting), posttraumatic play, regressive behaviors (e.g., bed wetting, thumb sucking), temper tantrums, hyperactivity

---

School-Age Children (Ages 6–11)

Somatic: Loss of energy, physical complaints (e.g., headache, stomachache), sleep disturbances

Cognitive: Believing in supernatural forces; distractibility; distortions about causes of disaster; intrusion of unwanted images, sounds, smells, and memories; poor concentration; poor school performance and grades; vulnerability to anniversary reactions

Emotional: Anger, denial, expression of guilt over past activities, helplessness, loss of interest in pleasurable activities, moodiness, sadness, self-blame, tearfulness, trauma-related and generalized fears, worry

Behavioral: Startle response, aggressive behaviors (e.g., fighting), hyperactivity, hypervigilance, problems in peer relations, repeated retelling of trauma and trauma related play, social and emotional withdrawal

---

Adolescents (Ages 12–18)

Somatic: Eating disturbances, loss of energy, physical complaints (e.g., headache, stomachache), sleep disturbances (e.g., insomnia)

Cognitive: Attention and concentration problems, poor school performance, memory problems, recurrent intrusive visual images, thoughts, sounds, and smells

Emotional: Anxiety, belligerence, denial, fear of growing up, grief reactions, guilt for being alive, shame, humiliation, depression, resentment, suicidal thoughts, wish for revenge, poor impulse control, rage, despair

Behavioral: Startle response, acting-out behaviors, accident proneness, disruption of peer relations, premature entrance into adulthood, social withdrawal and isolation, deviance, delinquency, school refusal, lack of responsibility, loss of interest in pleasurable activities, alcohol/drug use

Self: Sense of hopelessness, isolation, increased self-focusing and self-consciousness, loss of self-confidence, low self-esteem, negative self-image, personality changes, pessimistic world view, high level of worries and concerns about future, a sense of foreshortened future

---

Note: Dogan-Ates (2010), adapted from Lystad, 1984; Miller et al., 1993; Monahon, 1993; Murray, 2006; Norris et al., 2002; Pynoos & Nader, 1993; Sugar, 1999; Zubenko, 2002

person's psychological reserves and make it more difficult for them to cope with a current trauma. In addition, stressful circumstances (poverty, discrimination, family problems) after a trauma are likely to complicate a person's recovery (Carlson, 1997).

Herman (1997) emphasized that the most essential characteristic of a trauma is that it causes both terror and helplessness in the victim. It is because of these elements that our capacities and innate systems of self-defense become overwhelmed and disorganized. She theorized that the features of one's usual responses to danger are not effective in a traumatic situation and remain activated in an "altered and exaggerated" state (p. 34) long after the trauma itself is over. These effects impact physiological arousal, emotion, cognition, and memory, and also separate these from each other, so the victim may experience intense emotion without being able to remember the event, or may describe horrific memories with no emotional reaction.

Another view of the impact of trauma is proposed by Janoff-Bulman (1992), who focused on the effect on one's "fundamental assumptions" about the world. These personal theories help us make sense of, and interpret, our experience. Human beings tend to resist changing these basic assumptions, but when a trauma occurs, these assumptions may be shattered, causing a psychological crisis. The fundamental assumptions shared by most humans are these: "The world is benevolent, the world is meaningful, the self is worthy" (p. 6). It is these basic beliefs that a traumatic experience destroys. Janoff-Bulman also proposed that although all trauma survivors feel vulnerable and less safe and secure after the event, trauma that is intentionally caused by others (criminal assaults, interpersonal violence, terrorism, war atrocities, etc.) contradicts the belief that human beings are basically good. In fact, survivors may believe that evil is a potent force, and trust in others is no longer easily bestowed. Although this perspective is not reflected in the diagnostic criteria for PTSD or other trauma-related disorders, it is often seen clinically: Trauma survivors often grapple with basic existential questions about the meaning of events and their own lives.

When the symptoms of PTSD subside, the person may not be symptom free. For example, the intrusion symptoms may diminish, but physical complaints, symptoms of arousal and hypervigilance, and depression may still persist and need attention.

Older Adults

About 8% of adults over age 65 have been diagnosed with PTSD in their lifetimes. Current PTSD is estimated to be about 4% in that population. Rates are much higher for combat veterans and former prisoners of war (POWs), and older women report higher rates of IPV. There are also many older adults who do not meet clinical criteria for a diagnosis who experience troublesome symptoms related to trauma (Kaiser et al., 2002).

Trauma in older adults is a complicated picture. Effects of trauma may be disguised by co-occurring physical health problems, cognitive changes, current stressful life events, and other mental health concerns. This stage of life is characterized by loss (of home, work, physical skills, loved ones, etc.), which may impact the way trauma is experienced. Age also interacts with the social, economic, cultural, and historic context of different settings (Cook et al., 2001). Most of what is known about elderly trauma survivors is based on studies of three groups: war veterans, Holocaust survivors, and victims of recent disasters (Averill & Beck, 2000; Cook & O'Donnell, 2005).

Cook and O'Donnell (2005) highlight obstacles to accurately assess the effects of trauma (and possible PTSD symptoms) in older adults: Self-disclosure was less acceptable in earlier times, self-reliance was the standard, psychological problems were considered evidence of weakness, open discussion and information about trauma and PTSD was not available, and mental health problems are frequently attributed to physical concerns in this life stage. Understanding these challenges will help the counselor understand what might appear to be resistance in these clients and to respond with understanding and concern.

There is conflicting evidence about whether earlier exposure to trauma is protective or whether it increases vulnerability to later trauma (Busuttil, 2004). Older persons who experienced a trauma at earlier periods of life may exhibit either the development or re-emergence of a variety of trauma-related symptoms, particularly intrusive memories, avoidance of reminders of the trauma, sleep problems, and acute difficulties coping with current loss (Grossman et al., 2004). Many of these individuals will have shown only mild symptoms when they were younger, but as age-related cognitive declines appear, PTSD symptoms may be amplified. It has been suggested that the symptoms increase because the capacity to inhibit intrusive memories has been diminished. Other experts believe that with retirement comes more time to reflect on past experiences, which may precipitate PTSD in later life (Busuttil, 2004). Various types of dementia affect the prefrontal cortex, where the mechanisms for stopping thoughts and responses are located. Short-term memory is often impaired while long-term memories perseverate. Another possible explanation for the increased emergence of PTSD is that whatever coping capacities the individual used earlier are no longer functional, allowing the symptoms to emerge.

An interesting study examined PTSD in elderly residents of Lockerbie, Scotland, during the 1988 air disaster there (Livingston et al., 1992, 1994). A total of 270 people (on the plane or on the ground) died. In their first study conducted within the first year of the disaster, researchers compared 31 elderly with 24 younger subjects and found that both groups had similarly high rates of PTSD, but the elderly group was more likely to also have depression. Predictors of PTSD in the elderly, but not the younger group, were losing friends and seeing human remains.

Livingston et al. (1994) were able to follow the residents at 1 through 3 years after the event. At 1 year after the event, 84% of the elderly survivors met criteria for a diagnosis of PTSD. Symptoms of PTSD declined over time, but almost 16% of the sample still met criteria for PTSD 3 years after the event. This pattern is similar to that found in younger trauma survivors: While many symptoms remit over time, for some they persist for years. There are likely to be many factors involved in predicting which trauma survivors will have persisting PTSD, but some believe that the intensity of exposure (in this case, loss or injury to close friends and family) and the type of trauma (human caused) are very influential.

Gordon Turnbull (1998), a local psychiatrist, was immersed in counseling local residents, witnesses, and first responders. His experience led to a book on trauma and to working with hostages and survivors of war. He stressed that in the 4 weeks immediately after the incident, people experienced acute stress reactions. Only some of those people went on to develop PTSD. Turnbull realized that PTSD is "the mind's natural reaction to a terrifying unnatural event." He also saw firsthand how vicarious trauma affected those who counseled those directly affected. A man who helped at the crash site (he was in the military) suffered from severe PTSD before being diagnosed 32 years later! He is currently active as a fundraiser for a charity that provides care to veterans (Brown, 2011; Cameron, 2022).

Treatment Options and Considerations

As we discuss treatment options (Clark et al., 2015), there are several points to keep in mind. First, we emphasize that not everyone who experiences a traumatic event will develop a diagnosable disorder and that many with symptoms and diagnoses recover without treatment. Nevertheless, it is important to screen for symptoms in anyone who has experienced a trauma because many people who could benefit from trauma-related treatment are overlooked when their symptoms do not meet the criteria for a diagnosis. Some clients will seek help with symptoms that they do not realize are associated with traumatic experiences, and a brief screening may alert the clinician to that possibility. In the immediate aftermath of a trauma or disaster, people affected need assistance in managing the consequences: locating food, shelter, and medical care; gaining access to a wide range of community services; and assistance managing other stressors.

There are several extensive reviews of efficacy studies that provide treatment recommendations for PTSD based on evidence from high-quality research. The Agency for Healthcare Research and Quality and the Patient-Centered Outcomes Research Institute found strong evidence for CBT and CBT-mixed (CBT-M) and moderate evidence for cognitive processing therapy (CPT), cognitive therapy (CT), and EMDR. Their criteria were reduction of symptoms and not meeting criteria for PTSD diagnosis. The report also lists approaches that have inadequate evidence at this time (Forman-Hoffman et al., 2018a). These researchers located only a few studies that compared different approaches and indicate that effectiveness was better for CBT exposure therapy than for relaxation, CBT-M was more effective than relaxation for PTSD symptom reduction. Similar effectiveness was found for

CBT exposure and EMDR for PTSD symptoms. Because depression is often a comorbid diagnosis, treatment for PTSD may alleviate depression symptoms; CBT exposure and CBT exposure plus cognitive restructuring were equally effective for depression.

Pharmacological interventions with moderate effectiveness were fluoxetine (Prozac), paroxetine (Paxil), and venlafaxine (Effexor). The only available comparative study evaluated the effectiveness of a psychotherapeutic treatment (EMDR) and pharmacological treatment (Prozac), and results were inconclusive. We also recognize that most mental health professionals (with the exception of some licensed psychologists with specialized training) do not prescribe medication. However, getting information about medications (and consulting with a prescribing physician) can ensure treatment is coordinated.

Also important is that, to date, there is no empirical evidence on how treatment approaches affect clients with different characteristics and/or types of trauma experience. This means that mental health professionals need to rely on clinical judgment and consultation to create a treatment plan. They also must obtain training and supervision in those approaches they may use, because fidelity of use affects client outcomes (Forman-Hoffman et al., 2018b; Whiteside et al., 2016)

The APA conducted an updated review of the report cited to determine whether any more recent research would change those recommendations. They had only minor changes. For PTSD in adults, the panel recommended CBT, CPT, CT, and prolonged exposure therapy (PT) and suggested BEP (brief eclectic psychotherapy), EMDR, and narrative exposure therapy (NET). For pharmacological treatment they suggest Prozac, Paxil, Zoloft, and Effexor.

We will review several of the treatment approaches, but first we want to mention trauma-informed care, a term that is widely used but not well understood. This refers to a perspective that considers the likelihood that trauma—especially complex and cumulative trauma—to be the origins of many aspects of mental and physical disorders (Clark et al., 2015). It requires understanding that current problems may be extensions of the original attempt to cope with the trauma. The initial response to the trauma may or may not have been effective at the time but have become impediments to well-being. This framework also recognizes that interpersonal trauma erodes trust in others, so building trust with the therapist is a critical first step. Trauma-informed professionals are mindful of their own reactions to painful narratives of trauma and monitor their own needs for self-care. The final tenet of this outlook is that the individual must be understood in context, knowing that such characteristics as race/ethnicity, gender, age, culture, sexual orientation, are features of the environment in which the trauma occurred. Because treatment strategies vary somewhat by the age of the client, we describe the options by developmental stage.

Children

In general, children and adolescents are brought to therapy at someone else's behest and are less than enthusiastic about the prospect. The therapist needs to work to engage the client and to help them understand the goals of therapy. When working with a child or adolescent who is reluctant or resistant, we often ask what they would like to achieve in treatment. Their answer is often a form of "to stop coming to these stupid appointments" (perhaps using more colorful language). Then we discuss what we need to do to reach that goal. They realize they will have to make some changes in order to terminate treatment, and we discuss how we will know that we have reached that point.

Another characteristic of some children and adolescents is their language, often filled with profanity. Sometimes that is to shock the therapist and see their reaction. More often, they speak this way in their social world, and especially if they are comfortable, they are prone to using their usual style of communication. If the therapist forbids the use of expletives, the youth may conclude the therapist is too old and stodgy to "get" them, and progress will be more difficult. In the same way that people tend to use their first language to communicate emotional content, kids use their usual social language when they speak of personal and emotional material.

Finally, many of the children and adolescents coming to counseling will have comorbid disorders and/or behavior problems in addition to PTSD. The clinician will need to develop a plan to deal with the behavior problems before PTSD treatment can begin.

Trauma-focused CBT (TF-CBT) is the approach with the strongest evidence of effectiveness overall, including for children, adolescents, and adults, and for all types of trauma (Clark et al., 2015). A meta-analysis of studies on effectiveness of TF-CBT treatments found that outcomes were more positive for individual therapy than group therapy, and therapy involving caretakers were more effective than treatments with children and adolescents alone (Gutermann et al., 2016). Outcomes were better for adolescents and older children than younger children, who may not have the cognitive skills needed to benefit from a CBT intervention. Guterman et al. note the few studies based on manualized CBT showed the best results. Several of these manuals are available for free download and are included in the Resources section at the end of the chapter.

TF-CBT is a structured intervention (Kliethermes et al., 2013). Children and caretakers each have individual sessions followed by conjoint sessions. Recall that a therapeutic relationship built on trust and respect must be established prior to initiating the steps. With some young people, that may take many sessions. It is also essential to identify any immediate safety concerns and develop a plan to respond should those arise between sessions.

Exposure: In CBT treatment, a technique that uses careful, repeated, detailed imagery of the traumatic event. The purpose is to help the client face the fear and gain control over the event

Many therapists will begin with a brief "check-in" and end with a brief activity (selected by the child and therapist together), such as drawing or doing a puzzle, to ease transition in and out of the session. The treatment components begin with skills and progress to exposure to trauma (imaginal or in vivo depending on the situation). The steps in this model, in order, are as follows:

1. psychoeducation (about trauma): What it is, how it impacts functioning, how one recovers

2. parenting skills: Behavior management strategies to deal with trauma-related behavior problem

3. relaxation: Learning to control the physiological effects of the trauma

4. affective expression and modulation: Learning to identify emotions and express them appropriately

5. cognitive coping: Learning how thoughts, feelings, and behaviors are inter-related

6. trauma narrative and processing: Processing traumatic memories to desensitize the client to trauma triggers and to change maladaptive cognitions related to the trauma (e.g., "It was my fault")

7. in vivo mastery of trauma reminders: Helping youth and caregiver to surmount generalized fear prompted by trauma triggers (e.g., "All men are bad")

8. parent–child conjoint session to practice skills

9. enhancing future safety and development (p. 186)

Medication

Psychological treatments are the first choice for treatment for children and adolescents. Although medications are sometimes provided to children with PTSD and comorbid disorders, they are more vulnerable to side effects, including weight gain and suicidality (Keeshin et al., 2020) and therefore require close monitoring. There is no U.S. FDA-approved medication for PTSD in children. Keeshin et al. are wary of using medication not fully tested on children but do note that some guidelines suggest prazosin (Minipress) whose symptoms include severe sleep problems. March et al. (2004) discussed using Prozac with and without CBT for treating depression in adolescents. Communicating with prescribing physicians is essential for ensuring the safety and effectiveness of medication; the progress in therapy is important information for the doctor.

Adolescents

TF-CBT is also the most recommended approach for adolescents and adults. The overview of that approach is given in the previous section.

Although *dialectical behavior therapy* (DBT) was not developed for PTSD treatment, DeRosa and Rathus (2013) argue that it is a well-researched treatment, with accumulating studies demonstrating the value pf DBT in adolescents, with some adaptations. Treatment requires 16–32 sessions for adolescents (adult treatment is longer), with less complex materials and supplementary materials for caregivers. The approach works to enhance emotional regulation, increase tolerance for distress, and learn mindfulness in the belief that these skills would be protective for adolescent trauma victims. Adolescents with complex PTSD often have difficulties regulating emotions and impulses, engage in self-destructive behaviors, have multiple types of illnesses, dissociate, have negative self-concepts, are hopeless about future, and have difficulties with interpersonal relationships. DeRosa and Rathus are not persuaded that is a necessary component:

> DBT treatment is comprehensive and requires strong commitment (and cost) to complete.
> It consists of individual therapy, a weekly multifamily 2-hour skills group, phone coaching to support use of the skills between sessions, and weekly DBT consultation team meetings for the clinicians. Adolescents also complete a weekly self-monitoring checklist, referred to as the diary card, to track specific behaviors, emotions, and skills used during the week. (p. 227).

Therapists then create an agenda for the session, with the following as priorities: life-threatening behaviors, therapy-interfering behaviors (of both client and therapist), problems the client is experiencing in their life, trauma and PTSD symptoms (which may be monitored via the diary card—perhaps technologically completed), and working on mindfulness and communication strategies. In the interest of space, we will not elaborate on the individual steps. This is also not yet evaluated as a treatment for PTSD in adolescence beyond a few small studies. Evidence of effectiveness may be found, but we recommend caution (and training) when considering this approach.

Eye movement desensitization and reprocessing (EMDR) is an approach with a body of empirical evidence demonstrating its value for treating trauma (Wesselman & Shapiro, 2013). The theory behind this approach proposes that ordinary experiences and stressors are assimilated into existing neural networks in the brain. Some processing may also occur through dreams. There are networks in the brain that store memories (including sensations, sounds, images, emotions) and link them to other networks to make sense of them. EMDR postulates that traumatic memories are not linked to existing networks, leaving them fragmented and unintegrated into the neurological connections. In EMDR, those memories are now processed. The approach also assists the client to formulate positive memories that support progress.

Readers interested in the neurobiological foundations for memory processing might refer to Bergmann's (2019) *Neurobiological Foundations for EMDR Practice* (second edition). This book provides current speculations (some would say explanations) of how EMDR uses what is known about how the brain processes information. Here, we will give a general overview of the eight phases in EMDR therapy, based on Wesselman and Shapiro (2013). The time for each stage varies with the client and therapist:

1. During history taking, the clinician identifies disturbing memories, current triggers, and positive images of the future.

2. reparation, when therapist explains the process (including bilateral stimulation) to the child. The authors provide an example: "EMDR makes upset feelings smaller and positive feelings bigger" and "helps the brain get stronger" (p. 206).

3. Assessment is the stage in which the client identifies their worst traumatic experience, including images, emotions, physical sensations, and negative beliefs. They also identify positive beliefs that would be helpful.

4. Desensitization uses the worst memory followed by bilateral stimulation eye movements, sounds or touch. The usual number of side-to-side eye movements is about 24. The client is asked to notice what they experience and then is instructed to "take a breath and let it go." They are then asked, "What's there now?" (p. 207).

5. Strengthen the positive cognition that was learned in the previous stage.

6. Scan the body for any sensations or movements that remain.

7. Begin closure.

8. Engage in reevaluation.

The stages involve considerable skill on the part of the therapist. Wesselman and Shapiro (2013) report that the number of sessions can be as few as one to three (with type I trauma) or months or years depending on the case. The possibility of resolving a trauma in a brief therapy is appealing to clients (costs, etc.), but predictions about duration of treatment should be avoided. It is imperative that a professional who is inclined toward this treatment get specialized training and supervision.

Adults

As with children and adolescents, CBT is widely regarded as the most effective treatment for trauma-related symptoms and PTSD. Since we have discussed the general principles of CBT, we will focus here on specific components that are believed to be important: *Exposure* refers to repeatedly experiencing the traumatic event, either in imagination or live (depending on the trauma), until the fear and anxiety are extinguished. In PTSD treatment, the client (or the counselor) recounts the traumatic experience as if it were still occurring while focusing on the most disturbing aspects of the trauma. This is done repeatedly until the fear response no longer occurs. This is called *habituation*. The recounting of the event can even be tape-recorded so that the client can listen between sessions to increase exposure. Live exposure does not mean reexperiencing the trauma physically but means facing reminders of the trauma (e.g., the site of one's house that was destroyed in a hurricane) frequently. Live exposure is often administered in graded increments, starting with less distressing reminders and working up to the most upsetting ones. The goal—habituation—is the same in imaginal and live exposure.

There are several techniques for using exposure in treatment. *Systematic desensitization* is a process in which the counselor and client construct a hierarchical list of memories or cues to the trauma. Then the counselor relates the memories or cues starting with the least distressing one while the client uses muscle relaxation, which has been taught to the client. The theory is that one cannot be both anxious and relaxed at the same time, so hearing the memory while relaxed prevents anxiety from occurring. After many repetitions, the memory is no longer associated with the anxious feelings—and then counselor then moves on to the next one. Eventually, the client is able to experience the memories and cues without the distressing emotional response.

Prolonged exposure is widely used in treatment of PTSD and is one of the CBT approaches (Riggs et al., 2006). It typically involves nine to 12 individual 90-minute sessions using four procedures: education about trauma and associated conditions, breathing retraining (learning controlled breathing techniques), in vivo (in real-life settings) exposure to trauma-related but safe situations, and repeated imaginal exposure to the trauma event. The cognitive processing occurs following each session of imaginal exposure. Homework usually includes in vivo exposure assignments and listening to tape recordings of the imaginal exposure exercise from the session. There are sources of explicit session-by-session guidelines for using this approach. Riggs et al. stress the importance of providing the client with a rationale for this technique. They also indicate that the counselor must convey confidence in the technique, expertise in using it, and confidence that the client has the ability to successfully complete the treatment. It is also important, as it is with all approaches, to form a strong alliance with the client and to praise and support their efforts and courage in addressing this disorder.

Cognitive therapy for trauma-related symptoms focuses on emotions other than fear (guilt, sadness) that may follow a traumatic experience, helps clients understand the meaning of the trauma, and helps them examine their basic belief structure so that the traumatic memories do not distort the client's view of self and the world. A 12-session protocol is summarized in Shipherd et al. (2006), who provide a full manual and forms that are used in this approach. Cognitive restructuring is a variation of cognitive therapy that teaches clients how to identify faulty thinking (overgeneralizing, catastrophizing, etc.) and then how to challenge and change those faulty notions. Sometimes, exposure may be used to test faulty assumptions (Livanou, 2001).

Some therapists incorporate stress inoculation training in treating trauma victims. This technique teaches clients methods to control anxiety. Techniques include slow deep breathing, progressive muscle relaxation, thought stopping, and guided self-talk. Again, exposure is sometimes incorporated (Brom et al., 2017; Livanou, 2001).

Older Adults

Research on effective treatments for elderly trauma victims is sparse, so Dinnen et al. (2015) suggest that treatments found to be effective with adults be used until more research is available. The few studies available are inconclusive, with exposure-based and EMDR treatments showing some promise in case studies. Of concern in treating elderly people is the likelihood of other psychiatric disorders being present as well, especially depression. Given that physical complaints are also more likely in this age group, consultation with a physician is essential. Medication is often used with the elderly (antidepressants, mood stabilizers, etc.), but caution is advised. First, it is important to determine whether the elderly client uses alcohol to avoid complications from interactions of prescribed medication with alcohol. An additional concern is prescribing medications to depressed elderly clients that could be used for suicide.

Another issue with the use of common treatment approaches with elderly trauma cases is whether exposure is beneficial (Cook & O'Donnell, 2005). One concern is that the emotional reaction aroused during exposure (intense fear and anxiety) has physiological effects (e.g., increased heart rate and respiration) that could have a negative impact on the health of an elderly client. Case studies of the effective use of EMDR with traumatized elderly clients have reported positive outcomes, and some proponents of this approach recommend this for elderly clients as a vehicle for life review.

Life review therapy is a treatment approach designed to assist elderly clients to rework conflict from earlier in their lives in order to reach understanding and acceptance (Cook & O'Donnell, 2005). Several studies found initial evidence of success using this approach with elderly clients with PTSD. Storytelling as treatment is a variant of the life review therapy with four elements that make this useful for resolving historical material.

Cook and O'Donnell (2005) noted that progress in treatment is typically slower for elderly victims. Also, due to age-related cognitive declines, educational elements should be repeated, and learning of new skills is enhanced when information is provided in several modalities (spoken, written, using diagrams, etc.). These experts also advise therapist flexibility in terms of logistical matters, which may be more challenging for older adults. Telephone or virtual consultations may have to replace in-person sessions when mobility is problematic and technology is available. For this reason, as well as other factors of life in old age, support systems may be lacking for elderly clients, and assistance with utilizing available support is an important element of working with this clientele.

Intimate Partner Violence

The DSM-V (APA, 2013) includes IPV under *Other Conditions That May Be a Focus of Clinical Attention* (p. 715). IPV is not a diagnosis at this time, but its mention in the DSM-V suggests that experts may believe that the associated disorders (PTSD, depression, etc.) do not capture the intricacies of this issue. Both women and men are victims of IPV, but women have more severe injuries and hospital visits and deaths from physical and sexual violence (Condino et al., 2016). Other groups also experience IPV, such as LGBTQIA+ persons, people with disabilities, people with atypical gender expression or identities, migrants and refugees, ethnic minorities, and Indigenous people. IPV intersects with larger societal contexts, including racism, classism, transphobia, ableism, and poverty (Oram et al., 2022). A large majority of research and practice focuses on women as victims and overlooks female perpetrators. Importantly, treatment for perpetrators is infrequently discussed, and approaches are almost uniformly punitive. We provide a brief overview of studies on both perpetrators and victims.

Mental health disorders are both predictors and outcomes of IPV for both partners. Conduct disorders and antisocial behaviors are risk factors for perpetration; for victimization, risk factors include prior victimization, homelessness and poverty, and the presence of children (Condino et al., 2016). Note in the section on children and adolescents in this chapter that IPV also has a significant impact on children in the household, so efforts to reduce this behavior have wide implications. We must also keep in mind that substance abuse is highly correlated with IPV, and treatment that does not address that is unlikely to be successful.

Programs for perpetrators are typically mandatory (via the justice system) and consist of psychoeducation linking responsibility for violence to males who are socialized to believe they are entitled to power and control in interpersonal relationships. The widely used Duluth model is an example of a widely used template for such treatment. These programs typically require 3–36 weeks of reeducation with the goal of engendering a more egalitarian attitude toward women. Condino et al. (2016) argue that the absence of attention to the perpetrator's personal trauma history, substance abuse, and possible personality disorders are impediments to effectiveness.

Group CBT approaches work to develop skills to reduce violent behavior. Those include anger management, relaxation, communication skills, and assertiveness instead of aggressiveness. Emotional aspects of IPV, including jealousy, are often incorporated into the psychoeducational components. Research is not robust enough to support (or disclaim) these approaches. However, data from victims finds that in about 33% of cases, a new instance of IPV occurs within 6 months (Condino et al., 2016).

A promising new treatment approach involves incorporating motivational interviewing (based on the stages of change model; Prochaska & Norcross, 2001) into perpetrator treatment (Silva et al., 2022). A systematic review found that programs incorporating MI reduced dropout rates in community samples and improved participants' readiness to change, along with perpetrators' ratings of the value of treatment, commitment to the program, and increased acceptance of responsibility for their behavior. Keep in mind that many variables (length of treatment, MI only, or MI in combination, etc.) makes it difficult to make conclusive statements about the efficacy of this approach, but it merits future attention and research. Training in MI is widely available.

A perspective on female victims of IPV is apparent in the data showing 21% of women experienced IPV by multiple partners; 5%–13% were victims of IPV for more than 20 years! (Condino et al., 2016). Mental health problems common among victims of partner abuse are depression, substance abuse disorders, and anxiety disorders, although PTSD is the most common (Rodgers & Norman, 2004). In many cases, when PTSD is resolved, symptoms of the other diagnoses are no longer observable or are greatly reduced, suggesting that PTSD is the primary disorder, with other disorders best considered PTSD symptoms instead of separate disorders. Hughes and Jones (2000) pointed out another reason for focusing on the PTSD diagnosis: It locates the cause as outside the client, thus diminishing the stigma associated with a disorder that has its origin within the individual. This may alleviate the sense of powerlessness that often is a feature of IPV victims.

Despite the high rates of IPV and the prevalence of trauma-related disorders in this population, IPV victims have been neglected in the research on effective treatment for PTSD. Because victims come to the attention of mental health professionals at times of crisis, basic safety needs, logistical challenges for housing and employment, childcare, and so on predominate and the mental health issues are in the background. Oram et al. (2022) propose that professionals in primary health care are often the first to encounter IPV victims and should receive training to recognize the importance of coordinating with mental health care.

A treatment, cognitive therapy for battered women (CTT-BW), includes elements designed to address PTSD (psychoeducation about the disorder, stress management and relaxation training, self-monitoring of maladaptive thoughts and speech, and talking about the trauma with exposure exercises as homework). There are also unique components for the battered woman: recognizing and changing dysfunctional beliefs; decreasing negative self-talk, especially related to guilt and shame; self-advocacy techniques; assertiveness training; managing unwanted contacts from former partners; and skills for recognizing potential batterers to avoid future IPV. Treatment is provided in 1.5-hour sessions twice a week, and usually includes eight to 11 sessions. The studies of treatment effectiveness excluded women who had not been out of the abusive relationship for at least 30 days, who were abusing substances, and who had psychotic disorders. Results were very promising both in the initial evaluation study (Kubany et al., 2003) and the subsequent study, which improved the research design (Kubany et al., 2004). Both studies included follow-up studies (at 3 months in 2003 and 3 and 6 months in 2004) that found treatment gains were maintained. The samples included ethnic minority women, and no differences in outcomes were detected between Whites and minority women. In the second study, both male and female therapists were used, and again no differences in client outcomes were found. Given the strong research evidence of the effectiveness of CBT on trauma-related disorders, and the encouraging outcomes in this well-designed research, this is an approach worthy of attention. There is a manual and client workbook for this protocol, and we encourage any readers who are interested in working with this clientele to investigate this approach more closely. The HOPE program (Helping to Overcome PTSD Through Empowerment; Johnson et al., 2011) incorporates many components of CBT for PTSD but is designed for delivery in shelters and includes basic life concerns and advocacy skills. Although both approaches report evidence of effectiveness, the research output is primarily from program developers and does not address long-term gains beyond 6 months. The few studies that assess long-term effects found new incidents of IPV assessed at 6 months to 3 years at a rate of 31%–44%. Finally, the research on programs for perpetrators and victims does not account for significant dropout rates.

A more recent concern in IPV is enacted via technology. Gilbar et al. (2023) provide the following explanation of the phenomenon:

> Cyber IPV includes monitoring a partner's online activities, exerting control over their online communications, making hostile threats, and/or sharing embarrassing photos via electronic tools. (p. 1948)

In their meta-analysis, Gilbar et al. found that Face-to-Face-IPV (F2F-IPV) and Cyberer-IPV (C-IPV) were highly correlated, and that correlation was not significantly different for males and females. A complete discussion of cyber-IPV is beyond the scope of this chapter, but research is ongoing, and undoubtedly more conclusive data will be forthcoming.

Before leaving this topic, we want to alert readers to novel treatments beginning to appear in both lay and scholarly literature. MDMA (i.e., ecstasy) treatment should be an adjunctive treatment to standard approaches. A randomized controlled trial of MDM-assisted therapy was conducted with 90 participants with severe PTSD and comorbid disorders (Mitchell et al., 2021). Participants received manualized treatment with MDMA or placebo and were assessed at baseline and 2 months after treatment for PTSD symptoms and functional impairment. The MDMA protocol involved three preparatory sessions and nine integrative sessions. Results showed that MDMA-assisted therapy was highly efficacious in clients with severe PTSD and had negligible side effects. This prestigious research group encouraged more extensive evaluation studies given the encouraging results.

Another new treatment is the administration via injection into the neck of stellate ganglion block (SGB). Rae Olmsted et al. (2020) reported greater reductions in the SGB group on PTSD symptoms than in the sham-treated group. All participants had baseline PTSD levels in the mild-moderate range, were taking other psychotropic medications, and were excluded if they had a substance use disorder, a traumatic brain injury, or recent suicidal ideation. Despite positive findings, this treatment is in preliminary stages of research but may attract more attention in the future.

The final novel treatment to be alerted to is the use of virtual reality in PTSD treatment (Health-Match. 2022) for PTSD sufferers who had not been able to visualize the traumatic event (necessary for exposure treatment). Virtual reality uses a headset that immerses the person in a realistic context that adjusts to head and other movements. According to HealthMatch Staff (2022), to date virtual reality has not been shown to be more effective than other treatments but may appeal to those who resist more conventional treatment. For example, 33% of American soldiers were unwilling to speak to a counselor but were willing to try virtual reality. A systematic review and meta-analysis analyzed virtual reality exposure therapy and augmented reality exposure therapy and found that virtual reality exposure therapy produced better outcomes than waitlist controls (Eshuis et al., 2021) but cautioned that the number of studies and number of participants were small. However, as we await future research, they believe virtual reality exposure therapy has potential to be effective, especially with clients who have not improved with other treatments.

We must mention that the APA (2017) has published the *Clinical Practice Guideline for the Treatment of Posttraumatic Stress Disorder (PTSD) in Adults,* which defines minimal competencies for all trauma treatment approaches and does not endorse a specific approach. Written for psychologists, the competencies readily apply to other mental health professionals. These guidelines are too lengthy to include here, but we advise professionals who expect to work with people who have experienced trauma to consider whether their own training has prepared them in line with these competencies. Given the concerns described next, readers might find the eight general trauma competencies (Appendix C; Cook et al., 2019), which we find very succinct and useful.

However, readers should be aware that the competencies were not universally applauded. For example, Silver and Levant (2019) commented that although the panel based their recommendations on scientific evidence, some find that the guidelines could limit clinician independence and might limit insurance coverage to "manualized, time-limited, cognitive-behavioral treatments" (p. 347). Evidence used to formulate these guidelines come primarily from randomized clinical trials, which are difficult and expensive to execute and may not include the range of factors that are associated with PTSD. Sufficiently large sample sizes are needed to conduct many types of analyses, and subsamples that include all factors of potential interest are rare; potential participants with multiple comorbid disorders are often excluded because of the potential confounding of results. Silver and Levant argue that clinician judgment is at the center of the treatment plan, and social and cultural influences may call for a combination of approaches. They recommend that revised guidelines should account for comorbid diagnoses (including substance use and personality disorders), cultural influences, and types of trauma (type I or II or complex trauma).

Another strong criticism of the APA guidelines argues that they give short shrift to cultural context, intersectionality, and systematic oppression of marginalized groups. This position reminds readers that trauma symptom expression varies as a result of these intersectional identities and that treatment that does not take culture (in the broadest sense) into account is likely to be ineffective at best and harmful at worst (Bryant-Davis, 2019).

Issues of Diversity

Here, as in each chapter in the book, we consider how trauma and responses to trauma are affected by gender, race/ethnicity, disability status, age, immigrant status, and language and cultural factors. We note that research does not always address these issues, which should affect both policy and practice. We hope this overview sensitizes our readers to be self-aware; to assess their own knowledge, attitudes, and skills; and to utilize consultation and supervision to ensure clients receive the most competent treatment.

Trauma affects individuals differently depending on a number of factors, including gender and race/ethnicity. For PTSD, differences in diagnosis (PTSD or not), symptom severity, and symptom expression have been detected by those categories. Some researchers (Ruglass et al., 2020) speculate that African Americans and Latinx groups are more likely to be exposed to traumatic events and thus have higher rates of PTSD. It is also possible that different groups are more vulnerable to develop PTSD after exposure, perhaps due to environmental differences. Ruglass et al. also consider whether the measures used to study PTSD in women IPV victims are invariant across demographic groups. Some studies utilize self-report for assessment while others use structured clinical interviews, which also may account for different findings.

One concern about the research that readers should keep in mind is the possibility that observed racial/ethnic differences are due to insensitivity of test instruments to cultural differences. Although there were no differences detected between African American, Latinx, and White women on rates of diagnosis, further analysis detected differences between White and African American and White and Latinx women on avoidance of trauma-related thoughts and a sense of foreshortened future (Ruglass et al., 2020). Differences may be accounted for by clinician biases; clinicians might

Hyperarousal: High level of physiological and psychological tension that occurs when the nervous system has been overwhelmed. Includes heightened startle reactions, agitation, and so on.

weight symptoms differently by group and/or participants may respond differently to clinician characteristics.

As we discussed earlier, veterans are at high risk for PTSD. Koo et al. (2016) examined existing data from 79,938 veterans of Iraq and Afghanistan deployments who had received treatment through the VA, had a PTSD diagnosis, and completed a PTSD screen before starting treatment. Results revealed these differences: Asian/Pacific Islander (A/PI) females and Black males were more likely to receive a PTSD diagnosis and to endorse most symptom clusters than White veterans. A/PI males differed only by having fewer participants who endorsed hyperarousal symptoms. Black and White women did not differ; Latinx women acknowledged symptoms of emotional numbing more often than did White women. Again, it is possible that the measures used were not culturally or gender neutral. Also, the data came from veterans who initiated mental health treatment, which may not generalize to all veterans of those conflicts. The importance of these findings is to stress the need for cultural competence in clinicians and to ensure they understand that the symptoms of PTSD may appear differently in some demographic groups.

Adults with intellectual disabilities (ID) also develop PTSD subsequent to a trauma at higher rates than the general population (Wigham & Emerson, 2015). They note the people with ID often have difficult childhood environments and relationships that can become more difficult when they transition to a form of independent living in adulthood. The researchers found a direct relationship between challenging life events and behavior problems in this population. Concerns regarding getting appropriate services include the difficulty of meeting criterion A for PTSD in the DSM-V because they may have difficulty identifying an event that is the focus of treatment. Reasons include secrecy and shame, especially when the trauma involved sexual abuse. In addition, many have challenges with communicating that may keep them from being able to describe symptoms. Wigham and Emerson express concern that the absence of a diagnosis, or incorrect diagnosis, could lead to inadequate treatment, or none at all. There are now assessments designed for this population, including self-reports and third-party identification, with adequate psychometric properties, that should be used with people with ID. EMDR, TF-CBT, and psychodynamic approaches had positive but small effects, and these authors recommend EMDR. A harmful outcome of misdiagnosis would be moving the individual to an institution because of misinterpretation of their behaviors and lack of understanding of their triggers. Medication is also widely used with this population (antipsychotics, often) that are not recommended for PTSD and that may have unpleasant or harmful side effects.

Parker et al. (2016) conducted a systematic review and meta-analysis of six papers that looked at the impact of natural disasters on older adults. They found PTSD symptoms were 2.11 times more likely in older adults than younger adults, and adjustment disorders were 1.73 times more likely in the older group. In their commentary on this study, O'Donnell and Forbes (2016) noted that the prevalence of other negative mental health outcomes (depression and anxiety) were not higher in the older group; this is puzzling since in studies with community samples not involved in a disaster, prevalence of PTSD declines after age 55. They speculate that the longer life span of women compared to men might account for this finding. They also propose that older adults often have more casualties in disasters that cause pain and stress and are associated with PTSD, and the physical vulnerabilities that accompany aging might engender increased fear in older adults, which would contribute to PTSD symptoms rather than depression. O'Donnell and Forbes suggest that psychological first aid be provided to everyone affected by the disaster, a more focused intervention given for those exhibiting signs of potential mental health problems, and intensive treatment be provided for those who develop mental health disorders.

Many people with a range of disabilities are more vulnerable to negative psychological and mental health outcomes of trauma, but we mustn't forget that disasters can be the cause of disabilities (amputations, TBIs, spinal cord injuries, death; Stough & Kelman, 2018). When a physical injury is the result of a disaster, the risk for mental health problems increases. In a natural disaster people with disabilities that affect mobility, or those with sensory disabilities, may not be able to reach safety. For example, Deaf people may not hear evaluation instructions, people with visual impairment may find their guide dogs confused by changes in the landscape, and so on. Shelters may not be accessible or may lack accommodations for various disabilities. Furthermore, emergency responders may not have training for assisting people with disabilities.

High rates of abuse and violent victimization are reported in people with disabilities around the world (Petersilia, 2001; Wigham & Emerson, 2015). Children with disabilities are physically and sexually abused at rates higher than nondisabled children. In addition to increased vulnerability, Charlton et al. (2004) observe that persons with disabilities typically have fewer protective factors that can buffer them from the effects of trauma. In fact, they have been found to be less resilient than nondisabled persons and are less likely to have appropriate treatment for trauma, particularly if the disabilities are cognitive and/or involve barriers to communication.

As law and policies reduced the number of disabled persons who are in institutions, one consequence is that some disabled persons are forced by poverty to live in unsafe environments. On the other hand, persons in institutions are also very vulnerable to victimization. Disabled persons who are dependent on others for care, including bathing, dressing, and toileting, are particularly vulnerable to abuse by caregivers (Cronin, 2005; Disabled Women's Network Ontario, n.d.), because resistance can result in the withholding of care. Because of their dependence, many persons with disabilities have been encouraged to be compliant with the wishes of caregivers, which makes them an easier mark for those who seek to take advantage.

Persons with physical disabilities may be unable or less able to defend themselves against violence due to challenges with mobility. Those with cognitive limitations may not have the skills to identify high-risk situations and may lack the vocabulary to provide an accurate account of the crime. And persons with intellectual disabilities or communication impairments are often not believed if they do report crimes, and when perpetrators are convicted, sentences tend to be light (Petersilia, 2001). On those rare occasions when a case involving a person with intellectual disabilities does go to court, the person does not receive any assistance with testimony. The adversarial nature of a trial, combined with the presence of the perpetrator, easily overwhelms an intellectual disabled person, and the experience can be traumatic and revictimizing.

Deaf children appear to have higher rates of physical and sexual abuse than hearing children, perhaps because the perpetrators assume they are unable to report the offenses (Durity et al., 2004). Some believe that the greatest risk for abuse occurs in residential schools, which Deaf children often attend. Factors that may increase the vulnerability of these children include the inability to partake of "incidental learning." Hearing children learn from overhearing private conversations of adults or siblings and may pick up information from television that is on in the background. Hearing peers may share information by whispering. These sources of information, that help prepare children to protect themselves from harm and victimization, are not accessible to Deaf children. This general lack of information may impair the child's social development, and they may have less understanding of what is appropriate in what situations. Further, Deaf children of hearing parents (as 90% of Deaf children are) may have restricted communication even with family, which may increase their need for intimacy, however inappropriate. In addition to the increased vulnerability of Deaf children to abuse, their ability to report and receive therapy is also limited by the limited availability of certified interpreters who can assist. Assessment of disorders is complicated by the lack of measures designed for this population.

Shaken Baby Syndrome: Constellation of symptoms of violent shaking of an infant or small child, including severe neurological damage and death.

Not only are children with disabilities more likely to be exposed to trauma and violence, but trauma and violence can actually cause some disabilities (Charlton et al., 2004). Child abuse and neglect in infancy increases the likelihood of developmental delays. The brain can be permanently affected by such abuse as "shaken baby," and even neglect can result in decreased brain size and other damage.

For helping professionals who work with persons with disabilities, it is worthwhile to inquire about past trauma, given the high incidence in the population. It would also be useful to check that such clients do have an emergency plan in place.

Counselor Issues

Working with trauma survivors is hard and emotionally taxing (Chatters & Liu, 2020). *Vicarious trauma* refers to detrimental effects in mental health providers that are the consequence of being exposed to trauma reported by clients (Jimenez et al., 2021). Clinicians with a personal history of trauma are particularly vulnerable to this phenomenon. Symptoms of this disorder are the same as those for PTSD, except that the experience itself is indirect. This is not synonymous with *secondary trauma*, which is not limited to mental health clinicians but applies more generally to people who are close to trauma victims and hear accounts of their experience. They may experience some symptoms similar to PTSD, but they tend not to be long-lasting. *Burnout* refers to the exhaustion associated with one's work and is not similar at all to PTSD. *Empathy-based stress* is a term coined by Rauvola et al. (2019) and defined as work-related stress (in any field) due to exposure to trauma and feeling empathy. That includes vicarious and secondary traumatization and *compassion fatigue*. These researchers emphasize the importance of closely monitoring themselves for symptoms, managing a work–life balance, attending to health and sleep, and when necessary, seeking therapy. Taking care of the provider ultimately affects the quality of treatment they provide to clients.

Two factors have been investigated as contributors to the constellation of symptoms experienced by clinicians who have experienced vicarious traumatization: personal trauma history and the percentage of trauma survivors treated by the counselor. Although results of the few research studies are mixed on personal trauma history, there is more consensus that the number or percentage of trauma survivors treated by a counselor is directly related to the symptoms of the counselor experiences (Arvay, 2001, Makadia et al., 2017).

One study examined factors that affected social workers who treated survivors of the World Trade Center attacks on 9/11 and found higher rates of PTSD symptoms in social workers who treated survivors than in those who did not (Boscarino et al., 2004). Several variables were identified that predicted symptom development: degree of exposure (number of clients treated), personal history of trauma, social support available, and environmental (work setting) factors.

Although there is insufficient research to support any specific prevention strategies, Zimering and Gulliver (2003) proposed four areas that are important: professional strategies, organizational strategies, personal strategies, and general coping strategies. We believe that the professional strategies are crucial. Even if a counselor specializes in trauma work, some limitation on the number of trauma survivors seen at any given time is essential. In addition, the availability of supervision to allow for debriefing and processing of emotional reactions is another necessity. Organizational strategies include having release time available and ensuring a safe work environment. Personal and general coping strategies are those any counselor should employ regardless of clientele: recognizing one's limits, engaging in self-care activities, and using a personal support system.

NOTE TO SCHOOL COUNSELORS

Earlier in this chapter, we discussed trauma and PTSD in children and adolescents. We know that acute stress disorder (ASD) and PTSD are not uncommon in school-aged youth. In addition to violent crime, either experienced or witnessed, conditions that have the potential to be traumatic include child abuse, IPV in the home, homelessness, poverty, school shootings, immigration, bullying, and natural disasters (National Association of School Psychologists, 2015). Educators have determined that youth with trauma experiences are more likely to drop out of school.

A qualitative study revealed obstacles that keep school counselors from working more effectively with trauma-affected children:

- They experience uncertainty about their role (e.g., they are not mental health therapists in the school setting but have those skills to assist children with issues that interfere with their educational experience).

- They are uncertain about confidentiality guidelines.

- They are uncertain about communicating with parents.

- The feel at personal risk (e.g., parents disagreeing with a suggestion for their child). In the current climate, parents can not only be vocal in their complaints, but can escalate to making threats.

- They feel overwhelmed by the many duties that keep them from working directly with youth in need.

School counselors have a significant role to play in identifying and providing services to these young people. Students who exhibit academic disinterest, behavior problems, poor attendance, and so forth may in fact be suffering from PTSD or subclinical trauma symptoms. Ongoing trauma can affect the developing brain, further complicating functioning in school (deficits with attention, emotional regulation, memory, etc.). Again, most children are resilient and recover from trauma, but a minority will have problems, including internalizing and externalizing behaviors. Rumsey and Milsom (2018) worry that these symptoms may be misunderstood or misdiagnosed as ADHD, oppositional defiant disorder, or conduct disorder, which would deprive them of appropriate interventions. School counselors are integral to identifying and supporting children affected by trauma. The following points summarize their recommendations for school counselors:

- Use systemic interventions.

  - Assume a leadership role in implementing trauma-informed practices in their schools. In a trauma-informed school, everyone understands trauma and its effects.

  - Recognize symptoms of trauma.

  - Provide trauma-informed interventions.

  - Avoid retraumatizing children.

- Take leadership in providing staff development for all people who work in the schools

- Be a strong advocate for trauma-informed policies and procedures

- Collect, analyze, and share data that guides decision-making

- Infuse a multi-tiered system of supports (MTSS) with trauma-informed practices at all levels.

- Develop collaborative relationships with families and communities.

A major challenge is the ratio of school counselors to students. The ASCA (n.d.) recommends a student to counselor ratio of 250:1. At the time of this writing, data from 2022 show that Illinois has the highest ratio at 693:1, and Vermont has the lowest at 186:1. A former teacher decries the insufficient staffing for school counselors, especially considering the high rates of mental health needs in the population.

Ethical Concerns

If a counselor works with clients who have experienced trauma in the form of IPV, there are two concerns. First, these clients have had their trust and safety deliberately violated, and they are likely to be reluctant to establish trust with anyone else, including the counselor. The counselor needs to be very careful not to misinterpret this reluctance as resistance, to address the safety issue in sensitive and careful ways, and to make establishing trust a primary treatment goal.

Because working with trauma victims is so difficult, and the danger of vicarious victimization exists, there are two extremes of possible reactions to this work to which the counselor must be acutely alert. Sometimes counselors overidentify with the victim (Dutton, 1992). This response can lead to problematic emotional responses on the part of the counselor. For example, the counselor may become visibly distressed, causing the client to feel the need to comfort the counselor and/or be more restrained in sharing information to avoid upsetting the counselor. If the counselor were to express extreme anger at the perpetrator, the client may find themself defending them. The other extreme that sometimes occurs in the counselor who works with these clients is to become emotionally distanced and detached in order to protect themself. This stance communicates to the client that their issues are not that important and that the violence that the client experienced is not understood by the counselor. Being alert to these possible responses to working with this clientele will help the counselor avoid unethical behaviors.

It is also essential that counselors focus on the needs of the client. Several authors cited in this chapter express concern that counselors avoid using exposure treatments because they are unable to cope with the client's negative emotional response. It is unethical to select a treatment approach that is less effective for a client because the counselor has personal difficulty tolerating strong emotions. In such cases, the counselor should not treat trauma cases, and when presented with a client for whom trauma is a central issue, the counselor should make a careful and considered referral to a specialist.

As with many other issues in this book, the counselor's personal history and its effect on the ability to provide ethical services needs to be addressed. Vicarious traumatization might be more readily experienced by a counselor with a history of trauma and violence, and listening to clients' reports of trauma may be experienced by the counselor as revictimization. The counselor must be sure that their own issues have been resolved before consenting to work with trauma survivors. Both supervision and personal therapy are strategies for ensuring that the personal and professional concerns are separated. Again, the reader must consider the ethical issue is the "boundaries of competence" ethical standard. Counseling trauma victims requires considerable specialized expertise and supervised practice, and counselors interested in this work must get both training and supervised experience in the techniques.

Summary

- Trauma and violence are experienced by most people in the course of their lives. Most people experience acute distress but recover within 6 months. Some will develop PTSD, and some of those will continue to have the disorder 10 years later.
- Disasters, one type of trauma, can be natural or human caused. Human-caused disasters seem to cause more psychological harm due to the violation of basic assumptions about the world, others, and self.
- Two types of trauma have been identified: type I traumas are single-incident events (hurricane, criminal assault); type II traumas are chronic and repeated (as in ongoing sexual abuse

or living in the midst of war). Complex trauma is characterized by multiple violent ongoing events that began at an early age.
- Many variables influence an individual's response: the severity of the trauma, prior traumatic experiences, mental health prior to the incident, gender, developmental level, and available support systems.
- PTSD is often found in combat veterans, refugees, and victims of IPV. These populations have unique issues that should be addressed in treatment.
- A variety of assessment tools are available to screen or diagnose PTSD. The generalist counselor will want to screen all new clients to identify any trauma history.
- The strongest evidence for effective treatment of PTSD and trauma-related symptoms is for cognitive behavioral approaches. EMDR is accumulating evidence of effectiveness.
- Most CBT approaches incorporate exposure and cognitive restructuring in the treatment protocol. Exposure (systematic desensitization, flooding, and implosion therapy) is designed to disconnect trauma reminders from the distressing emotional response using habituation and extinction. The cognitive elements address faulty thinking about the trauma (e.g., "I could have prevented it").

Flooding: A technique used in CBT in which the client continues to imagine the feared stimulus until the anxiety is extinguished

- Females of all cultures are more likely to have problematic or enduring distress following a trauma than males. Some research suggests that minorities experience greater degrees of trauma-related problems than Whites, but differences may be due to culturally insensitive instrumentation to measure reactions and/or to differential treatment following a disaster.
- Persons with disabilities are at elevated risk for many kinds of trauma and may have fewer resources to cope with trauma when it occurs.
- Natural disasters impact persons with disabilities disproportionately, as communication impairments and mobility difficulties can interfere with evacuation and sheltering.
- Specialized training is needed to employ trauma-related treatment approaches. Counselors must be alert to their levels of competence and their own tolerance for horrific content and strong emotions if they are considering specializing in this clientele.

Additional Resources

On the Web

- www.trauma-pages.com is a link to David Balwin's trauma info pages that contain links to so many other resources that it is truly a one-stop-shopping source.
- www.istss.org is the website for the International Society for Trauma and Stress Studies and is useful if you are looking for research and/or conference information.
- http://www.apa.org/topics/topictrauma.html is the APA's trauma resource section that also posts current information, sometimes in PDF form for downloading. They have current information and reports for psychologists responding to a variety of disasters worldwide.
- www.rainn.org provides information about a sexual assault hotline.
- http://www.sexaa.org/ This is the website for Sexual Addicts Anonymous, a 12-step self-help organization, that clients exhibiting compulsive sexual behavior might consider as an adjunct to treatment.

- https://pandys.org/ is a nonprofit organization with resources for survivors of sexual assault and rape.
- https://www.nctsn.org/ is a resource for both clients and counselors for overall trauma treatment.
- https://www.loveisrespect.org/ is an organization that addresses domestic violence, with the hopes of preventing abuse from happening. It is primarily for adolescents, but there are good resources for adults as well.
- An online training program for working with trauma is available at https://www.timfletcher.ca//.

In Print for Counselors

- *Too Scared to Cry* by Lenore Terr is a classic on trauma.
- *Trauma and Recovery* by Judith Herman is also widely read and authoritative.
- *Trauma in the Lives of Children* by Kendall Johnson would be an excellent addition to the library of any counselor who works with children who have been traumatized.
- *Empowering and Healing the Battered Woman* by Mary Ann Dutton is the most comprehensive and useful book for those who work with female victims of IPV.
- *Effective Treatments for PTSD*, edited by Edna Foa, Terence Keane, and Matthew Friedman, would be a good start for readers who think they might be interested in specializing in treating trauma survivors and are not sure which approach is best. For each approach, available research is described so that the reader can make informed decisions. Treatments are rated from level A (best evidence) effectiveness to level F (recently developed approach with no evidence).
- *Cognitive-Behavioral Therapies for Trauma*, edited by Victoria Follete and Joseph Ruzek, has more technical information on using CBT approaches.
- *Post-Traumatic Stress Disorder in Children* by Spencer Eth and Robert Pynoos is still relevant and provides useful techniques for a variety of types of trauma in children.
- *Seeking Safety: A Treatment Manual for PTSD and Substance Abuse* by Lisa M. Najavits is a manual primarily for the treatment of substance abuse and trauma and provides a structural approach for counselors.
- *TF-CBT Web* by Judith A. Cohen, Anthony P. Mannarino, and Esther Deblinger is both a manual and online workshop for counselors working with children and trauma.

In Print for Clients

- *The Post-Traumatic Stress Disorder Sourcebook* by Glenn Schiraldi is useful for clients, their support system, and the counselor. It also helps the client understand different approaches to treatment.
- *We Can't Get Over It: A Handbook for Trauma Survivors* by Aphrodite Matsakis contains four parts: understanding PTSD, the healing process, specific traumas (individual chapters on every type of trauma), and appendices with additional resources.
- *The PTSD Workbook* by Mary Beth Williams and Soili Poijula is most useful when the client has complex PTSD, as the majority of the book is devoted to topics geared to complex PTSD survivors.
- *Outgrowing the Pain: A Book for and About Adults Abused as Children* by Eliana Gil is a short, clear, highly readable, and cleverly illustrated book that provides straightforward guidance. Although it was published in 1983, I still find it one of the best to suggest.
- *The Courage to Heal* by Ellen Bass and Laura Davis can be an effective adjunct to treatment. An accompanying workbook allows clients to share. Although more recent editions of this classic do make mention of males, it is clearly a book for women.

- *Victims No Longer* by Mike Lew is by and for men. Readers may relate to the many personal stories interspersed with useful information, although others may be put off by the stories.
- *Wounded Boys, Heroic Men* by Daniel Jay Sonkin is a more practical book. Chapters on various approaches to healing are very clear, and clients are likely to find the suggestions helpful.
- *I Can't Talk About It* by Doris Sanford is for "the child who hasn't told … yet." The child talks to a dove about her secret and shameful experience with her father, and the dove (identified in the beginning as the spirit of God) provides gentle and wise counsel. Several of my young clients requested their own personal copy of this book.
- *Please Tell: A Child's Story About Sexual Abuse* is by Jessie, a 9-year-old survivor of sexual abuse. Illustrated by the author, this beautiful book is one that children can relate to. It may inspire some to tell or draw their own story.
- *Bastard out of Carolina* by Dorothy Allison is an excellent if sometimes disturbing novel about childhood sexual abuse. The story is set in the south in the 1950s and paints a harrowing picture of the physical and sexual abuse the protagonist suffers at the hands of her stepfather.
- *Monkey King* by Patricia Chao is a novel from the perspective of a 28-year-old Chinese American incest victim, hospitalized after a suicide attempt, who reflects on the incest she experienced at the hands of her father, the anger and grief she feels at her mother's refusal to believe her, and her sister's dismissal of her pain.
- *Mouthing the Words* by Camilla Gibb is set in England and tells the story of Thelma's struggles to integrate her experience of childhood abuse, ultimately requiring hospitalization. In both this and *Monkey King*, the wounded child has a mental breakdown requiring inpatient treatment. Readers should keep in mind that not every victim has a similar outcome.
- *Push* by Sapphire is a very quick and shocking read about an African American victim of sexual abuse. The first sentence, "I was left back when I was twelve because I had a baby for my fahver," sets the stage for this horrifying but enlightening tale.
- *The Sexual Healing Journey: A Guide for Survivors of Sexual Abuse* by Wendy Maltz is a book helping survivors of sexual abuse reclaim their sexuality.
- *The Body Keeps the Score: Brain, Mind, and Body in the Healing of Trauma* by Bessel van der Kolk details the effects trauma has on both the body and mind and gives advice on dealing with these impacts.

Novels for Counselors and Clients

- *The Kite Runner* by Khaled Hosseini is a favorite of mine. The crucial scene in the book is traumatic for Hassan, but also for Amir. We think reading the book with that in mind would be a worthwhile exercise for those interested in untreated trauma.
- *The Boy Who Loved Anne Frank* by Ellen Feldman is a moving work of fiction that chronicles the experience of Peter, who was described in Anne Frank's diary. It is an original perspective on a Holocaust survivor, and one we highly recommend.
- *The Return of the Soldier* is Rebecca West's first novel, published in 1918. She describes the return of a shell-shocked soldier to his elegant English estate. Although we know much more about PTSD now, this short novel gives a glimpse of history that is beautifully written.

Film and Television

- *Jackknife* helps the viewer understand PTSD in Vietnam veterans.
- *The Deer Hunter* is another film about PTSD in Vietnam veterans.

- *Behind the Lines/Regeneration* provides an example of shellshock in World War II based on an outstanding novel (part of a trilogy by Pat Barker) about real historical figures.
- *Sophie's Choice* is a classic film about a Holocaust survivor that should not be missed.
- *Bastard out of Carolina* is fairly true to the novel and may shock some readers with the degree of violence portrayed. The mother's response to the abuse is a good topic for discussion.
- *Ultimate Betrayal* is an enlightening and powerful film about adults sexually and physically victimized as children, based on actual situations, and highlights the ramifications for adults who decide to confront their abusers.
- *The Tale* is a powerful film based on the true story of Jennifer Fox. It depicts the grooming of a child and shows the lingering and troubling effects 35 years later. We don't want to spoil the emotional impact of this film by mentioning details, but rest assured that this is a very important work.
- *Scouts Honor: The Secret Files of the Boy Scouts of America* is a documentary that exposes the horrific sexual abuse of many young scouts by scout leaders. We meet many victims and hear how their lives have been affected. We also learn of the lengths the organization went to in order to keep their despicable secret.
- *Surviving R. Kelly* is a docuseries about the women who were affected by R. Kelly's trauma and sexual abuse and how it has affected them and how they have found healing.
- *Room* is based on a novel about a young mother and her son trying to escape captivity.
- *Precious* is a movie surrounding a female who has experienced trauma and abuse throughout her life and how she copes with these factors and eventually finds healing.
- *The Invisible War* is a documentary based on the struggle for justice among U.S. military in regard to sexual assault.

Exercises

1. If you have been persuaded that it is important to inquire about trauma experiences during your initial sessions, how will you do so? If you would use an assessment instrument, which one will you use? If you determine that PTSD is a likely diagnosis, what will be your next step?

2. Assume there has been a shooting (one shooter and one victim, but many witnesses) at a local school. The staff asks for your help and wants to know how you would approach the situation. What will your strategy be?

3. Many organizations solicited mental health workers after 9/11 and Hurricanes Katrina and Rita for short-term volunteer counselor assistance. What concerns would you have about that? How would you protect yourself from secondary traumatization?

4. You are a consultant for a shelter for victims of domestic violence, and you are asked to devise a screening method so that staff can refer those clients who need more intensive mental health services. What will you suggest?

5. Assume you are a school counselor whose school includes many military families whose soldiers are deployed in Iraq. What kinds of programming will you devise to educate children and parents about this situation? How would you work with a child whose dad has just returned, and the child reports that the father is "not the way he used to be"?

6. Watch one of the movies recommended and identify the traumatic event and the symptoms of PTSD, and indicate what approach you would take with this client. If you are going to refer the client to someone else for treatment, discuss how you will explain this to the client.

7. Visit a shelter for battered women in your area. Find out how they assess for PTSD and how they provide mental health services to the women and their children. In a brief report, make recommendations for changes or additions to the program.

8. Read *The Kite Runner* and write about or discuss the effects of the central trauma on both Hassan and Amir. Look for evidence of the diagnostic criteria in both characters. If you had the opportunity to treat Amir in the United States, what approach would you take?

9. Read Feldman's *The Boy Who Loved Anne Frank* and decide if Peter has PTSD. Then discuss the treatment he receives and compare it to what is known today about effective treatment for PTSD.

10. Watch or rewatch any of the Hollywood films mentioned and discuss the portrayal of PTSD in the characters. Also talk about treatment and whether you believe it would have been helpful.

11. Develop an initial interview protocol that includes nonsuggestive, nonsuppressive questions about sexual abuse. Consider how and when in the interview you will ask your questions.

12. Assume a child or adolescent you are working with reveals that they were sexually abused 3 years ago by an extended family member. How will you proceed? What will you tell the client about your obligation to report? What will you do if the client says that the perpetrator lives in another state now and is no longer a danger but the client fears the repercussions on the rest of the family if they find out?

13. Assume you are working with an adult survivor of sexual abuse who has made good progress in therapy and indicates that they want to have a family session that includes the perpetrator. The client wishes to confront the perpetrator in this setting in order to achieve closure on the abuse and to express the feelings to the perpetrator and the rest of the family. How will you decide if this is an appropriate intervention? How will you prepare the client for the session if the decision is to proceed?

14. Assume you are working with a child or adolescent client who is a known victim of sexual abuse. There are three other siblings in the home, none of whom has reported sexual abuse. The client is struggling with feelings of "why me?" which contribute to their sense of somehow deserving the abuse. How will you work with this issue?

15. An adult comes to you for treatment and reveals at intake that in the last few months they have had intrusive thoughts and flashbacks of episodes of sexual abuse from childhood that were not previously remembered. What will you tell the client about these memories?

16. You receive an invitation from a local high school to give a presentation on childhood sexual abuse. School officials are hoping the talk will encourage some youth to seek help for this problem. Assuming a 45-minute presentation, what will you present?

17. You have one male client who was sexually abused as a child and four female clients with that experience. You are considering forming a support group but are concerned about including only one male. How will you make the decision?

18. Consider the case of Mark. Assume you had a referral from a middle school teacher concerned about his withdrawal and isolation. Discuss or write about how you would approach an initial interview with this child and how you would proceed.

Appendix A: Diagnostic Criteria: Posttraumatic Stress Disorder in Individuals Older Than 6 Years

Note: The following criteria apply to adults, adolescents, and children older than 6 years.

A. Exposure to actual or threatened death, serious injury, or sexual violence in one (or more) of the following ways:

1. Directly experiencing the traumatic event(s).

2. Witnessing, in person, the event(s) as it occurred to others.

3. Learning that the traumatic event(s) occurred to a close family member or close friend. In cases of actual or threatened death of a family member or friend, the event(s) must have been violent or accidental.

4. Experiencing repeated or extreme exposure to aversive details of the traumatic event(s) (e.g., first responders collecting human remains; police officers repeatedly exposed to details of child abuse).

   Note: Criterion A4 does not apply to exposure through electronic media, television, movies, or pictures, unless the exposure is work related.

B. Presence of one (or more) of the following intrusion symptoms associated with the traumatic event(s), beginning after the traumatic event(s) occurred:

1. Recurrent, involuntary, and intrusive distressing memories of the traumatic event(s).

   Note: In children older than 6 years, repetitive play may occur in which themes or aspects of the traumatic event(s) are expressed.

2. Recurrent distressing dreams in which the content and/or affect of the dream are related to the traumatic event(s).

   Note: In children, there may be frightening dreams without recognizable content.

3. Dissociative reactions (e.g., flashbacks) in which the individual feels or acts as if the traumatic event(s) were recurring. (Such reactions may occur on a continuum, with the most extreme expression being a complete loss of awareness of present surroundings.)

   Note: In children, trauma-specific reenactment may occur in play.

4. Intense or prolonged psychological distress at exposure to internal or external cues that symbolize or resemble an aspect of the traumatic event(s).

5. Marked psychological reactions to internal or external cues that symbolize or resemble an aspect of the traumatic event(s).

C. Persistent avoidance of stimuli associated with the traumatic event(s), beginning after the traumatic event(s) occurred, as evidenced by one or both of the following:

1. Avoidance of or efforts to avoid distressing memories, thoughts, or feelings about or close associated with the traumatic event(s).

2. Avoidance of or efforts to avoid external reminders (people, places, conversations, activities, objects, situations) that arouse distressing memories, thoughts, or feelings about or closely associated with the traumatic event(s).

D. Negative alterations in cognitions and mood associated with the traumatic event(s), beginning or worsening after the traumatic event(s) occurred, as evidenced by two (or more) of the following:

1. Inability to remember an important aspect of the traumatic event(s) (typically due to dissociative amnesia and not to other factors such as head injury, alcohol, or drugs).

2. Persistent and exaggerated negative beliefs or expectations about oneself, others, or the world (e.g., "I'm bad," "No one can be trusted," "The world is completely dangerous," "My whole nervous system is permanently ruined").

3. Persistent, distorted cognitions about the cause or consequences of the traumatic event(s) that lead the individual to blame himself/herself or others.

4. Persistent negative emotional state (e.g., fear, horror, anger, guilt, or shame).

5. Markedly diminished interest or participation in significant activities.

6. Feelings of detachment or estrangement from others.

7. Persistent inability to experience positive emotions (e.g., inability to experience happiness, satisfaction, or loving feelings).

E. Marked alterations in arousal and reactivity associated with the traumatic event(s), beginning or worsening after the traumatic event(s) occurred, as evidenced by two (or more) of the following:

1. Irritable behavior and angry outburst (with little or not provocation) typically expressed as verbal or physical aggression toward people or objects.

2. Reckless or self-destructive behavior.

3. Hypervigilance.

4. Exaggerated startle response.

5. Problems with concentration.

6. Sleep disturbance (e.g., difficulty falling or staying asleep or restless sleep).

F. Duration of the disturbance (Criteria B, C, D, and E) is more than 1 month.

G. The disturbance causes clinically significant distress or impairment in social, occupational, or other important areas of functioning.

H. The disturbance is not attributable to the physiological effects of a substance (e.g., medication, alcohol) or another medical condition.

Specify whether:

With dissociative symptoms: The individual's symptoms meet the criteria for posttraumatic stress disorder, and in addition, in response to the stressor, the individual experiences persistent or recurrent symptoms of either of the following:

1. **Depersonalization:** Persistent or recurrent experiences of feeling detached from, and as if one were an outside observer of, one's mental processes or body (e.g., feeling as though one were in a dream; feeling a sense of unreality of self or body or of time moving slowly).

2. **Derealization:** Persistent or recurrent experiences of unreality of surroundings (e.g., the world around the individual is experienced as unreal, dreamlike, distant, or distorted).

   Note: To use this subtype, the dissociative symptoms must not be attributable to the physiological effects of a substance (e.g., blackouts, behavior during alcohol intoxication) or another medical condition (e.g., complex partial seizures).

Specify if:

With delayed expression: If the full diagnostic criteria are not met until at least 6 months after the event (although the onset and expression of some symptoms may be immediate).

Appendix B: Diagnostic Criteria: Posttraumatic Stress Disorder in Children 6 Years and Younger

A. In children 6 years and younger, exposure to actual or threatened death, serious injury, or sexual violence in one (or more) of the following ways:

1. Directly experiencing the traumatic event(s).

2. Witnessing, in person, the event(s) as it occurred to others, especially primary caregivers.

3. Learning that the traumatic event(s) occurred to a parent or caregiving figure.

B. Presence of one (or more) of the following intrusion symptoms associated with the traumatic event(s), beginning after the traumatic event(s) occurred:

1. Recurrent, involuntary, and intrusive distressing memories of the traumatic event(s).

   Note: Spontaneous and intrusive memories may not necessarily appear distressing and may be expressed as play reenactment.

2. Recurrent distressing dreams in which the content and/or affect of the dream are related to the traumatic event(s).

   Note: It may not be possible to ascertain that the frightening content is related to the traumatic event.

3. Dissociative reactions (e.g., flashbacks) in which the child feels or acts as if the traumatic event(s) were recurring. (Such reactions may occur on a continuum, with the most extreme expression being a complete loss of awareness of present surroundings.) Such trauma-specific reenactment may occur in play.

    4. Intense or prolonged psychological distress at exposure to internal or external cues that symbolize or resemble an aspect of the traumatic event(s).

    5. Marked physiological reactions to reminders of the traumatic event(s).

C. One (or more) of the following symptoms, representing either persistent avoidance of stimuli associated with the traumatic event(s) or negative alterations in cognitions and mood associated with the traumatic event(s), must be present, beginning after the event(s) or worsening after the event(s).

Persistent Avoidance of Stimuli

    1. Avoidance of or efforts to avoid activities, places, or physical reminders that arouse recollections of the traumatic event(s).

    2. Avoidance of or efforts to avoid people, conversations, or interpersonal situations that arouse recollections of the traumatic event(s).

Negative Alterations in Cognitions

    3. Substantially increased frequency of negative emotional states (e.g., fear, guilt, sadness, shame, confusion).

    4. Markedly diminished interest or participation in significant activities, including constriction of play.

    5. Socially withdrawn behavior.

    6. Persistent reduction in expression of positive emotions.

D. Alterations in arousal and reactivity associated with the traumatic event(s), beginning or worsening after the traumatic event(s) occurred, as evidenced by two (or more) of the following:

    1. Irritable behavior and angry outbursts (with little or no provocation) typically expressed as verbal or physical aggression toward people or objects (including extreme temper tantrums).

    2. Hypervigilance.

    3. Exaggerated startle response.

    4. Problems with concentration.

    5. Sleep disturbance (e.g., difficulty falling or staying asleep or restless sleep).

E. The duration of the disturbance is more than 1 month.

F. The disturbance causes clinically significant distress or impairment in relationships with parents, siblings, peers, or other caregivers or with school behavior.

G. The disturbance is not attributable to the physiological effects of a substance (e.g., medication or alcohol) or another medical condition.

Specify whether:

With dissociative symptoms: The individual's symptoms meet the criteria for posttraumatic stress disorder, and the individual experiences persistent or recurrent symptoms of either of the following:

1. **Depersonalization:** Persistent or recurrent experiences of feeling detached from, and as if one were an outside observer of, one's mental processes or body (e.g., feeling as though one were in a dream; feeling a sense of unreality of self or body or of time moving slowly).

2. **Derealization:** Persistent or recurrent experiences of unreality of surroundings (e.g., the world around the individual is experienced as unreal, dreamlike, distant, or distorted).

   Note: To use this subtype, the dissociative symptoms must not be attributable to the physiological effects of a substance (e.g., blackouts) or another medical condition (e.g., complex partial seizures).

Specify if:

With delayed expression: If the full diagnostic criteria are not met until at least 6 months after the event (although the onset and expression of some symptoms may be immediate).

Appendix C: Eight Cross-Cutting Trauma-Focused Competencies

1. Demonstrate understanding about trauma reactions and tailor trauma interventions and assessments in ways that honor and account for individual, cultural, community, and organizational diversity.

2. Demonstrate understanding and ability to tailor assessment and interventions to account for developmental lifespan factors at time(s) and duration of trauma as well as time of contact.

3. Demonstrate the ability to understand, assess, and tailor interventions and assessments that address the complexities of trauma-related exposure, including any resultant long- and short-term effects (e.g., comorbidities, housing-related issues), and person–environment interactions (e.g., running away from home and being assaulted).

4. Demonstrate the ability to appropriately appreciate, assess, and incorporate trauma survivors' strengths, resilience, and potential for growth in all domains.

5. Demonstrate understanding about how trauma impacts a survivor's and organization's sense of safety and trust.

6. Demonstrate the ability to recognize the practitioners'

   a. capacity for self-reflection and tolerance for intense affect and content,
   b. ethical responsibility for self-care, and
   c. self-awareness of how one's own history, values, and vulnerabilities impact trauma treatment deliveries.

Adapted from J. M. Cook, Elana Newman, and The New Haven Trauma Competency Group, "A Consensus Statement on Trauma Mental Health: The New Haven Competency Conference Process and Major Findings," *Psychological Trauma: Theory, Research, Practice, and Policy*, vol. 6, no. 4, p. 303. Copyright © 2014 by American Psychological Association.

7. Demonstrate ability to critically evaluate and apply up-to-date existing science on research-supported therapies and assessment strategies for trauma-related disorders/difficulties.

8. Demonstrate the ability to understand and appreciate the value and purpose of the various professional and paraprofessional responders in trauma work and work collaboratively and cross systems to enhance positive outcomes.

CHAPTER 7

Suicide

Suicide is the most frequent crisis situation for mental health professionals in all settings. It is also one of the most challenging and stressful situations a clinician ever faces, regardless of how much experience and training the counselor has. In our careers as counselors, we have each intervened many times with individuals contemplating suicide. Several former students and clients who are now leading satisfying and productive lives at one time needed to be hospitalized for serious and lethal attempts to take their lives. We are gratified to know professional skills allowed us to intervene successfully in so many cases. There were also times when we were unable to prevent a suicide, and one particular story will be the case study for this chapter. We share the story because we hope by doing so others can learn from the experience.

CASE STUDY

There have been many situations over the years when I have intervened with a suicidal client, and all had a positive outcome, with the client safe and obtaining help—except one. I tell the painful story of this situation because it illustrates every counselor's worst nightmare. It is a difficult story for me to tell. I have changed some details in order to protect the privacy of others, but the essential information is unfortunately accurate.

Although this event occurred over 30 years ago, I remember it vividly. I was working as a counselor in a high school where the admission process for potential students included an initial interview by a counselor. Students completed an application form and a problem checklist, which were reviewed during the interview. Most students checked a fair number of problems on the checklist of 240 issues often reported by adolescents, and one thing that stood out about John, age 17, was that he checked only two. John's response to my expression of surprise at the small number of concerns, and to my inquiries about many items that other students often checked, made it clear that he was very invested in being "normal" and being able to handle difficult situations, including his parents' divorce and other stressors. At the time of this initial contact, John was living away from home and working to support himself, and he expressed a desire to earn his high school diploma. With my assistance, he selected his classes and enrolled.

Attendance was a requirement of the school, and students who exceeded a specified number of absences were dropped from the program, with the option to reenroll when their circumstances (internal or external) would allow them to attend regularly. John was quickly dropped from the program his first term due to absences. At the next opportunity to enroll, he applied for readmission. We met again and talked about what had interfered with his

(Continued)

attendance the previous term (including difficulties with his work schedule), and he insisted he now had everything under control and was ready to commit to school. Nevertheless, his lack of attendance again quickly resulted in his second dismissal from the program. Other students mentioned him occasionally in conversation, often referring to his reckless driving behavior.

When he came to see me for the third time about reentering, I pointed out that when students had been dismissed three times, they were considered a low priority for available openings, and that it was therefore important that he consider whether this was the best time to try again. He acknowledged the obstacles but appeared determined to be successful this time. I encouraged him to come to see me so that I could support his efforts to stay in school and assist him if problems arose. He agreed to do so. The second day of the new term, he telephoned me to say he would be absent but that he would communicate with me and come to see me the next day. He did so and said his relationship with his girlfriend was not going well and that their late-night arguments had resulted in his oversleeping and missing school. He reported that the previous evening their conversation had been very productive, and she agreed that his education was a priority. He attended an entire day of school and stopped by before leaving to say his day had gone well.

The next morning, I was in my office meeting with a student in crisis. The secretary always honored my request not to interrupt such sessions, so I was quite surprised when the intercom buzzed. She said I had a call that she thought I should take, because the student had been calling every few minutes for the last hour. It was John, of course, and I answered, intending to say I would call him back when I was free. The quality of his voice when he answered made it obvious he was in distress. Mindful of the other upset student in my office, who could hear my end of the conversation, I said he sounded distressed, and he replied, "Yes." I said something about being glad he called and that I was with another student right then and would be glad to call him or meet with him later in the morning. I could tell he was crying, and I said something like, "I'm worried that you are thinking of hurting yourself." He responded with more sobs. I asked if he would come to school and meet with me. When he declined, I assumed he did not want to risk being seen by other students in his emotional state, so I said I would meet him at a local coffee shop close by if he preferred. He declined again, and I assumed the same reason was involved. I foolishly said I would come to his home, and he thanked me, said that would be much better, and he then provided directions to his rural address. I explained that I would need some time to finish my current session, and then I would leave. I told him approximately when to expect me.

As soon as the other student left my office, I attempted to call John back and confirm the appointment and let him know I was on my way. When there was no answer, I became alarmed and rushed out the door. My fear was that he would have driven his car dangerously on a mountain road, perhaps after drinking alcohol, and killed himself. In my panic, I hurriedly told the secretary where I was going and left. She handed me one of the earlier phone messages he had left, which I stuffed in my pocket. I read it later: the message was that he wanted to thank me for all my help. My alarm escalated, and I drove to his home.

When I approached John's rural home, I noted with relief that his car was there. I knocked on the door and was answered only by the dog's barks. I remember still the terrible sense of dread I felt, and I ran across a field to the closest neighbor to call the police. It turned out that the neighbor was related to John and was certain my fear was unfounded. She reported that John frequently listened to loud music in his room using headphones and would not hear the door. I repeated my wish to call the police, but she insisted she accompany me back to his home. The door was unlocked, and the aunt walked to his room, with me following. I could hear her cry and saw only the legs on the bed when I realized what had happened.

I called the police, who arrived about 15 minutes later to this rural home. I also called the school, told the principal what was happening, requested that a faculty meeting be scheduled for late that afternoon, and that the district's crisis response team be contacted and asked to send representatives.

The aftermath included meetings with the police, the family, and staff at the school, and the next day meeting with groups of distressed students. In a small school, news travels quickly, and news of this kind brings up many issues in students, both those who knew and those who did not know the deceased. In meeting with the police and the family, I learned that four notes had been left (although I was not privy to the contents), that John had told his brother earlier in the morning that he was going to kill himself and the brother told him to call his counselor. The lethal method was a gunshot to the head.

I know some of my colleagues both in the school and in the community believed I was responsible for the suicide and/or that I could have prevented it had I responded more appropriately and effectively. Although I will never
know if that is the case, guilt and self-doubt plagued me for a long time. It may be that John pulled the trigger as
soon as he hung up the telephone and that the police would only have found his body. It may be that if I asked the
other student to leave, I could have kept him on the phone and provided other options. That I think is more likely. I
didn't think quickly enough, and the one mistake for which I hold myself most culpable is not staying on the phone
when I realized John's level of distress. I could have signaled the other student to wait outside and been able to
assess the situation more directly. I don't know if that would have changed the outcome, but it is the professional
response I wish I had made. My assumption about his refusal to meet anywhere but at his home was faulty, and
this was not a time for assumptions.

My own help and support came from the members of the school district's crisis response team, who listened
to my story as often as I needed to repeat it, who assured me that I was not responsible for the death and encouraged me to continue doing this work. They also provided direct assistance in managing the students who needed
support and assistance in the days following the suicide. I definitely needed the support; rumors quickly spread
about what had occurred and what my involvement had been. In fact, I still remember the sick feeling in my stomach when, not very long after this incident, I was in a district-wide meeting of counselors. Someone introduced
the story with something like "I heard that a [irresponsible—I don't remember the word used, but I know it was not
supportive] counselor ..." When the person finished, I said, "That was me." The silence that followed was not a
comfortable one, to say the least.

Personally, I struggled with guilt and self-doubt and wondered if I should leave the profession. I did not. I know I
did not cause the suicide. I will never know if any of the things I wish I had done and said would have prevented it,
but I have come to accept the uncertainty. There was also definitely a long-term impact on my professional behavior; I know that I am now hypervigilant when there was the slightest hint of suicidal ideation, but I also developed
strategies for consultation and collaboration so that I never made decisions in isolation again. Although I can't
say for sure, I don't think I've avoided dealing with suicidal individuals, but I have definitely been overly cautious in
responding to individuals who express any level of suicidal ideation. If I were to make another error of judgment with
a client, it would to over-react in a case of low lethality.

Definition and Description of the Problem

Self-murder, self-inflicted death, deliberate self-annihilation, self-destructive acts with intent
to die—these are among the definitions found in the literature. Suicide is usually a conscious,
planned, and premeditated act but can also be impulsive and unplanned (particularly in adolescents), a desperate attempt to end unbearable pain. A suicidal event (thought, gesture, attempt,
threat) may be what brings the person to see a counselor, but it is often the case that the reason for
seeking help is something other than suicidal thinking. Counselors may also work with survivors
of suicide (friends and loved ones of someone who completes an act of suicide), and when a client
completes a suicide, professionals must cope with their own survivor issues.

Graduate training programs are inconsistent about training students in the management of
suicidal clients, so many readers may have had only perfunctory coverage of this topic in their
coursework. For example, a survey of 226 school counselors found that 38% of participants had
not received training in suicide prevention (Becnel et al., 2021). Doctoral programs in clinical
psychology are also remiss in this regard; one study found that only 35% of programs offered
training in working with suicidal clients (Mackelprang et al., 2014). While this chapter does not
pretend to be a comprehensive manual on suicide, readers will gain an awareness of the issue
and how they might respond in their work setting. Experts recommend that counselors need

information about suicide risk assessment and treatment of suicidal clients (Foster & McAdams, 1999), along with clinical training and preparation for the possibility of a client suicide. We will address each of those topics.

Prevalence

According to the most recent data available from the CDC (2023b) 48,183 people took their own lives in 2021, which reflects an increase of 4% over 2000. That figure does not include the 12.3 million Americans who had seriously considered suicide, 3.5 million who made suicide plans, and 1.7 million who attempted suicide. In 2021, suicide was the second most frequent cause of death for people 10–14 and 20–34 years old. Youth suicides, and plans and attempts, increased during the pandemic (Bridge et al., 2023; Durante & Lau, 2022), while adult rates declined from 2019 to 2020 (Park, 2023).

A word about terminology: We object to the phrase *successful suicide* to describe someone whose suicidal act was fatal. We prefer the term *completed suicide* to avoid the connotation that suicide is a successful solution to a problem. Suicidal *ideation* refers to thoughts of suicide that are nonspecific as to plan or timing (e.g., "Sometimes I think I'd be better off dead"). We use the term *gesture* to refer to an act that is meant to imply suicidal intent but that is of very low lethality (e.g., making a very superficial cut on the wrist, taking five aspirin) and is intended to be a cry for help. A suicidal *attempt* is more lethal (e.g., taking a bottle of sleeping pills) and implies that the person believed their action would result in death (even if that belief was based on inaccurate information) and, if the individual survives, it is because someone intervened or interrupted the act. *Suicidal behaviors* refer to all of the above.

While the overall suicide rate is sufficient cause for concern, these rates vary sharply by demographic groups. Males commit suicide at almost four times the rate for females. Men who are 75 and older have the highest suicide rate of all age groups. Among the elderly, suicide attempts are more often fatal than in any other group. The racial/ethnic groups with the highest rates of suicide are American Indian/Alaskan Natives and non-Hispanic Whites. The CDC also finds that veterans, LGBTQ+ youth, persons with disabilities, adults ages 35–64, residents of rural areas, and workers in certain occupations are over-represented among those who die by suicide (CDC, 2023a).

Across age groups, firearms are the most frequently used method of suicide, accounting for 54.6% of all suicides in 2021 (58% for males, 33% for women). Suffocation (including hanging) was the next most common method, accounting for 25.08% (27% men, 27 % women), followed by poisoning (including drug overdoses) with 11.6% (8% men and 29% women). Rates varied somewhat by age, with 28% of suicides among in people ages 15–24 being the result of suffocation and 7.6% due to poisoning. The only age group for which firearms were not the most common method was age 10–14, in which suffocation accounted for 56% of suicide deaths and firearms 36.7% (National Institute of Mental Health (NIMH, 2023). Although men commit suicide at four times the rate of women, women attempt suicide at three to nine times the rate of men. College students commit suicide at a lower rate than their nonstudent peers.

Other demographic variables have also been found to increase the risk for suicide. For example, the rate of suicide among divorced or separated men is as high as that of married men (Kposowa, 2000). Comparing religious affiliations among persons who have made a suicide attempt, one study found that 8% of Muslims, 6% of Catholics, 5% of Protestants, and 3.6% of Jewish respondents acknowledged having made an attempt. People in high-status occupations (e.g., physicians) have higher rates of suicide than those in lower status positions, and those who experience a decrease in status (for whatever reason) are at increased risk. A serious, chronic physical illness is also associated with increased risk for suicide (U.S. Department of Veteran Affairs, n.d.), especially in the elderly.

Risk Factors

Suicide occurs throughout the life span. Some individuals are more likely than others to contemplate or commit suicide, due to the presence of risk factors that render them more vulnerable to this behavior. Being aware of these developmental and risk factors helps the counselor direct prevention and intervention efforts where they are most needed.

The most important predictor of suicide potential is a history of previous attempts. The more prior attempts, and the more lethal those attempts, the greater the current risk of suicide. Gathering such information is essential in any evaluation of suicide risk. It is important to keep in mind, however, that over-relying on this risk factor is dangerous, since more than two thirds of completed suicides occur with the first attempt (Mann, 2002). Nonsuicidal self-harm is another potent risk factor for suicidal behaviors (Williams et al., 2021).

There are other known risk factors that can be grouped into those that predispose an individual to suicide or increase their vulnerability (chronic factors and traits) and those more immediate situational factors that may impel the individual to act (Haley, 2004). The following is an overview of those factors.

There is ample evidence that suicide is associated with the presence of psychiatric disorders, diagnosed or not. Over 90% of suicide victims have a psychiatric disorder (often undiagnosed), most often a mood disorder such as bipolar disorder or depression (Mann, 2002). When these disorders are combined with either a personality disorder or substance abuse, the risk is substantially elevated. Again, although this is a well-known risk factor, it is important to keep in mind that most people with psychiatric disorders do not commit suicide. The implications for mental health professionals are twofold: the importance of correctly diagnosing and treating mood disorders and the need for ongoing monitoring of suicide risk in clients with mood disorders.

Substance abuse, particularly alcohol, is a potent risk factor. In fact, in those with a history of attempts, alcohol abuse is the strongest predictor of a subsequent suicide. In addition, for children and adolescents, parental alcoholism elevates their risk for suicide. Experts theorize that alcohol use in a depressed person leads to suicide by acting as a depressant (which alcohol is) and by reducing impulse control. Individuals, particularly those who are dually diagnosed with a mood disorder and substance abuse, require close monitoring. In adolescents, acting-out behaviors may mask underlying depression, and it is important to be thorough in evaluating younger clients for both disorders. There are prevention programs in schools that include a screening for depression for all students, although schools may be wary of parental objections to such practices.

There are also genetic factors in suicide, meaning that the tendency toward suicidal behaviors and thoughts is, at least in part, inherited. Evidence of genetic influence has been found in twin and adoption studies, which show a greater incidence of suicide in those whose biological parents have committed suicide and greater similarity between identical than fraternal siblings. The genetic influence in suicide is about the same as heritability of major psychiatric disorders, such as bipolar disorder and schizophrenia.

A history of suicide of a close family member increases the risk. In adolescents, the suicide of a friend or family member elevates the risk of suicide. Other conditions that are risk factors for suicide include physical or sexual abuse in childhood, head injury or neurological disorder (e.g., epilepsy), and cigarette smoking. In children, witnessing the abuse of another elevates their risk for suicide. Those individuals who lack problem-solving skills and who have difficulty coping with stress are more vulnerable to suicidal thinking and actions. Problems in the family system may exacerbate these existing skill deficits, leading to a desperate act. The old adage "suicide is a permanent solution to a temporary problem" seems apropos to such circumstances.

An important risk factor, particularly in adolescents, is LGBTQ+ status. Numerous studies have found higher rates of suicide ideation, attempts, and suicides among gay, lesbian, bisexual, and trans-gendered adolescents and young adults than in the general population. That risk factor is reduced when the individual has a supportive family and social group (Madireddy & Madireddy, 2022).

Environmental variables that increase the risk of suicide are living in a rural area, access to guns, poverty and unemployment, and social isolation. Researchers found that 50% of people who committed suicide did not have a single close friend. The presence of a serious medical illness or condition may elevate suicide risk. This may explain, in part, the high rate of suicide in the elderly, whose health status may be a factor, along with social isolation. Across age groups, people with HIV/AIDS commit suicide at much higher rates than the general population.

In addition to these risk factors, there is often a precipitant—an event close in time to the suicide that was the "last straw" in the life of a vulnerable individual. In children and adolescents, the precipitant is often the loss of an important relationship via death, break-up of a romantic relationship, or relocation. In the elderly, concern about medical conditions is often a precipitant. Protective factors include the absence of risk factors, a sense of hopefulness, having the responsibility for children, having strong social support, and having access to mental health care.

Digital Media and Suicide

The role of digital media in suicide is complex. Digital media may prevent suicide but can also enable vulnerable users to harm or kill themselves. In this section, we outline the positive features of online suicide material and those that promote or support suicidal actions. We discuss how texting has been used in productive and harmful ways and consider the issue of suicide contagion. One systematic review of literature on digital media and suicide found that of the 51 articles the researchers examined, 18 studies found negative effects of digital media, 11 reported positive effects, and 17 had mixed effects on suicidal behavior (Marchant et al., 2017). There has been a rapid increase in suicide forums and blogs on the subject (e.g., 3% of search results in 2007 to 18.5% in 2014), while even greater increases in sites that evaluate and discuss specific suicide methods (9% to 21.7% in the same time period). Sadly, results for help sites decreased from 13% to 6.5% (Cohen-Almagor & Lehman-Wilzig, 2022). Clinicians should be familiar with these phenomena in order to be alert to how their clients engage with digital media around suicide.

On cause of anxiety about the negative impact of internet sources are the sites or forums that actively promote suicide, even to the extent of providing detailed instructions for specific methods for ending one's life. Such sites may be found inadvertently; results of a search for information or for help with suicidal impulses may bring up such sites. It is common for people looking for information, forums, pro-suicide sites, support, and so forth to use a search engine to locate those sites. An interesting study compared the results of a search of commonly used search terms related to suicide (in both English and Spanish) on Google, Bing, and DuckDuckGo. Their results demonstrated that Google brought up the least amount of harmful content of the three. The researchers also revealed that 53% percent of Google searches included information about suicide hotlines compared to 35% for Bing and 10% for DuckDuckGo. Overall, searches in Spanish produced fewer results considered harmful but were also less likely to include information about available and reliable support. Searches for specific methods of suicide were, unsurprisingly, more likely to generate harmful results.

Another worrisome issue is the effect of digital media coverage of celebrity suicides on vulnerable persons. A study in Japan found that there was an increase in suicides when young people, women, and entertainment figures' suicides (known as the Werther effect) were discussed on Twitter, especially among those who were surprised by the news (Fahey et al., 2018). Relatedly, a phenomenon known as suicide contagion may operate when fragile individuals come upon videos, reports, or discussions of suicide in online media (Borge et al., 2021). The glamorization of suicide may seem appealing to those who are already having suicidal ideation. Readers may recall the controversy about the book and subsequent Netflix series 13 *Reasons Why* (Yorkey, 2017) that told the story of a girl who committed suicide and left a series of recordings that described the reasons for her action. The series included graphic depictions of traumatic events that could trigger young viewers. An increase in suicides occurred after the Netflix version aired (Borge et al., 2021). The story also depicts the effects of suicide on survivors, considered by some to provide cautionary perspectives that might act as a deterrent. While some readers praised the book highly and encouraged adults to read it (particularly to be able to discuss it with youth who read it), others believed the book glorified suicide and was dangerous for young people to read, fearing it would encourage some vulnerable youth to view suicide as an option. Clinicians who work with early adolescents may want to familiarize themselves with this title/program to be aware of its potential impact. Although teachers in some schools required the book (Kaufman, 2017), others sent warnings to parents about the series. However, the series was so popular it would be prudent to inquire if an adolescent client had read or seen the book and explore their reactions, being alert for any suicidal ideation or plan.

Cohen-Almagor and Lehman-Wilzig (2022) provide several examples of individuals who died by suicide who were influenced by various forms of digital media. In one case, a person live-streamed his suicide, which was watched by many people, none of whom intervened until he was already dead; some of the witnesses urged him to take more pills to ensure his attempt was lethal. These scholars also described "insult forums" (p. 108) on which perpetrators gather to hurl demeaning and humiliating insults at victims, some of whom were encouraged to commit suicide. They cite findings from survey research that 7.5% of respondents indicated they had searched for information about suicide online; of those who made a serious attempt, 70% reported accessing online information. It seems that online platforms, including chatrooms and forums, are particularly dangerous for fragile individuals already contemplating suicide, however vaguely.

Although social networks in general have been implicated in encouraging suicide, the reality is much more complicated. While pro-suicide sites can be instrumental in pushing an ambivalent person to act, in general, social networks are more likely to provide a vehicle for finding social support, especially from peers. In fact, some individuals seriously contemplating suicide reveal those thoughts/plans on social media, which provides an opportunity for others to intervene and provide support and resources. The flip side of gaining support from social media is that for some, the experience may engender feelings of isolation and alienation (Cohen & Biddle, 2022) if the response is other than what they hoped for. Another conundrum is whether and how social media sites encourage or discourage susceptible users. For example, TikTok, currently extremely popular, does not allow material that normalizes or promotes suicide or other destructive behavior, but they distinguish between posts that include personal experiences with suicide and those that actively promote it. They contend that hearing the stories of others who have struggled might be helpful; when user searches for suicide-related posts, they are directed to local and national support lines (Canady, 2021). Digital media users are often adept at circumventing provider restrictions; it is unrealistic to assume that a site does not contain pro-suicide content or to think that age constraints are enforced.

Platforms are available to assist people contemplating suicide. Cohen et al. (2022) found that "clarity, brevity, and immediacy" (p. 1) were essential characteristics of online support locations. Furthermore, the young adult participants felt that sites that were suicide specific, young adult specific, and geared to students. Although not part of their study, it is reasonable to think that other populations (e.g., elderly, chronically ill, LGBTQ+) might also find that most support sites don't understand their specific context.

Although not yet verified by empirical studies, the impact of social comparison may be associated with suicidal behavior, especially among vulnerable youth. Many images and content on popular social networks are carefully curated and often edited to present an ideal image. Posts that show exciting adventures and achievements may induce negative social comparisons, contributing to depression, eating disorders, and other symptoms that are associated with suicidal behaviors.

Texting has become a ubiquitous communication method and can be especially helpful to persons who prefer to communicate that way. However, there is the potential to use if for harmful purposes. In 2020, a young woman was convicted of involuntary manslaughter for texting her boyfriend messages prodding him to commit suicide. She spent almost a year in jail (Fieldstadt, 2020). A recent innovation for people in crisis is the required accessibility of a national hotline (988), available by phone or text 24/7 (Conforti, 2022) to communicate with a trained interventionist. In August 2022, 361,140 communications were received at 988; 88% were answered by a counselor while 12% were disconnected before the counselor answered the call (Howard, 2022). This is in addition to the Crisis Text Line (text HOME to 741741), which has fielded 5,565,224 conversations since August 2013. One counselor I know prints these numbers (and a local crisis center number) on the back of her business card and points that out to clients or students when she first meets them.

Today's mental health professionals need to be aware of new developments online that might influence a suicidal individual, hopefully to decide to live and seek help for troubling issues or events. They also need to be conversant with sites that are unhelpful or dangerous to be able to recognize when using digital media is not in clients' best interests.

Theoretical Perspectives

Researchers and practitioners have long sought to develop a theory that would help understand the complex factors that are involved in suicidal behaviors (Bauman, 2008). Hopefully, a theory would provide some direction to developers of prevention and intervention efforts. A theory offers a lens through which a clinician can be alert to potential indicators of suicidality and use those to assess lethality and develop a treatment plan. Several theories have been proposed, and we describe the most-cited ones here. The suicide trajectory model proposed by Stillion et al. (1989, in Stillion & McDowell, 1996) is based on the premise that a combination of biological, cognitive, psychological, and environmental risk factors interact to bring the individual to consider suicide (suicidal ideation). This model applies across the life span and may be useful to keep in mind as a framework for understanding suicidal clients. Suicidal ideation begins when the combined pressure from the four risk factors overtaxes the individual's coping skills. Once suicidal ideation has occurred, if a triggering event ("last straw") is added to the mix, the individual engages in suicidal behavior. From this perspective, *biological factors* include male gender and a genetic predisposition to depression. *Cognitive factors* include rigid, inflexible thinking patterns, and the presence of certain cognitive distortions. Depression, hopelessness and helplessness, low self-esteem, and inadequate coping skills are *psychological factors*, and loss, negative family experiences and/or life events, and availability of lethal means are *environmental factors*. Stillion and McDowell discuss how this model applies to individuals at various life stages, including children and adolescents. In children, impulsivity (considered a biological factor) is more prominent than at other life stages. In the psychological domain, a sense of inferiority and the *expendable child syndrome* (belief that they are unworthy and that their death would not be a loss to anyone) are risk factors particular to this age group. Cognitive risk factors at this age include immature understanding of death and the concreteness that is characteristic of children's thinking at this age, while environmental factors focus on the home environment. In adolescents, the biological factor includes puberty, the psychological factor focuses on identity development, and the cognitive factor includes the disillusionment that may come from the newly emerged ability to think hypothetically (about such things as an idealized world). In the environmental factor, conflicts in the family are risk

| Long-term pre-disposing risk factors (genetics & personality traits) | + | Short-term risk factors (including environmental stressors & psychiatric dx) | − | Protective factors (hope, social support, access to mental health care) | + | Precipitating factors (e.g., legal problems unwanted pregnancy, loss) | = | Current risk of suicide |

FIGURE 7.1 A model for determining risk of suicide

factors as is abuse. A model that attempts to describe the vulnerability to suicide is useful, particularly when viewed as a formula (Figure 7.1). Thinking of suicide in this way reminds us that suicide has multiple causes, and the counselor's role once the immediate crisis has passed and the client's safety is assured is to assist the client in addressing all of the factors involved (Matthews & Paxton, 2001).

Joiner's (2005) interpersonal theory of suicide (IPTS) was innovative in that it attempted to explain why some persons who have suicidal thoughts do not proceed to more serious suicidal behaviors (attempts or completed suicides) while others do act on those thoughts. Joiner proposed that two beliefs or perceptions are fundamental to suicidal ideation. When thwarted belongingness (feelings of alienation or isolation), perceived burdensomeness (belief that their existence is a burden to others), and hopelessness (belief that things will never improve) are all present, suicidal ideation is more likely. IPTS suggests that in order for ideation to result in lethal attempts/completions, an additional factor must also be present: acquired capability. Since humans are innately fearful of pain and death, and seek to avoid it, those obstacles to suicide must be overcome in order for the person to move from ideation to more serious behaviors. Acquired capacity (not fearful of death and high tolerance for pain) is necessary; ITPS considers childhood trauma and previous attempts to be factors in acquired capacity. Ma et al.,(2016) noted that a systematic review of the research testing this theory did not find evidence that the presence of the three conditions (thwarted belonging, perceived burdensomeness, and acquired capacity) were predictors of ideation or attempts.

The integrated motivational-volitional model (IVM; O'Connor & Nock, 2014) contends that the path to suicidal behavior has two phases: motivational and volitional phases. The former phase includes various factors that are believed to contribute to the development of suicidal ideation or intent, whereas the latter phase focuses on factors that influence the move from ideation to attempt. Although IVM proponents acknowledge that absence of belongingness and feelings of being a burden are key concepts in ITPS, this theory proposes that feelings of defeat and entrapment are central concepts (O'Connor & Nock, 2014). IVM posits that when feelings of defeat and entrapment are present, "motivational moderators" (p. 75) are the factors that increase the likelihood of a serious attempt. We will not list all the potential factors here, but we note that those factors are classified into four groups: personality and individual differences (many which are biologically based), cognitive factors, social factors, and negative life events. IVM adherents do not discount the value of hopelessness as a potential predictor of suicidality; they believe that the broad range of factors considered in their theory is more important.

Klonsky and May (2015) praised Joiner's theory but also recognized its limitations. They used it as a springboard for their expanded model they call the "ideation to action" framework (p. 115). According to this theory (also called the three-step theory, or 3ST; Dhingra et al., 2019) suicidal ideation begins when an individual experiences pain (physical or psychological/emotional). Since humans are conditioned to avoid pain, when they do experience painful feelings, they act to avoid them; one way to do that is to stop living. The corollary of that proposition is sometimes pain is viewed as punishment for living, leading to thoughts of suicide. If a person experiencing pain also becomes hopeless, believing that the pain will never stop, this condition (pain plus hopelessness) is fertile ground for suicidal ideation to appear. However, when connectedness is also present, it mitigates suicidal thoughts when pain and hopelessness are present. Klonsky and May defined connectedness as an attachment to something outside the self, but not only to people. One may feel connected to their work or to other purposeful or meaningful activity that serves as an impetus to stay alive.

The final requisite condition for moving from ideation to more serious suicidal behavior is the capacity to take such an action. Although Joiner (2005) also proposed that a capacity to make an attempt is necessary, Klonsky and May (2015) developed a more specific explication of the mechanisms by which that capacity can develop: dispositional (e.g., genetic attributes), acquired (adaptation to pain and death that result from repeated experiences with deadly situations), and practical (knowledge and access to deadly methods). To summarize, the "ideation-to-action" framework posits that suicidal ideation will lead to suicidal behavior when both pain and hopelessness are present, connectedness is absent, and the individual has the capacity due to knowledge and access to lethal methods (firearms, medication, rope, etc.).

Dhingra et al. (2019) point out that empirical evidence supporting these theories is scant, due partly to the low base rate of suicidality. Nevertheless, for counselors, having a theoretical framework is helpful in conceptualizing a case and creating a treatment plan.

Assessment

When a mental health professional suspects or believes that a client is considering suicide, an immediate assessment of risk is in order. Unlike other types of assessment, in which care is taken to include a variety of measures and sources of information to assist in decision-making about an individual, suicide assessment must be done immediately and accurately. The goal of a suicide assessment is to determine the client's level of current risk in order to take appropriate action. This aspect of suicide assessment engenders understandable anxiety in counselors, both experienced and neophyte, because the consequences of making an error are so serious.

We describe in detail several widely used assessment approaches. Some readers may already be familiar with these, but in the event they are not, we want to be sure the reader has some basic tools available. There are both formal and informal assessment tools. Informal tools do not have norms or guidelines for interpretation, nor are there psychometric data on their reliability and validity (Ghasemi et al., 2015; Runeson et al., 2017). Counselors should not rely on these tools to provide a definitive determination of suicide risk, but they are helpful in guiding the kind of information the clinician will want to obtain.

The National Institute of Mental Health (2021) provides a useful four-item tool to screen for suicide risk that includes recommendations based on the responses. This tool can be used with anyone age 8 and older. The American Academy of Pediatrics (n.d.) has similar guide.

There are two widely used informal assessment tools that can be quite useful in determining the level of risk for suicide, although we have been unable to find the original source of these methods, nor is there any evidence of accuracy. Each uses an acronym to help the clinician remember to inquire about all pertinent issues. The SLAP method in Box 7.1 is used when the clinician learns of a client's suicidal ideation.

One potent risk factor for suicide is a previous attempt. When the clinician learns that there has been such an attempt, the DIRT method, shown in Box 7.2, is a useful tool to assess the seriousness of that attempt.

Another scale that utilizes an acronym as a mnemonic device for clinicians is the SAD PERSONS scale (Patterson et al., 1983). This scale has also been adapted for use with children and adolescents

BOX 7.1 **The SLAP Method of Suicide Assessment**

S = How *specific* is the plan? Has the client thought about details? Does the client have a time frame? Has the client made special arrangements to make sure the plan works? A client whose plan is more specific is at higher risk. For example, a client who says, "I'm going to take some pills" is a lower risk than one who says, "I'm going to pick up a refill on my prescription for Valium and take them all with a stiff Bloody Mary."

L = How *lethal* is the plan? Firearms are the most lethal, along with jumping from high places or jumping in front of moving cars. Hanging, overdose, and cutting can also be lethal but can more easily be reversed if the person has second thoughts and are also more easily interrupted by others. The more lethal the plan, the higher the risk.

A = How *available* is the method? If the client intends to shoot themself in the head, do they have a gun, or do they plan to go to a store and buy one? Does the client who intends to overdose on barbiturates already have them, or will they have to make an appointment and request a prescription? Does the client who intends to use a knife have a knife selected? The more available the means, the higher the risk.

P = Are others in close *proximity*? Are there significant others who could interrupt or interfere with the plan? Are there others whose help can be enlisted (e.g., to remove firearms from the home, flush medication, remain with the client, etc.)? The greater the distance and isolation of the client, the higher the risk.

BOX 7.2 **The DIRT Method of Assessing the Severity of an Attempt**

D = How *dangerous* was the attempt, or how lethal was the method used?

I = What was the client's *impression* of the lethality? In this case, the clinician wants to know how lethal the client believed the method to be. For example, taking 10 Tylenol may not be highly lethal from a medical perspective, but if the client *believed* they would die, that is more important in assessing the seriousness of the attempt.

R = What was the probability of *rescue*? Did the client take pills when others were at home? Did the client expect a friend to arrive? Did client announce their plan to others? Did they choose a public place (e.g., a school restroom) where they was likely to be observed and stopped?

T = What was the *time* frame of the most recent suicide attempt? The more recent the attempt, the higher the current risk.

(Juhnke, 1996). This scale is more formal, in that there are guidelines for interpretation. This method is easily learned and used and is a systematic approach that the counselor can use in a crisis situation. The scale and interpretation are described in Box 7.3. Note that reliability and validity of suicide assessments are problematic for ethical reasons. No researcher would choose not to intervene in the case of a client assessed at high risk for suicide in order to test the validity of the scale.

Juhnke (1996) noted that some modifications would make this scale more appropriate for use with children; his modified version is the Adapted Sad Persons Scale (A-SPS). Goldston (2003) noted that there is no research providing data on reliability of validity of this measure, but there are few measures that do have such data. Juhnke's modifications include revised scoring for several letters in the acronym: age (adolescents 15 or older are scored, while younger children are not scored on this item). Social support is scored 1 if the child has no close friends. N signifies negligent parenting, family stressors, or suicidal modeling by parents or siblings, and the final S = school problems.

BOX 7.3 **The SAD PERSONS Scale for Assessing Suicide Risk**

Scoring: 1 if present, 0 if not present

S = Sex	Score if the person is male.
A = Age	Score if the person is under 25 or over 45.
D = Depression	Score if there are signs of depression.
P = Previous attempt	Score if there was a previous suicide attempt.
E = Ethanol (alcohol)	Score if there are symptoms of substance abuse.
R = Rational thinking loss	Score if person is psychotic, disoriented, has bizarre thoughts, is confused, irrational, and so forth.
S = Social support loss	Score if person has lost (via death, break-up) a close relationship recently.
O = Organized plan	Score if the person has a fairly detailed plan that is lethal.
N = No lover, mate, spouse	Score if person does not have a committed relationship.
S = Sickness	Does person have a chronic, serious, or terminal illness?
Intervention	
0–2	Send home with follow-up appointment.
3–4	Close follow-up, consider hospitalization.
5–6	Strongly consider hospitalizing, depending on follow-up arrangements.
7–10	Hospitalize or commit involuntarily.

Box 7.3a: Adapted from William M. Patterson, et al., "Evaluation of Suicidal Patients: The SAD PERSONS Scale," *Psychosomatics*, vol. 24, no. 4. Copyright © 1983 by Elsevier B.V.

Box 7.3b: Adapted from Gerald A. Juhnke, "The Adapted-SAD PERSONS: A Suicide Assessment Scale Designed for Use with Children," *Elementary School Guidance & Counseling*, vol. 30, no. 4. Copyright © 1996 by American Counseling Association.

Juhnke recommends scoring each factor on a scale from 1 to 10 (except sex) and offers recommendations based on scores:

0–29	Encourage counseling services.
30–49	Strongly recommend counseling and follow-up services, contact parent or guardian, get "no-suicide" contract.
50–69	Have formal evaluation for hospitalization unless follow-up arrangements and counseling plan are highly reliable.
70 +	Arrange for immediate hospitalization.

An unpublished instrument for the assessment of suicidality in high-risk prisoners (Giles, 1997) contains one item that we have not seen elsewhere, and that we now ask routinely as part of a suicide assessment: "What is one thing that could happen to you that would push you to actually try to hurt yourself?" The response gives important information to the clinician. The person may deny current suicidal plans or intent but reveal that "if my boyfriend left me," or "if something happened to my mother," the equation could change very quickly. Such a response alerts the counselor that the person has not ruled out suicide as an option and provides clues to the type of stressors the person does not feel capable of managing. Sometimes individuals say something such as "Nothing, I would never consider taking my life no matter how bad things get," which is important to know in planning treatment. Another useful question is "What would stop you from killing yourself?" which may indirectly identify the precipitant or stressor and/or give an indication of protective factors the client may have.

The mnemonics described, although helpful and widely used, do not have any empirical support. The SIMPLE STEPS model was developed because a number of the others approaches focus

BOX 7.4 **The SIMPLE STEPS Mnemonic for Assessment of Suicidality**

S = Suicidal: The person states they intend to kill themself.

I = Ideation: Pervasiveness of suicidal thought. Response to question "On a scale of 1–10 how likely are you likely to kill yourself in the next 3 days?"

M = Method. How the person intends to kill themself, including how lethal and available is the method and how complete the plan is

P = Perturbation: How distressed and how much emotional pain

L = Loss: Loss of people or objects of personal significance

E = Earlier attempts: Including details of past attempts

S = Substance use: Including alcohol and drugs, and if taking medication, how compliant

T = (Lack of) Troubleshooting skills: Ability to problem-solve and consider alternatives to suicide

E = Emotions/diagnosis: Including emotional states associated with suicide, including mood disorders and personality disorders

P = (Lack of) Protective factors: Personal strengths, supportive people, community resources

S = Stressors and life events: Current and past stressors

on risk factors but do not take protective factors into account. An interesting study of the model tested the utility of the model (see Box 7.4) using the contact sheets from a sample of 13,423 callers to a suicide hotline over a 6-year period (McGlothlin et al., 2016) and examined the relationship between SIMPLE STEPS scores and separate assessment of lethality. The regression analysis demonstrated that all the variables in the model were associated with the degree of lethality of the caller and that the strongest relationship was with troubleshooting, emotion and diagnosis, verbalizing suicidality, and protective factors.

An assessment designed for college students with good psychometric properties and items that relate to the consequences of alcohol abuse in that setting is the Young Adult Alcohol Problems Screening Test (YAAPST; Hurlbut & Sher, 1992; personal communication, July 17, 2003). Since the initial article, the authors have added several useful items, which can be obtained by contacting Dr. Sher.

There is an eventuality in suicide assessment that calls for advance planning. If you have a suicidal person in your office, and you believe they need either hospitalization or close monitoring by family members along with counseling, how do you make arrangements and consult with colleagues without leaving the person alone? One should absolutely not leave a client alone, even for a few minutes, if there is any chance they will panic and leave. I (SB) once was called to the emergency room to assist the family of a client because the family was too distressed to provide needed information. The doctor left the bedside to consult with me, and while he was doing so, the student (who had taken medication with alcohol and was barely conscious) managed to disappear! Security was called and there was high drama until she was located. At that moment, she wanted to die and did not want anyone to stop her. (She is now a professional adult with her own family.)

So how do you remain with the client, contact parents/hospital/police, and inform your supervisor or consult with colleagues? One way that works well (in the absence of "panic buttons") is to prearrange a code with someone in the office. The code might be a fictitious doctor's name. Then, you can tell the client that you will need to cancel an appointment with your doctor in order to continue your meeting. When you call your own office, you say, "Would you please cancel my appointment with Dr. Tarasoff? I'm with a client and can't leave right now." This is a signal to the person on the phone that you have a difficult situation and need your supervisor or colleague to knock on the door. When she does so, you can tell the client you'd like to invite this person in because you trust them, and you would like their help. You can then discuss your concerns in brief and ask this person to make the phone calls, and so forth.

Readers who are interested in technical information and psychometric properties of suicide assessment measures for children and adolescents will find a book (*Measuring Suicidal Behavior and Risk in Children and Adolescents*) published by the APA (Goldston, 2003) to be an excellent reference. Although not a recent publication, for readers seeking an in-depth coverage of the topic, *Harvard Medical School Guide to Suicide Assessment* is still a valuable source (Jacobs, 1999).

Treatment Options and Considerations

While the first consideration is always to provide for the client's safety and prevent suicide, once that goal has been accomplished, it is important to address underlying issues so that the risk of future attempts is reduced. There are three essential components of suicide intervention: assessment of risk, removal of means of suicide (e.g. guns, medications), and diagnosis and treatment of the psychiatric disorder. Risk assessment was discussed in the previous section. One strategy, often used in conjunction with the assessment process, is the "no-suicide contract." This technique is controversial, and we focus on it in later.

The need to remove means of suicide (firearms, medications, etc.) is obvious: Recent data show that the most common method of suicide in young people is hanging, which presents a challenging problem because of the many common objects that can be used (e.g., belts, shoelaces, scarves, etc.). The counselor must evaluate the level of cooperation and reliability of family members or whoever will provide safety monitoring in the crisis period. For example, are parents or family members willing to remove all firearms and knives from the home? Are they willing to remove all medications (prescription or not) to a locked cabinet and dispense only the necessary dosage to the client? If there is resistance, or claims of inconvenience, the individual might need to be hospitalized for safety reasons. Are family members willing and able to take time from work during the acute period to ensure the client is not left alone? How seriously do family members consider the attempt or threat? If the counselor has misgivings about the family's ability to provide close monitoring and follow-up services, hospitalization is a reasonable consideration.

There are clients who threaten suicide unless certain conditions are met ("If you don't …, I'll kill myself). Such demands can be seen as manipulative behavior and may engender negative reactions on the part of clinicians and family members. Although such behavior may in fact *be* manipulative, one must realize that the individual does not believe their needs would be met unless the response is coerced. Dr. Motto (1999) recommends that even if the client is being manipulative, if the demand is realistic and feasible, it can be met and later explored with the client (e.g., "How have you come to believe that others will not respond to your requests without being coerced?"). If the demand cannot be met, it is suggested that the reasons for refusal be made clear, and in response to the threat the message should convey that, ultimately, suicide is an individual's decision and that if the person does choose to end their life, you will be sad, but not guilty. Motto suggests that by making clear that others will not feel guilty, one possible motivation for suicide (to punish others) may be removed.

Some mental health professionals use no-suicide contracts with clients as a strategy to manage risk. Such contracts are typically used in acute crisis situations, when there is elevated risk for suicide and usually include two elements: a commitment from the client not to act on suicidal impulses and an agreement from the client to contact the clinician if the urges to suicide become difficult to resist. Although this technique is widely used, there is little research on its efficacy. A critical element in deciding whether a no-suicide contract is appropriate to a particular case is the strength of the therapeutic relationship. If the client and counselor have a positive and strong bond, the client is more likely to take the contract seriously. If the client has no investment in the relationship, they may say or sign anything in order to avoid more intrusive interventions and may have no commitment to adhere to the agreement. I (SB) remember a student who came to school one day with hospital bandages on his wrists. When I inquired, he told me he had made a serious suicide attempt and that he had been hospitalized the night before. I expressed surprise that he had been released, considering the severity of the injuries, and he told me he had signed a no-suicide contract in order to be released. When I asked if he intended to uphold the agreement, he said something like, "What can they do to me if I violate the agreement and kill myself? Sue me?" This comment made a strong impression on me, and I am very cautious about relying on such contracts to ensure client safety.

A major disadvantage of this contract is that the counselor may consider this the extent of risk management with suicidal clients. At best, a contract can be one component of a much larger safety plan involving significant others and removal of means. Further, such a contract may inadvertently restrict the client's expression of suicidal thoughts and impulses, fearing that such revelations will be seen as a violation of the contract that will result in hospitalization. Some clients may see the contract as an effort on the part of the clinician to cover themselves to avoid legal ramifications should the client eventually commit suicide—which they may interpret as the counselor being more concerned with self than with the client. The clinician will have to weigh all these factors in the decision to use a no-harm contract. Once the suicidal crisis has been managed, it is necessary to diagnose and treat any psychiatric disorders, and in the case of clients who are already diagnosed, to reevaluate the treatment plan.

Children

Thankfully, the rate of suicide in prepubertal children is low (~8%; Frangou, 2020), but it is the second leading cause of death in children 10–14 years old. Chances are good that many child suicides are not so designated; it is difficult to get a ruling of suicide in a child's death, with investigators more likely to assume accidental causes (e.g., gunshot or poisoning) due to lack of evidence of intent (Davis, 2004).

The lower rates for this age group can be explained by a number of factors, the most important of which is their limited cognitive ability for planning and carrying out a suicide. In addition, thinking at this age is primarily concrete, and thinking about the future (which, when bleak, may influence suicidal thinking in adolescents and adults) is not well developed, which serves as a protection from hopelessness. Young children have more limited information and access about lethal methods of suicide and are less likely to have problems with depression or substance abuse, which elevate risk in older individuals (Goldman & Beardslee, 1999).

Assessment of suicidal thoughts is difficult with young children. First, they are likely to be uncomfortable talking to a "stranger" about personal material. Second, their verbal abilities and vocabulary may not be sufficient to express these ideas. Skillful use of play and art therapy approaches may allow a clinician to detect suicidal thinking in a child. Children who are questioned about suicidal ideation or attempts may also deny such ideas for fear they will get in trouble if they tell the truth.

When children are diagnosed with a depressive disorder, medication is one of the options. With increasing publicity about increases in suicidal behavior in children taking antidepressants, physicians are more cautious about prescribing these drugs. The use of medication to treat depression in children and adolescents has received a great deal of publicity, much of it misleading. According to the American Academy for Child and Adolescent Psychiatry and the American Psychiatric

Association (2018), "Antidepressant medications can be effective in relieving depressive symptoms in children and adolescents. Approximately 55–65% of children and adolescents will respond to initial treatment with antidepressant medication" (p. 9). The organization acknowledges that more research is needed to increase knowledge about the use of antidepressants with youth. In an FDA review, 2,000 children treated with SSRIs were studied, and no completed suicides occurred. However, the rate for other suicidal behaviors (including attempts) was 4% for those treated with SSRIs and 2% for those who received placebos. They caution that any child or adolescent taking antidepressant medication should be closely monitored. In clinical trials, one in 10 children experienced adverse side effects.

In their review of the research on the use of medication for depression in children and adolescents, Emslie and Mayes (2001) noted that research has examined effectiveness at different points in treatment. For acute treatment, tricyclic antidepressants were not found to have a clinically significant effect over a placebo. However, all but one study found a substantial effect for fluoxetine (Prozac) at this stage of treatment, with more subjects recovered using fluoxetine than a placebo and no difference in response between children and adolescents. Since children and adolescents have a high rate of recurrence of depression after recovery, it is important to examine the effects of continuation of medication beyond the point at which symptoms are no longer present. Only one study of continuing medication was reported, and findings demonstrated effectiveness of fluoxetine over placebo for preventing relapse and increasing the amount of time before relapse occurred. There was no information available on the effect of long-term treatment with medication in children and adolescents.

Several SRRIs now have FDA approval for use with children as young as 6 years old, but physicians can prescribe other medications in what is known as "off-label use" (SAMHSA, 2020). SSRIs are used with children and adolescents because they have fewer side effects than older tricyclic antidepressants but have a small risk for suicidality in that age group (Edinoff et al., 2021). While Prozac contains a warning for use with children, another SSRI (paroxetine, i.e., Paxil) was specifically advised against by the FDA. Research is likely to increase in the future, as the FDA Modernization Act of 1977 required manufacturers of certain medications approved for adults but used with children to conduct studies on children (Emslie & Mayes, 2001). Even when medication is utilized, it should not be the only treatment. SAMHSA (2020) has an excellent review of suicidal behaviors and treatment options for children and adolescents.

Adolescents

Since about 30% of adolescent suicides are repeat attempts, follow-up after the initial assessment and treatment intervention with a suicidal teen is particularly critical. In the large majority of cases, those who eventually commit suicide will die by the same method used in their first attempt, and the first few months following the initial attempt are the time of greatest risk (Spirito et al., 2000). Among suicide attempters, substance-abusing teenage males have the highest risk for eventually completing suicide. The best predictor of additional attempts is the lethality of the initial attempt; the presence of a mood disorder and/or ongoing conduct and behavior problems are additional predictors. Adolescent suicide attempters are also at greater risk for death by other means, including vehicle accidents, homicide, and overdose.

A major concern with adolescents is that there is often poor compliance with outpatient treatment. Researchers have been unable to identify factors that contribute to better compliance, but there is some evidence that the type of treatment may be important. In one study, the best rates of compliance were with medication, followed by individual therapy, with poorest compliance for family therapy. Given the importance of follow-up with this age group of suicide attempters, there are some strategies that may improve involvement in treatment following a suicide attempt. First, when an assessment or hospitalization is completed, a specific appointment for counseling should be set. At this time, the adolescent and their parents or guardians should be given information about therapy, and the importance of restricting access to lethal means should be emphasized. They need to understand that not only firearms, but medication, toxic household chemicals, cars, belts, and shoelaces, can all be used for suicide, and they must be highly vigilant during and following the acute crisis. Phone numbers to use in emergencies should be provided (with 24-hour coverage), and some potential stressors should be identified and possible coping strategies discussed. For example, if the adolescent has been hospitalized and has missed school, they should anticipate that friends and classmates may ask where they have been. An answer that is acceptable to the client should be planned and rehearsed. Any barriers to involvement in treatment should be discussed (e.g., transportation) and strategies devised to ensure participation. Phone reminders the day before appointments may be helpful. Finally, suggesting brief therapy (e.g., six sessions) may counter the client's or family's belief that treatment is endless. See the section on Digital Media and Suicide in this chapter. Online resources are now widely available and may be more appealing (or less onerous) to adolescents. They should be informed of suicide hotline numbers for 24/7 assistance.

What kind of treatment is effective? While empirical studies are few, there are clinical suggestions that are useful to consider in treatment planning. First, the motivation for the suicide needs to be explored so that alternative strategies and more effective ways of coping with the underlying issues can be generated. For example, if an adolescent attempted suicide because of perceived alienation from friends and family, they can be helped to develop more effective social and communication skills to increase social support. They also will need to accept the reality that not everyone will like them. Other cognitive techniques may help adolescents more realistically assess the nature and severity of their problems (to counter the tendency to catastrophize) and to generate alternatives for resolving problems. For many adolescents, learning to manage intense emotion (e.g., anger) will be useful, as will modifying negative self-talk and learning relaxation methods. Since depression is so strongly linked to suicide, it is useful to know something about treatment approaches found to be effective with this disorder.

Interpersonal Therapy for Adolescents

In addition to medication, a form of therapy has been found to be effective for depressed adolescents—interpersonal psychotherapy (IPT-A). IPT is a brief treatment with the dual goals of identifying and treating depression first and then identifying and treating the interpersonal problem areas related to the depression. The problem areas are grief, personal role disputes, role transitions, and interpersonal deficits. For adolescents, an additional problem area may be single-parent families. The focus is on the present rather than the past (Harrington et al., 1998). Curry (2001) utilized criteria for considering treatment to be efficacious; it proved superior to placebo or other treatment in a randomized, controlled trial, and the research design included a treatment manual, a defined population, reliable and valid outcome measures, and appropriate statistical analysis. When the criteria have been met in more than one research setting, the treatment is considered "well established." ITP-A is considered "possibly efficacious" because only one research group meets the criteria. Mufson et al. (1999) found that following a 12-week IPT-A treatment program, the treatment group reported fewer depressive symptoms than the control group, were rated as significantly less depressed by clinicians, reported significantly better functioning with friends and dating relationships than the controls, and showed better problem-solving skills than controls.

One other study compared IPT with CBT and wait-list controls with Puerto Rican adolescents and reported a significant impact on self-reported symptoms of depression as well as improved self-esteem and social adaptation with IPT (Rossello & Bernal, 1999). Unlike the Mufson et al. (1999)

study, these researchers did not measure diagnostic status after treatment, nor did they utilize the Mufson et al. modification of the problem areas. Hollon et al., (2002) noted that previous studies found both IPT and CBT more effective at reducing depressive symptoms than the control condition, with IPT having a greater effect. The additional benefit of improved self-esteem and social adaptation was found in the IPT group only.

CBT

CBT is based on the notion that depression is associated with faulty cognitions or maladaptive coping behaviors (Curry, 2001). CBT treatment differs in emphasis according to development, with children receiving more behavioral interventions and the focus in adolescents on cognitive strategies (Hollon et al., 2002). All of the six controlled studies of CBT with children prior to 2001 were conducted in the school setting and examined self-reported depressive symptoms. Nine controlled studies investigated the effectiveness of CBT with adolescents, most using an experimental design with subjects randomly assigned to groups. Curry concluded that in children with severe depression, CBT has demonstrated efficacy in symptom reduction. Other researchers found CBT more effective than systematic behavioral family therapy or nondirective supportive therapy (Hollon et al., 2002).

Combined Treatment

What does research suggest is the best treatment for depression in children and adolescents? Clinical trials with 439 adolescents aged 12–17 at 13 sites around the country found that fluoxetine (Prozac) in combination with CBT was superior to either the medication or therapy alone and a placebo alone (March et al, 2004). A positive response to treatment for those participants who received the combined fluoxetine and therapy was 71%; for fluoxetine alone, 61%; for therapy alone, 43%; and for the placebo group, 35%. Regarding suicidal behaviors, the rates in the fluoxetine alone and the placebo alone were similar. However, there were more suicidal behaviors in the therapy plus medicine group, which the research team found confusing. They speculated this may relate to the small number of cases.

In a critique of recent research on the controversy regarding the use of medication with children and adolescents with depression, Dubicka and Goodyer (2005) concluded that basic psychoeducation should be the first effort at treating the problem. If the depression does not remit, and is mild, CBT should be provided; if it is severe, fluoxetine and CBT should be used together. They add that if there is not a response in a reasonable time to the combined treatment, alternative SSRIs should be considered. Interestingly, these authors comment that adverse effects of medication must be documented, but there is no requirement to record information about adverse effects of therapy, which they believe could also occur.

While family problems may underlie the suicide attempt, the clinician might want to defer family therapy until the adolescent is more stable and has acquired some skills to communicate effectively. In fact, it may work best to consider the adolescent the client and to invite family members as "consultants" at some point in the treatment program.

College Students

The comparatively low rate of suicide among college students does not mean counselors working with this population should be any less vigilant about suicide than those working with other groups. Suicide is still the third leading cause of death in this group (Welding, 2023). A survey of a nationally representative sample of college students found that 10% had seriously considered suicide in the previous year. It is likely that college students who engage in suicidal behavior have not met developmental challenges earlier in life, so are not equipped with necessary coping skills (Schwartz & Whittaker, 1990). Surveys of college students who attempted suicide reveal that there are particular issues that are mentioned often as the precipitant: grade problems, loneliness, money problems, and problems in romantic relationships. In addition to these precipitants, other risk factors included legal problems, parent problems, and hopelessness and helplessness. Substance use elevated the risk for suicidal behavior, and joining a sorority or fraternity served as a protective factor.

A major concern with this group is that they tend not to seek counseling services, and thus problems that could lead to suicidal behaviors continue unresolved when treatment could be a great benefit. Outreach to college students is an important component of counseling this population. Unfortunately, as Moezzi (2021) eloquently argues, mandatory suicide prevention is far from universal in American institutions of higher education. In one study, only 12% of students reported receiving any suicide awareness at their institution. There are some aspects of college life that may push a vulnerable student to suicide: leaving home (and social support networks), facing new academic and social pressures, and sleep deprivation. In addition, several serious psychiatric disorders, such as schizophrenia and bipolar disorder, begin to appear in this age group, adding to the risk factors. The prevalence of substance abuse on many campuses is an additional complication for many students.

Some colleges have begun to utilize screening for depression and suicide and other mental health problems, in some cases using online surveys that students can take in their own homes. It has been suggested that a freshman survey on an intake form would help identify students at risk, and a follow-up could inform them of available services. It has been reported that college students who commit suicide are 150 times more likely to have a psychotic disorder than their peers. Screening to identify such students would allow for early intervention and treatment. Because of the relationship between substance abuse and suicide, substance abuse screening can be an important element of a suicide prevention plan for college students.

Several groups of students are an elevated risk. Foreign students, who may be struggling with separation from family and adjusting to a new culture in addition to any risk factors they already have, are particularly vulnerable. Other students who come from communities that are markedly different from the university setting are also at risk, as social isolation and a new setting add to the pressure of increased academic expectations compared to their high school experiences. Programs on campus that help introduce freshman to campus would benefit from the inclusion of campus counselors and community resources on the program.

Since many students, particularly freshman, live in residence halls, resident assistants and hall directors need to be well trained in identifying students at risk for suicide and in intervention and referral techniques. In one university, counselors from the campus counseling center are each assigned to a residence hall and form relationships through workshops and other programming for both students and staff. With such an arrangement, if students need to be referred for services, the counselor will be more familiar and less threatening to students than if they had never met.

Adults

As with other age groups, the presence of risk factors is the backdrop for suicidal behavior. Adulthood is characterized by starting families and establishing careers. Young adulthood is a time of peak mental and physical performance, and for many this is the time in which their roles as partners, parents, and workers are defined. In Erikson's (1982) terms, early adulthood is focused on achieving intimacy, and in those who do not accomplish this task successfully, the outcome may be isolation. In middle adulthood, persons are concerned with generativity (or leaving something behind for future generations); when this does not occur, the individual experiences stagnation. In this period of life, most adults experience increased responsibilities as well as opportunities to make significant contributions to work and family. Many adults begin to reflect and evaluate the course of their lives (the "midlife crisis"). For some midlife adults, changes such as launching the last child may precipitate feelings of loss along with a heightened awareness of their own mortality. These tasks of adulthood may generate the precipitating events for suicide in vulnerable persons.

Working with suicidal adults requires the same skills for working with suicidal individuals at other stages of life. Recognition of risk factors, assessment of the ability to cope with stressful life events and assessing for substance abuse and mental disorders (particularly mood disorders) provides the counselor with basic information about how vulnerable the individual might be to suicidal behaviors. With adults, it is always important to be sure clients have had recent complete physical examinations, as some psychological symptoms (e.g., depression) can be linked to physical conditions (e.g., thyroid function). Because adults will have had more life experience than younger clients, they may benefit from attention to how they have coped with stress before, with a focus on enhancing coping skills. It is important to assess the level of social support, which is a protective factor against suicide. In America today, there is much mobility, and the availability of family is often compromised as a result. Clients may need assistance in establishing new networks of support, so the counselor must be aware of community resources that clients may be encouraged to access. Researchers found that the mobility factor most closely associated with nearly lethal suicide attempts is the number of moves in the previous year (Potter et al., 2001).

Treatment for suicidal adults follows the same model as treatment at other ages. Research has found cognitive behavioral treatment and medication to be the most effective, with interpersonal therapy for depression also showing positive results. Because of the central role of family in the lives of most adults, involving family members in treatment and/or using some strategies from family therapy is generally helpful. Simon (2004) stresses the importance of acknowledging the adult's status when working with potentially suicidal individuals: Refer to them by last name and inform them immediately about issues of confidentiality and involving spouses or other family members in safety plans. Assessing the likelihood of compliance with treatment is important, as the best plans will not be effective if not followed. It is essential to inquire about substance use and abuse, as this elevates suicide risk and may require targeted treatment once the suicidal crisis is stabilized.

The Elderly

Erikson (1982) described the task of older adults as seeking integrity, a sense that one's life had purpose; the opposite pole is despair. Physically and cognitively, many older adults face loss of physical abilities, sensory acuity, and intellectual facility as aging increases sensory loss (hearing declines, vision deteriorates), more frequent and serious medical illness, and some cognitive slowing. These developmental characteristics may be a factor in the high suicide rates observed in this age group.

Given the relatively high rates of suicide in the elderly (especially elderly males), this is an important population to discuss. Older Americans who commit suicide are less likely than younger people to signal their intent or provide clues to their plans and less often use suicidal behaviors to cry for help. They are more likely to make lethal attempts and to plan carefully to avoid surviving the attempt. Additional risk factors that appear in this age group may alert counselors that suicide is a possibility. Losing a spouse increases the risk for suicide, with the greatest risk being in the 1st year following the death (Osgood & Thielman, 1990). Social isolation also increases risk, particularly if the elderly person is also depressed or has another serious mental disorder. The single most common reason for suicide given by elderly (when a reason is known) is health status, with as high as 35% of suicides in this group being associated with a physical illness (Conwell, 1997). The increasing number and seriousness of health problems creates many stressors for elderly, such as concerns about access to health care and medication, inability to manage ordinary daily tasks, and reduction in activities. If an elderly person has also made a suicide attempt earlier in life, they are 20 times more likely to commit suicide than those who had no previous attempt.

Depression may not be diagnosed in the elderly, who can be successfully treated. Mental health professionals working with an elderly clientele need to take a careful history to determine the presence of chronic risk factors and to get an accurate picture of their current status. Asking about suicide is an important part of history taking, and this should not be overlooked in this population.

Counselors can also serve as advocates for better vigilance on the part of physicians. While many elderly people may not seek mental health treatment, they are likely to see a physician. Most elderly people who commit suicide have seen a physician within 30 days of their death, and some within a week. If primary care physicians are most likely to see elderly clients, they need to be educated about the risk of suicide. There are numerous treatment options for this group, including medication, psychotherapy and counseling, electroconvulsive therapy, life review therapy, supportive group therapy, and environmental changes. It is essential that access to lethal means be prevented. One expert suggested that elderly people need to have three things in their environments: connectedness, effectance (a sense of control over one's life and the ability to make choices), and identity. Living conditions, whether at home or in an institution, need to provide for these needs, and counselors again can be advocates for these conditions. Dr. William Thomas has taken these needs into account in designing a unique nursing home. His ideas are applied in the Green House Project (Shapiro, 2005).

A final word on counseling geriatric clients: Since suicide is more prevalent in this group than any other, and because there are so many unique stressors for this age group, the effective counselor will need to involve a multidisciplinary team, including medical doctors, in order to be successful in preventing suicide in this clientele.

Survivors of Suicide

A completed suicide affects a wide range of people—friends, family, and counselors among them. Although grief and bereavement are covered in a separate chapter, there are unique aspects to this process when the deceased died by suicide. Several former clients come to mind. One young woman, age 16, had been romantically involved with a talented and popular young man for about a year, and the relationship was becoming very serious. The girl decided that they were too young to be so serious and told the young man she thought they should date others. He hung himself that evening. She was devastated, both by the loss and by the reactions of peers, many of whom were quite vocal about how she had "killed" her boyfriend. Instead of being supported in her grief, she was taunted by comments from others and eventually had to change schools in an effort to get beyond this terrible period in her life.

Another young man, age 15, shared that his mother had committed suicide when he was 9 years old. He found her body when he arrived home from school. Although he had a very loving and supportive father and grandparents, he suffered from chronic depression. He was tormented by questions: "Why did she not want to see me grow up?" "She must have known I'd be the one to find her. Didn't she care what that would do to me?" "Didn't she love me?" Every significant event in his life—positive or negative—brought those questions to the forefront. There were times when he entertained suicidal thoughts himself and needed to be closely monitored by his father (who clearly had his own struggles with his wife's death). At one point, he visited his mother's grave and left some poetry he had written to express his feelings, in the hopes that this act might relieve some of his pain. I suspect this incident will resurface at various times in this young man's life, with variations on the questions taking new meaning as he reaches milestones in his own life.

In addition to the emotional impact of the suicide, there are elements of this kind of death that add stress for family members. Death by suicide generally involves investigations by police and may result in attention from the media. Each of these procedures is difficult to cope with at a time of tragic and unexpected loss. In addition, some religious denominations have restrictions on the rites available to those who die by suicide, and planning for services may be complicated. The assistance of a family friend or pastor with managing these intrusions can lessen the burden for the family.

Survivors of a death by suicide generally struggle to make sense of the death. Questions of *why* trouble survivors, and the fact that the answer may never be known is particularly difficult. Even when there is a suicide note, the content often raises more questions than it answers, and survivors ultimately must accept that their questions will remain unanswered. An additional burden for survivors is often guilt. They may blame themselves for acts they perceive contributed to the decision to suicide ("If only I had not said such mean things to him") or feel responsible because they did not recognize the signs or intervene to prevent the suicide ("If I had come home earlier, I could have stopped her"). Emotionally, it is confusing to survivors who feel rejected or abandoned by the deceased ("I must not have been very important to her") and at the same time they experience anger ("How could you do this to me?").

Among adolescents, we have noticed that when there is a peer death (accident or suicide being the most common cause of death), there is a tendency for many students to describe themselves as "best friends" of the deceased. Whether or not this is fact, it makes sense for counselors to respond to their grief. The loss of a peer at this age makes their own mortality apparent, and youth may appear to experience exaggerated bereavement when in fact they are grieving both the loss and the loss of the illusion that they will live forever.

These emotional reactions may be experienced in a context (real or imagined) of isolation or stigmatization by others. Survivors may believe others hold them responsible or have other negative beliefs, and they may feel a lack of social support at a time when such support is very much needed. Because family relationships may be strained at such a time, individual survivors may feel they cannot talk about suicide or their feelings in the family. In fact, family members themselves are at elevated risk for suicide.

What might be helpful to survivors of suicide? Counseling may be offered and sometimes is accepted. However, in those cases in which the deceased was receiving counseling and then completed suicide, the survivors may feel anger and distrust of counselors, who were unable to prevent their loss. In these cases, groups of suicide survivors provide support from others who had a similar experience. Hospice groups in many communities offer special support groups for survivors of suicide. For others, who are reluctant to engage in any social networks, bibliotherapy may provide some helpful information. Helpful books will be listed in the Resources section at the end of the chapter.

Screening for Depression

In elementary-age children, depression is often expressed as bodily complaints. Frequent stomach aches and headaches are observed. Anxiety about school (not wanting to go to school, excessive worrying about school performance) is another way depression is exhibited in children of this age. They may be extremely fearful of being separated from parents, develop temper tantrums and behavioral problems and be irritable or agitated. Such symptoms may not raise a red flag to the uninformed observer, and such children are often treated as discipline problems. Underlying sadness and hopelessness may not be easily detected, and poor self-esteem and expression of guilt may not be associated with possible depression. The counselor may be the only person who is aware of the link between such a pattern and possible depression, and as such has an opportunity to intervene and refer the child for further evaluation.

In adolescents, sadness and hopelessness may be more obvious, and withdrawal from friends and previously enjoyed activities is another sign. Changes in eating and sleeping patterns, poor school performance, and low energy are other signals. The challenge with adolescents is that many teenagers experience these symptoms on occasion, and adults may dismiss them as "just being a teenager." In adolescents, we are more likely to find drug and alcohol abuse (which may be initiated as a kind of self-medication of unpleasant feelings) and suicidal thoughts and behavior, so identifying untreated depression is particularly important.

Children and adolescents may mask their feelings and may have difficulty verbalizing what they are experiencing. The observant counselor can pay attention to other means of expression that provide clues to the inner world of the child. Play, art, and writing are activities that may reveal clues to a depressed child. Drawings that look sad and morose, or contain damaged or morbid images and gloomy colors, may signal sadness or preoccupation with fears and death. Stories and other writings, particularly in adolescence, may reveal thoughts and feelings that are not openly talked about. Adolescents may appear angry rather than sad.

Various behaviors might also lead a counselor to wonder about possible depression. When a child suddenly develops behavior problems, or seems unusually (for that child) irritable, distractible, and easily frustrated, depression may be behind the behaviors. Disciplinary referrals are likely to increase, and the counselor should make note of this. In addition, unexpected changes in grades and school performance may be more than laziness or lack of interest; sleeping in class may also signal underlying mood problems.

Children who exhibit one or more of the symptoms described should be screened for depression. It is important to clarify what is meant by screening. Screening is *not* diagnosing. Screening is a way to learn whether symptoms are present and how severe they are. Students who score above the cutoff should be referred for a more thorough evaluation by a physician and/or psychologist. The referral to a physician is important because there are some medical conditions that will produce symptoms similar to depression, and those should be ruled out and/or treated. There are several well-researched screening tools that are available and easy to use in the school setting; these are described in Table 7.1. All are self-report measures. I encourage you to contact publishers

TABLE 7.1. Screening Instruments for Depression

Instrument	Appropriate For	Written at Reading Level	Number of Items	Comments
Children's Depression Inventory (CDI)	Ages 7–17	First grade	27 items in the regular form Also available in a 10-item brief form of the most important items	This screening inventory has three statements after each stem, and the child marks the one that is most like them. Quick to administer and score. Available in Spanish.
Reynolds Child Depression Scale (RCDS)	Ages 8–12	Second grade	30 items	Easy to administer and score. Available in Spanish.
Reynolds Adolescent Depression Scale (RADS)	Ages 13–18	Third grade	30 items	Easy to administer and score.
The Beck Depression Inventory for Youth (BDI-Y)	Ages 7–14	Second grade	20 items	Students respond to statements by indicating how frequently a statement is true for them.
Center for Epidemiological Studies—Depression Scale for Children (CES-DC)	Ages 12–18	Sixth grade	20 items	Scoring is straightforward.

or go to publishers' websites for further information. Counselors may wish to compare costs, ease of scoring, and psychometric properties in deciding which inventory would be most useful in their setting.

Issues of Diversity

Members of diverse groups experience additional risk factors beyond those typically encountered by White Americans. Counselors must be sensitive to these differences and work to provide treatment that is responsive to the needs of all clients. Ideally, we would have a more diverse population of counselors; in locales where that is not the case, counselors would do well to create collaborative relationships with diverse professionals who work in other settings whom they can call on when needed.

Race and Ethnicity

Because suicidal behaviors vary across race, ethnicity, and other demographic characteristics, some knowledge of the most apparent differences in necessary. However, it is critical that mental health professionals treat these characteristics as generalizations and avoid assuming that they apply to every member of that group. This section will present some patterns that might be relevant to clients from those groups. We stress the importance of avoiding stereotypes in working with vulnerable clients.

African Americans

In their study of ethnic differences in patterns of suicide over the life span, Garlow et al. (2005) examined records of suicides in Fulton County, Georgia, from 1994 through 2002 and found that rates and patterns mirrored those reported in national samples. As in other studies, African Americans commit suicide at lower rates than Whites, and African American females had the lowest rates of all groups. Among victims younger than 20, significantly fewer African Americans tested positive for substances at time of death than did Whites in the same age group. In attempting to account for their findings, these researchers noted that although the rates of psychiatric disorders (including depression) have been found to be similar in both groups, the availability of mental health treatment for African Americans is limited and of lesser quality. Perhaps as a consequence, young African Americans may be reluctant to seek treatment. Counselors must conduct outreach with this population and provide culturally sensitive and culturally compatible treatment for depression and other disorders that are linked to suicidal behaviors.

On the other hand, African American culture may mitigate against suicide. The protective factors of family support and religiosity are suggested to explain the overall low rates of suicide in this group, and the widely held attitude among African Americans that suicide is not acceptable also may serve as a protection. Counselors need to access community support, and in an intervention it would be advisable to consider including extended family members as well as clergy. Based on this study, the best prevention strategies would be those that serve to strengthen the protective factors (and those that include screening for depression.)

Joe et al. (2006) demonstrated that Blacks are not a homogenous group. They discovered that Black men of Caribbean birth or ancestry had the highest rate of suicide attempts compared to other Black men and women. They also found that the highest rate of suicidal behaviors occurred in the late teens and early 20s. Suicidal behaviors in this age group were more impulsive than those at later ages, which tended to be more planned. The highest risk for progression from suicide ideation to planning to attempt was in the 1st year after the onset of ideation, so this is a crucial period for intervention. As in other groups, those with suicide ideation who had a psychiatric disorder were significantly more likely to attempt suicide than those without such a disorder.

Hispanics/Latinos/Latinx

Although Latinx youth in the United States commit suicide at lower rates than other ethnic groups, they are much more likely (particularly females) to make suicide attempts (Canino & Roberts, 2001). The Latinx or Hispanic group is not homogeneous, and although the following discussion will generalize some concepts, there are intra-group differences depending on country of origin. Suicide ideation and attempts of Latinx American youth (Mexican American, Puerto Rican, and Dominican American) are higher than rates among comparable youth in their country of origin. This fact may provide some insight into the increased ideation and attempts: acculturative stress. A detailed discussion of that concept is beyond the scope of this chapter, but acculturative stress refers to a number of stressors such as conflicts in values between cultures, perceived discrimination, language difficulties, and perceived poor opportunities. Family support and positive expectations about the future appear to protect against acculturative stress and thus protect against suicidal behaviors. Counselors would be wise to consider acculturation factors in planning suicidal prevention, intervention, and postvention. The protective factor of family support is important, but many counselors face a language barrier when communicating with Spanish-dominant or monolingual Spanish-speaking clients. Parent training and education programs are usually presented in English, excluding those parents who are not fluent in the language. The need for more bilingual and bicultural counselors to serve this group is critical.

American Indians/Native Americans/Indigenous Americans

American Indian youth have the highest rate of suicide among all groups (APA, 2019). These youth experience many of the risk factors as other groups but also have added risk factors unique to this group: social disintegration and cultural conflict (Metha & Webb, 1996). While some tribes have maintained their separate cultural identities, others have integrated with the majority culture. For many American Indian youth, adopting the majority cultural values means a loss of pride in their culture and decreased self-esteem. High rates of alcoholism and suicide may be the effect of "social alienation, social confusion, and self-hate" (p. 25).

Gary et al. (2005) believe that suicide among American Indians is a fatalistic suicide, a reaction to the historical regulation by the dominant culture, including loss of their land, exploitation of natural resources, forced relocation, and forced assimilation (e.g., boarding schools). These experiences have led to pessimism about the future, and suicide may be the result. Living conditions on many reservations are substandard, with high unemployment and inadequate health and education facilities and services. In addition to the high rates of suicide, these authors point out that American Indian youth die at high rates from preventable injuries, some of which may actually be suicides. Previous research found that for a large sample of Navajo adolescents in grades 6–12, risk factors for suicidal behavior included feelings of alienation from family and community, having a friend who made a suicide attempt, and use of alcohol on a regular basis. Family history of suicide, a history of physical abuse and violence in the family, and sexual abuse were additional risk factors. Protective factors were also detected. Girls were protected by attention in the family, positive feelings about school, and caring by family and other adults. For boys, positive experiences at school, participating in traditional activities, good academic performance, and caring by family and other adults were the most prominent protective factors. For both boys and girls, support and caring by tribal leaders was a protective factor. Another previous study on Northern

Plains reservations found that commitment to cultural spirituality was associated with reduced suicidal behaviors. In addition to common risk factors, an additional risk is the presence of guns in homes. As many American Indians hunt for food, guns are among the basic tools found in the home of many families.

Metha and Webb (1996) cite LaFramboise and Bigfoot, who observed that the governmental pressures to assimilate (via boarding schools and prohibition of Native language use in government schools for many years) may have created only one road to freedom: suicide. Further, some cultural attitudes may make suicide a more viable option to at-risk individuals. The self-control that is admired in the culture may cause some youth who are experiencing psychological problems to internalize those problems. In some tribes, death is not as feared as it might be in other cultures, and the belief in ongoing contact between the human and spirit world may diminish the fear as well. In some tribes, large ceremonies (sometimes involving giveaways) that occur after a death, including a suicide, may be attractive to vulnerable youth.

Implications for counselors include the high need for suicide awareness programs for American Indians in schools and communities (Metha & Webb, 1996). Parent education is also crucial, and often difficult to implement. Outreach should be ongoing and should include personal visits and tribal liaison personnel to encourage involvement in programs and activities. To increase attendance at programs for suicide awareness, counselors can encourage the use of raffles and food as an incentive for attendance and support the use of tribal members as speakers. Finally, staff training in suicide awareness for all professionals working with American Indians should be mandatory and should include follow-up sessions on a regular basis.

In addition, intervention strategies should employ traditional Native practices (e.g., the healing circle and the medicine wheel and traditional ceremonies), and the role of the counselor might be to refer to tribal sources for these practices. When the only mental health providers are non-Native Americans, the use of traditional healers is especially important for avoiding conflicts with cultural beliefs. Involving family when a person is at imminent risk and bringing members of the extended family into the consultation may increase the effectiveness of the intervention. As involvement in traditional cultural practices is a protective factor, encouraging and supporting that involvement is a useful preventive effort (Gary et al., 2005).

Asian Americans/Pacific Islanders

Although no literature speaks to specific risks for suicide in Asian American/Pacific Islanders, suicide is the third leading cause of death in youth in this group aged 10–24; this group should not be ignored in efforts to reduce suicide. Suicide is also the eighth highest cause of death among Asian and Pacific Islander males of all ages. Chung (2002) noted that Asian American youth are considered prone to depression. She cites racism, the absence of Asian teachers and professionals in the school system, conflict with parents (students are likely to be more acculturated than parents), and parental emotional unavailability as unique risk factors for this group.

LGBTQ+

Sexual minority youth are also at higher risk for suicide than their heterosexual peers (Russell, 2003). For this group, an additional risk factor is the possibility of abuse from relatives and family members who reject the child's sexual orientation. These students are often victims of violence and bullying at school as well. The adolescent task of identity formation may be difficult for sexual minority youth because of societal attitudes (Kirk, 1993). Although attitudes have evolved over time, there are still people and places where discrimination and hostility persist. Social support from other LGBTQ+ peers, family support, and self-acceptance of the sexual minority identity are protective factors. School counselors must be available to these students and be advocates for measures to protect them in the school environment. Further, with student consent, school counselors can provide parents with information about community resources that might be helpful as they adjust to their child's sexual orientation.

Overall, members of these diverse groups experience additional risk factors not present in White students. School counselors must be sensitive to these differences and work to provide programming that is responsive to the needs of all students. Ideally, we would have a more diverse population of school counselors; school counselors would do well to create collaborative relationships with diverse professionals who work in other settings whom they can call on when needed.

Persons With Disabilities

There is strong evidence that having any disability increases risk for suicide (Centers for Disease Control and Prevention, 2023c; Charlifue & Gerhart, 1991; Hartkopp et al., 1998;). We provide an overview of what is known about the relationship between some types of disability and suicide, but it is far from inclusive. We recommend that mental health professionals carefully assess for suicide in all clients, particularly those with disabilities.

Hartkopp et al. (1998) examined the records of 888 men and women with spinal cord injuries. The rate of suicide was higher than that in the general population (also found by Charlifue & Gerhart, 1991), but the rate declined over time. The highest rates were immediately following the injury. Poisoning was the method in 48% of the suicides. Risk factors were previous psychiatric diagnoses and previous attempts. In fact, 22% of those who committed suicide sustained their spinal cord injury in a suicide attempt, and two of those eventually committed suicide using the same method. These researchers made several surprising discoveries in the data. First, rates of suicide were higher in those patients who had almost complete physical recovery from the spinal cord injury. They theorize that it may be easier to adjust to an extreme loss (total paralysis) that is clear and definite than from a condition that is less certain. They also suggest that perhaps less support is provided to these individuals because their prognosis is so much better. An additional surprise in the findings is that the rate of suicide was higher for women than for men. The authors speculate that women's self-image is more often tied to their physical appearance, making it more difficult to cope with physical disabilities. For older women who have been caretakers in marriage, the reversal in roles necessitated by the disability may feel intolerable. The final important point is that even those who are quadriplegic are able to commit suicide (via poisoning).

Charlifue and Gerhart's (1991) study of suicide in individuals with spinal cord injuries compared those who committed suicide with a matched control group. The most important factors were identified: family disruption prior to the injury, depression, alcohol abuse, apathy or withdrawal, weight loss, anger, and destructive behavior after the injury. This combination of factors was found to predict suicides with 80% accuracy. This suggests that these factors are signals that should alert providers that intervention by mental health professionals would be helpful.

Patients with traumatic brain injury (TBI) are also at high risk for suicide, with a rate of four times that in the general population (Simpson & Tate, 2007). León-Carrión et al. (2001) found that clinical depression, known to be associated with suicide in the general population, is associated with suicidal ideation in TBI patients, even after more than 18 months following discharge from the hospital. Of the TBI patients in their study with depression, 65% were found to have suicidal tendencies. These patients needed more emotional support than they received because they had difficulty coping with stress, dealing with complex situations, and using abstract reasoning. The authors recommended against using exclusively cognitive approaches treatment with this group who needed assistance managing emotions and needed instruction in social skills. Simpson and Tate (2007) found elevated risk in those clients with a history of psychiatric or emotional disturbances after the injury, substance dependence, or both. They also found that those who made repeated attempts did so within a circumscribed period of time, suggesting a need for close monitoring for up to a year after the initial attempt. They found that the most effective method for preventing suicide was limiting the availability of methods (medications, sharp objects, etc.)

Persons with epilepsy have a risk for suicide that is 22% higher than in the general population (Henderson, 2006; Tian et al, 2016). Half of deaf people have felt suicidal, survey finds. Sander and Bell (2004) report a rate three times the general population, with higher rates for those with temporal lobe epilepsy. These authors suggest that cooperation between medical providers and mental health providers would be helpful for this population.

Another disability that appears to be associated with an increased suicide risk is an HIV-positive diagnosis (Kalichman et al., 2000). Among those at greatest risk are those HIV-positive persons who also abuse drugs, are socially isolated, and lack social support. The risk appears to be greatest soon after the positive diagnosis is confirmed, suggesting that suicidal thoughts may diminish with time after the diagnosis. However, it is possible that there will be an increased risk if AIDS symptoms appear. In their diverse sample, the presence of suicidal ideation was highest among White gay men who were currently experiencing symptoms. The researchers were surprised to find that suicidal ideation was higher among those who had disclosed their HIV-positive status to close friends and family. They speculated that when such disclosures are met with rejection, the consequence is psychologically devastating. Standard and effective treatments have been developed that inhibit the progression to AIDS; currently a diagnosis of HIV positive may be less frightening.

Multiple sclerosis (MS) is also associated with higher rates of suicide (Feinstein, 2002). Men who were diagnosed prior to age 30 were at higher risk. In his comparison of suicidal and nonsuicidal MS patients, Feinstein (2002) found that living alone, having severe depression, and a lifetime diagnosis of an alcohol abuse disorder predicted increase suicide risk in the MS patients. Perhaps the most important finding of this research was that many of the suicidal and depressed patients had not been treated for their mental health issues, despite the efficacy of both medication and psychotherapy for depression in MS patients.

Persons with sensory disabilities (blindness, deafness), like the disabilities described, have increased risk for suicide. It is important for mental health practitioners to keep in mind that the rate of disabilities increases with age, so the elderly, particularly those with visual impairment, neurological disorders, and malignant diseases are especially vulnerable and should be assessed (Waern et al., 2002). Half of deaf respondents to a survey conducted by a charity in Glasgow, Scotland, reported they had considered suicide, with those who became deaf having greater risk than those who were born deaf (Henderson, 2006).Those with low vision, in contrast to those with complete blindness, demonstrate more depression, hostility, and anger (Kaldenberg, 2005). Those who become blind later in life experience grief at the loss of their sight, which sometimes becomes severe enough to precipitate suicide or attempts (De Leo et al., 1999). Those persons who had progressive diseases that lead to blindness had the greatest risk of suicide, greater than those with complete blindness. That is, the risk of suicide in those with visual impairments is greatest when sight remains but the prognosis is blindness. These authors also report that adults who had procedures resulting in the restoration of sight were at elevated risk for suicide, perhaps due to the unanticipated impact of the change.

In summary, we reiterate that clients with disabilities are vulnerable to suicidal ideation, and clinicians need to be sure to assess for suicide in these clients. Perhaps more important, we hope that mental health practitioners advocate for more collaboration between the medical community who provides treatment for the physical aspects of disabilities and the mental health providers who can address the very important psychological consequences of these disabilities. The research described is strong evidence of a need for mental health services to clients with disabilities. Physicians treating these disabilities must be educated about the importance of referring clients to mental health professionals to address the serious risk of suicide.

Counselor Issues

There is no doubt that working with suicidal clients is demanding and at times overwhelming. A counselor's skills are tested, and counselors fear any mistake can have disastrous consequences. It is essential that counselors have their own support systems available to debrief these situations, provide professional consultation, and assist in managing their own emotional response.

In situations of such high stress, counselors must not overlook the basic qualities that make them effective in all situations. In their own anxiety, counselors may inadvertently communicate to the client that their interest in the client is only to prevent the suicide rather than a concern for the client's overall well-being (Hanna & Green, 2004). The counselor must communicate empathy for the client: a deep understanding of why this person considered taking their own life. The client must believe that they are worthy of the compassion and support of the counselor, and this requires empathy on the part of the counselor. The counselor also must continually monitor their reactions to the client and be sure that any negative feelings are kept in check (and processed with colleagues or in supervision) so that these issues do not interfere with their relationship with this fragile client. Counselors need to explore their own beliefs and fears about suicide and death and be able to separate those needs from those of the client. Counselors who have experienced suicide in their own families must be acutely aware of the tendency to be emotionally raw and recognize their own limitations for working with suicidal clients. Counselors must be aware of the ethical principle not to abandon clients, but referring clients to a more specialized professional may be in the best interest of the client when the referral is made skillfully and at the appropriate time (Remley, 2004).

Recordkeeping and documentation become even more important in the case of a suicidal client. Documenting all aspects of the case is necessary. Documentation should include any consultations with other professionals (dates, times, nature of contact). Records should clearly indicate steps that were taken to ensure the client's safety and to notify appropriate persons of the danger. When the counselor makes an assessment of suicidal risk, notes should indicate not only the method of assessment but the rationale for all decisions made in the case. Some experts suggest that the no-suicide contract is helpful for documentation, but if this strategy is used, it is important to note how and why the counselor believed this was appropriate.

A NOTE TO SCHOOL COUNSELORS

School counselors may be involved in all aspects of suicide, from prevention programs and activities to intervention with suicidal students, and, unfortunately, with response services to students following a completed suicide. School counselors are resources for students and educators, administrators, and family members who seek the advice and expertise of the counselor for addressing this challenge. "Counselors are on the front line for identification, prevention, intervention, and postvention of suicidal behavior. As oppressive as that may feel to counselors, it is nonetheless a fact" (Stefanowski-Harding, 1990, p. 334).

Despite their crucial role, specific training for the school counselors' role in dealing with suicide is lacking in most graduate training programs (Foster & McAdams, 1999). CACREP guidelines do not require training for suicide response, and most programs, even those not accredited, follow Council for Accreditation of Counseling and Related Educational Programs (CACREP) guidelines in designing their curricula. If an elective course in crisis intervention or suicide is available, not all students will have that training. Thus, most school counselors rely on general counseling skills and techniques and professional training workshops and other sources, for their skill development. I hope this chapter provides additional knowledge and resources.

(Continued)

While the roles in prevention, intervention, and postvention are similar at elementary and secondary levels, there are some important differences. Curriculum approaches to suicide awareness are not recommended for elementary students, but classroom guidance lessons that address many of the risk factors for suicide are typically conducted by the counselor. At these times, the counselor needs to be alert to students whose reactions suggest they need further assessment. Although rare, suicides in elementary students do occur, and any mention of suicidal thoughts or behaviors should be taken seriously regardless of the age of the child. Elementary counselors usually provide group counseling and guidance to students, and grief groups are not uncommon. Parental contact tends to be more frequent at the elementary level, so counselors may have more information about family climate and changes in the family than do secondary counselors. Secondary school counselors with large caseloads may not have the opportunity to get to know each student well, and thus may not have had the opportunity to build a trusting relationship with the student who is referred for suicidal concerns. Despite these differences, the roles of school counselors at all levels are much more similar than different.

MTSS is a useful framework for the schools' role in suicide reduction. Universal efforts target the general population (all students) and have as a goal increasing awareness and knowledge of suicide along with enhancing resilience in students in order to prevent suicidal ideation from emerging. Universal programs are usually components of the curriculum (e.g., health) delivered by teachers or school counselors in a classroom setting. Some programs include a screening component, by which students at risk for developing suicidal behaviors are identified, either by staff or by students themselves. These students are encouraged to seek assistance in order to prevent the emergence of suicidal behaviors. One of the resources for students at risk is the school counselor.

Targeted efforts target those who are known or believed to be at risk for developing suicidal behaviors. These students may be identified by screening procedures and may be referred by self or others (parents, teachers, administrators) or by contact from outside agencies (police, health providers). Services to these students may take the form of support groups, other counseling groups (e.g., self-esteem building), monitoring, and programs designed to address other risk factors (e.g., substance abuse) and thus indirectly impact the risk for suicide. Even programs for new students (e.g., buddy systems) can be considered secondary prevention of suicide, as transitions are known stressors that increase risk for suicide in vulnerable students. These prevention efforts are often provided, initiated, and monitored by the school counselor.

Intensive individual intervention involves actions directed at those who have already been affected by a suicide, including students who have made an attempt and return to school and students who have been exposed to the suicide of a friend or family member. The goal of this step of MTSS is to reduce the level of distress and assist students in returning to their former level of functioning. This includes monitoring for signs of increased suicidal ideation, as loss is frequently a precipitant of suicidal behavior. Again, it is the school counselor who is largely responsible for providing these services.

The role of the school becomes one of intervention when a student has been identified as suicidal. The student is provided with support, while the counselor assesses the lethality of the student's suicidal behaviors. The assessment strategies described in this chapter are useful for this purpose. The tools for screening for depression in children and adolescents are also helpful in this regard. At this point, it is important to note that the school counselor has a responsibility to notify the parents or guardians and assist them in obtaining appropriate services for the student, from outpatient counseling to hospitalization. The school counselor must also notify the administration according to established procedures.

One of the most difficult aspects of dealing with suicide in the school is responding to the suicide of a student. It is important to recognize that there is a fine line to walk between ignoring and glamorizing a suicide while providing support to those students who are most affected. In addition, a topic that receives too little attention is that of the impact of a student suicide on the school counselor, who may be providing support for students, family, and teachers, and whose own needs are often given short shrift.

For school counselors interested in implementing a suicide prevention and intervention program, there are clearly a number of models from which to choose. They vary in the degree of empirical support for effectiveness, and in target populations (staff, parents, students, community resources) and other components, so counselors can determine the best fit for their environments—and they do not have to reinvent the wheel!

Ethical Concerns

There are a number of ethical standards that apply to the school counselor dealing with suicidal students. The ACA's code of ethics is clear about the counselor's duty to warn in the case of imminent danger. That section of the code also mentions the importance of consulting with others when there is any uncertainty. Another section of the code emphasizes that the limits of confidentiality should be discussed with all clients at the beginning, so the need to break confidentiality in the case of a suicidal client should not be a complete surprise. Box 7.5 contains the relevant sections of the ethical code.

BOX 7.5 **Sections of the ACA Ethical Code**

B.1.b. Respect for Privacy

Counselors respect the privacy of prospective and current clients. Counselors request private information from clients only when it is beneficial to the counseling process.

B.1.c. Respect for Confidentiality

Counselors protect the confidential information of prospective and current clients. Counselors disclose information only with appropriate consent or with sound legal or ethical justification.

B.1.d. Explanation of Limitations

At initiation and throughout the counseling process, counselors inform clients of the limitations of confidentiality and seek to identify situations in which confidentiality must be breached.

B.2.a. Serious and Foreseeable Harm and Legal Requirements

The general requirement that counselors keep information confidential does not apply when disclosure is required to protect clients or identified others from serious and foreseeable harm or when legal requirements demand that confidential information must be revealed. Counselors consult with other professionals when in doubt as to the validity of an exception. Additional considerations apply when addressing end-of-life issues.

Box 7.5: American Counseling Association, 2014 ACA Code of Ethics, pp. 6-7. Copyright © 2014 by American Counseling Association.

The other ethical issue related to suicide is that of boundaries of competence. Counselors are expected to practice only in areas in which they have sufficient training. As suicidal clients can be on any counselor's caseload, regardless of specialty, it is essential that all counselors obtain and advocate for training in suicide prevention, intervention, and postvention. That section of the code is given in Box 7.6.

While this chapter is not a substitute for such training, it is a good first step to meeting the requirement of competence to treat suicidal individuals and to do so with respect for the many aspects of diversity that may affect their needs and responses.

BOX 7.6 **Sections of the ACA Ethical Code**

C.2. Professional Competence

C.2.a. Boundaries of Competence: Counselors practice only within the boundaries of their competence, based on their education, training, supervised experience, state and national professional credentials, and appropriate professional experience. Whereas multicultural counseling competency is required across all counseling specialties, counselors gain knowledge, personal awareness, sensitivity, dispositions, and skills pertinent to being a culturally competent counselor in working with a diverse client population.

C.2.b. New Specialty Areas of Practice: Counselors practice in specialty areas new to them only after appropriate education, training, and supervised experience. While developing skills in new specialty areas, counselors take steps to ensure the competence of their work and protect others from possible harm.

C.2.c. Qualified for Employment: Counselors accept employment only for positions for which they are qualified given their education, training, supervised experience, state and national professional credentials, and appropriate professional experience. Counselors hire for professional counseling positions only individuals who are qualified and competent for those positions.

C.2.d. Monitor Effectiveness: Counselors continually monitor their effectiveness as professionals and take steps to improve when necessary. Counselors take reasonable steps to seek peer supervision to evaluate their efficacy as counselors

Box 7.6: American Counseling Association, 2014 ACA Code of Ethics, p. 8. Copyright © 2014 by American Counseling Association.

Summary

- Suicide is a problem for all age groups, with White males over age 65 having the highest rates of all groups.
- The most frequent method of suicide in all age groups (with the exception of ages 10–14) is firearms. Restricting access to guns is an important prevention and intervention strategy.
- Researchers have identified factors, known as risk factors, that elevate a person's risk for suicidal behavior. The more risk factors present, the higher the risk for suicide.
- Among risk factors, a previous attempt is the strongest predictor of future suicide. Also highly correlated with suicidal behavior are depression and substance abuse. Thus, methods to reduce those problems will reduce suicidal behavior.
- There are a variety of suicide assessment tools available, from formal standardized instruments (e.g., the Beck inventories) to informal methods using acronyms. The most important assessment method is the careful clinical interview, gathering information about thoughts, plans, and lethality.
- No-suicide contracts are widely used, but the counselor must not rely on these as the sole method of suicide prevention.
- Counselors must break confidentiality to ensure the safety of a suicidal client. Informing all clients of limits to confidentiality at the beginning of counseling makes this easier for clients to accept.

- Research to date suggests that medication, medication and CBT combined, CBT, and interpersonal therapy for depression are useful approaches for treatment.
- Counselor self-care takes on particular importance when working with suicidal clients.

Additional Resources

On the Web

- http://www.suicidology.org/ is the website for the American Association of Suicidology. The links to other resources on this site are exceptionally thorough and include resources for specific groups (e.g., suicide of a sibling).
- http://www.afsp.org/ is the website for the American Foundation for Suicide Prevention.

In Print for Counselors

- *Suicide Across the Lifespan: Premature Exits* by Judith Stillion and Eugene McDowell.
- *Suicide Across the Lifespan: Implications for Counselors* by David Capuzzi.
- *How to Prepare for and Respond to a Crisis* (second edition) by David Schonfeld et al. This is brief book with step-by-step information that includes many sample documents that a team would find helpful.
- *Suicide Prevention in the Schools: Guidelines for Middle and High School Settings* by David Capuzzi provides sound information and many handouts that could be used in prevention programming.
- *Night Falls Fast: Understanding Suicide* by Kay Redfield Jamison has the unique quality of having been written by a psychiatrist who has made a suicide attempt herself.
- *No Time to Say Goodbye: Surviving the Suicide of a Loved One* by Carla Fine is a very helpful perspective on the experience of survivors written by someone whose husband committed suicide.
- *Ordinary People,* a novel by Judith Guest, presents a serious suicide attempt by an adolescent in a gripping and complex portrayal that helps dispel many of the myths about suicide.

Film and Television

- *Remembering Tom* focuses on the survivors of an adolescent suicide—his parents and two siblings. What is so helpful about this video is that we see how differently each of the family members responds to the loss and how differently they grieve. Their process of coming to grips with suicide includes counseling, and counselors can see what was effective.
- *Choice of a Lifetime* profiles a number of individuals who came very close to committing suicide but did not. Each one talks about what led them to that point, what stopped them (in some cases, others intervened), and how they have lived their lives differently since that time. The video includes representatives of a number of high-risk groups, including the elderly, sexual minorities, Native Americans, and other minority group members. Counselors can learn a great deal from listening to these honest and self-aware individuals describe their experiences with suicide.

Exercises

1. Counselors need ongoing practice doing a suicide assessment. Assume you are working with a client who experiences a significant loss (e.g., romantic breakup), and you are aware that there are several risk factors present. Role-play the interview in which you assess for current suicide risk.

2. Assume you conclude that the client in question 1 is at imminent risk for suicide. How will you notify family members? What will you recommend? Assume the family members arrive in your office. Role-play your session with the family.

3. If you are a school counselor in training, consider that you have a student who you have determined is at high risk for suicide and that the stressor is conflict with parents. How will you handle informing these parents, and how will you ensure that doing so does not increase tension at home?

4. Watch the movie *Harold and Maude* or *Ordinary People*—what risk factors were present in Harold or Conrad's cases? How does their recovery fit with your understanding of protective factors and treatment?

5. The documentary *The Choice of a Lifetime: Returning From the Brink of Suicide* is an outstanding (although unfortunately difficult to obtain) documentary in which six individuals describe their personal experience with suicide. Discuss your reactions to the persons in the video.

6. Watch the video *Fatal Mistakes: Families Shattered by Suicide* and discuss the feelings experienced by counselors. Although this video, available from the American Society for Suicide Prevention, weaves factual information with personal testimony of survivors of suicide, the vignettes may evoke emotions that counselors should explore as a vehicle to understanding their own reactions to suicide. One concern with both this video and another video available from American Foundation for Suicide Prevention (*The Suicidal Patient*) is that counseling is not mentioned as a source of help to clients. Write a letter to the producer of the movie discussing your concern about this omission and explaining how counselors can be effective helpers for suicidal individuals.

CHAPTER 8

Eating Disorders

Health professionals have proclaimed obesity a major health problem in the United States. At the same time, the current status of eating disorders has been called "an epidemic" (Buckland, 2022). And, there are many people who do not meet diagnostic criteria for these disorders who have problematic eating behaviors. Many of the behaviors that are characteristic of eating disorders are the extremes of a continuum, with most of the behaviors occurring to some degree in the population as a whole. Twenty-three percent of 8-year-old girls and 18% of 8-year-old boys reported they "always" wished they were thinner (Shapiro et al., 1997), with comparable results being found in several countries in the United Kingdom (Littleton & Ollendick, 2003). Among college females, 49% reported *bingeing* experiences and 31% used compensatory behaviors (self-induced vomiting, laxatives, diuretics, exercise) to control weight (Lipson & Sonneville, 2017). Perhaps most telling are the results of a study conducted in England: 58% of females in a large sample of 12- to 15-year-olds listed "appearance" as the biggest concern in their lives (ANRED, n.d.a.)!

Purging: Getting rid of excess calories by self-induced vomiting, misusing laxatives, diuretics, and enemas, or exercising excessively

Bingeing: Eating large quantities of food (usually high-calorie) at a time

These disorders develop in a sociocultural context that is essential to understand. The quest for the ideal body is widespread in Western societies, which assume that this ideal is attainable and that those who reach this standard will have a better life (Ellen, 2018). Think for a moment about the ubiquitous symbol of female beauty, Barbie, who has influenced the beliefs of countless little girls since 1939. If Barbie were a real woman, she would be 6 feet tall and 101 pounds. Her body mass index (BMI) would be 13.7; a person with a BMI below 17.5 is anorexic. Barbie is thinner than female models and anorexics, with extreme measurements at the neck, wrist, waist, and hips (Norton et al., 1996). Due to her low percentage of body fat, Barbie (if real) would no longer have menstrual periods, nor would department store mannequins (if real) on which current fashions are displayed (Rintala & Mustajoki, 1992). The average American girl between 3 and 11 years old owns seven Barbie dolls. What message are they receiving about their appearance? Interestingly, the proportions of the Ken doll are much closer to reality.

CASE STUDY

Maria is one of seven children in a family headed by her Anglo American father and Mexican mother. The family came to the United States when Maria was a toddler, and a sense of fear due to her illegal status pervades her childhood. She observed her mother in a subservient role toward her father. When Maria started school, she attended a school with mostly Anglo peers, where she struggled with English and believed she was inferior to her classmates.

When she was 8, a number of traumatic events occurred. The family was living in a motel managed by her father. They had only two rooms to themselves, and children had to share beds. Her older half-brother sexually molested her during this time. Maria did not tell anyone about this, but her mother once caught her brother fondling her. Although she told him to stop, she did not take any other measures to protect Maria and prevent recurrence. At this same time, Maria's mother had a traumatic late-term miscarriage that made her less available emotionally to the surviving children. Also at this time, Maria began wetting the bed, for which she was shamed and beaten.

Maria's father's unstable employment forced the family to move to another community, where her father was again unable to maintain a job. He decided to move himself to another city across the country seeking work, while Maria's mother and the children remained in the southwest town until he settled in the new location. After her father's departure, Maria's mother began drinking heavily and going out with men. One of her mother's boyfriends also sexually molested Maria. Her mother's abuse, both verbal and physical, increased; Maria believes she was the special target of her mother's abuse because her father always made a point of saying she was the "apple of his eye," incurring the jealousy of both her mother and her siblings. Her father did not send promised funds. The family's economic circumstances were dire, and Maria vividly remembers the crisis when they were evicted room their home. Somehow, they managed to survive, but in very marginal circumstances. Other children teased Maria about living in a shack and wearing goodwill clothes.

In her family, Maria was "parentified"—given responsibilities that really belonged to a parent. She kept the house and yard clean, cooked meals, and cared for her younger siblings. In reaction to the chaos and upheaval in her childhood, Maria became a perfectionist. She makes sure she is not the inferior being that she believed her childhood self to be. She tends to black-and-white thinking and has worked hard to discard her belief that her value as a human being is totally dependent on her weight, with thin = good and fat = bad. Maria also has a strong need to control. She is afraid if she doesn't keep everything in control, she will find herself back in the unpredictable state she knows too well from childhood.

Maria had never been told about the facts of life, and when she experienced her first real menstrual period, she was frightened by the blood, thinking something was terribly wrong. When she approached her mother in fear, her mother laughed at her. Mother and siblings began making fun of Maria's body, calling her "fat ass" and a whore. Her mother was always trying to look thin and was highly critical of women who were "fat." Maria's first diet was at age 12 or 13, using diet pills she stole from a local store.

Maria idolized her distant father. After Maria's eighth-grade year, her father went to live in Mexico and took Maria with him. She chose to leave her mother and siblings to live with her father because she anticipated a closer relationship with her "hero" and was surprised when he dropped her off to live with a Mexican family. She attended a private school where most other students were wealthy and "snobby." This time, it was difficult to attend school speaking only Spanish, and she again felt "less than" her peers. Maria lost her virginity at age 15 to the father in that household. At this point, she began restrictive dieting and running and exercising to an extreme. After the sexual incident, she moved in with another family that she describes as somewhat better, but she later moved to a border city with her father and his new wife, again hoping for the close relationship that never developed. There she met a 23-year-old man with whom she remained for 5 years, eventually marrying him. This man was possessive and controlling and made it very clear that she must be thin, sometimes pushing on her stomach to emphasize his point. Maria became pregnant but had a premature Caesarian delivery, and the baby died within a month.

Maria moved to back to a southwestern city when she ended this marriage. She was living alone when she heard from a friend about bingeing and purging and decided to try it. She had a boyfriend by then, who always complimented her when she was thin. She began to receive numerous compliments on her appearance when she lost a great deal of weight. This gave her a sense of power, and she would relish the feeling of being the thinnest one in the room. She felt in control. When she binged, she always ate "comfort foods" and felt numb afterward.

When she purged, she would feel euphoric, as though she had gotten rid of difficult feelings. Maria's eating disorder also served to keep her distance from others. She says, "I thought that by looking good on the outside, I could hide my vulnerabilities, secrets, and issues."

When the eating disorder was most severe, Maria would binge and purge three or four times a day. As a result, she began to feel anxious and emotionally distraught and was perpetually tired and without energy. For brief periods of time, she would stop purging but would start a cycle of overexercising. Maria describes these behaviors as self-abusive; she was angry with herself and wanted to punish herself.

Maria felt her life was out of control. She was binging and purging all the time. She found a therapist in the phone book, and in the second session told the therapist about her eating disorder. The therapist became visibly upset, said Maria needed to see someone else who specialized in that disorder, gave her the card of the specialist, and rushed her out the door. Maria describes that interaction: "She acted as though I had told her I had the plague." Several days later, she got an appointment with the therapist whom she has been seeing ever since—now 8 years. Maria has worked hard in therapy to recover from her eating disorder. She has had relapses, with a major one occurring when her father died in 1995. As a result of therapy, Maria came to understand her mother's behavior, and Maria has now repaired her relationship with her mother.

An essential component of Maria's treatment has been group therapy. Seeing other women with the disorder helped her feel less isolated and alone. Because her secretiveness about her behavior helped her maintain the behavior, exposing it to others in the group was an important step. In the group, Maria could observe something in others—their distorted body image—that she couldn't see at first in herself. She would then realize, "I do that too." In her group, Maria learned that being thin did not equal happiness. For her, the group was an available minilab where she could practice new skills before trying them in the real world. She also valued the opportunity to get to know other women. She had always viewed other women as threats and believes many women see other females as "competition." The group allowed her to form deep relationships with other women that helped her value her own femininity.

An important component of Maria's treatment has been medication, which she has been taking since her therapy began. In individual therapy, Maria has learned a great deal about herself, assisted by the skillful questions posed by her therapist. Homework assignments extended the process beyond the therapy sessions. Maria realizes that her issues encompass more than the eating disorder and values therapy for helping her become more satisfied in all areas of her life. "Exposing these things [my feelings of inferiority, insecurity] with a good therapist made "looking good" less of an obsession, because I realized that when I start feeling insecure about my body, it is never really about my body, but deeper issues."

The support and encouragement of her therapist gave Maria the motivation to return to school, where she has done very well. Maria has been married for 7 years to a man who appreciates and loves her regardless of her weight. Her husband has supported her therapy, even meeting at times with the therapist.

It is still hard to resist the pervasive message that thin is the ideal. Maria, like all of us, receives numerous subtle and not-so-subtle messages about what makes a woman beautiful or valued. She acknowledges that these messages are hard to ignore, but Maria focuses on eating a healthy diet and exercising reasonably. She is now able to look at her naked body in the mirror without disgust, and she loves her body for its efficient functioning. She thinks of her stomach as her "natural healer," as it alerts her when she is not eating well and taking care of herself.

Maria's therapist is a tall woman with a trim physique. Maria values the honesty of her therapist, who makes it clear to her clients on intake that she herself does not have, and has not had, an eating disorder. She does reveal her humanity to the clients (she is not perfect) and on the rare occasions when she does not eat a healthy diet, she shares that with her clients so that they understand that no one can eat "perfectly" all of the time. She advises clients to "hit the reset button" when that happens and get back on track. Maria values that both her advice and example.

Maria and her therapist have discussed termination of treatment, which Maria approaches with mixed feelings. She knows she has the tools to live a fulfilling life without bingeing and purging and has supportive people in her life who accept her unconditionally. She reflects, "I feel confident that I have the skills and knowledge I need to cope with whatever comes my way. I also know that I will not cope with things perfectly all of the time. My recovery is an ongoing learning process and whatever my progress is will be good enough."

Definition and Description of the Problem

Although eating disorders have existed throughout history, clinical attention to these behaviors has been relatively recent. Physicians first used the term *anorexia nervosa* in 1873. For the first part of the 20th century, doctors believed this disorder had a biological cause, such as a pituitary deficiency. In the 1930s, attention turned again to the psychological origins of the disorder, and this has remained the focus since then. The term *bulimia nervosa* was coined in 1979, almost a century later than anorexia. This does not mean the disorder did not exist; rather, identification of specific criteria for diagnosis did not happen until that time. In this chapter, we will often abbreviate the names of the disorders to *anorexia* or *bulimia* in the interest of space.

Anorexia Nervosa

Anorexia nervosa has the following characteristics (based on DSM-V-TR):

- Restriction of energy intake (e.g., food) relative to what is required to maintain body weight—leading to a significantly low body weight in the context of height and age
- Intense fear of becoming fat, despite being underweight
- Body image disturbance; inaccurate perception of weight, self-image based on weight alone, or denial of the seriousness of low body weight

There are two types of anorexia: *restricting type* (people losing weight primarily by dieting, fasting, or excessive exercising) and *binge-eating/purging type* (intermittent binge eating and/or purging behavior).

Eating disorders often have severe physical consequences. With anorexia, there are numerous potential medical complications that affect the endocrine system, the cardiovascular system, and the neurological system, as well as bones and metabolism. Menstrual periods may stop occurring or occur very sporadically. Anorexia often is associated with hair loss and dry skin, brittle nails, and sometimes results in a condition called *lanugo*, which means soft body hair found on the face, arms, and other parts of the body. *Electrolyte* abnormalities are common and can affect cardiac functioning. Dehydration and constipation are frequently associated with the disorder. Other than opioid use disorder, anorexia has the highest mortality rate of any psychiatric diagnosis (American Psychiatric Association, n.d.).

Electrolyte: Substance responsible for moving nutrients into cells and waste products out of cells

A fascinating study conducted in the 1950s by Keys et al. (1950) examined the effects of semi-starvation on adults. Researchers at the University of Minnesota recruited volunteers to participate in an experiment on the effects of restricted food intake on healthy adult men. The 36 healthiest (both physically and psychologically) of the volunteers were enrolled in the study as an alternative to military service. During the first 3 months of the year-long study, participants ate normally while researchers closely observed their eating habits, general behavior, and personality. For the next 6 months of the study, the men received half their former food intake. They lost an average of 25% of their previous weight. In the final 3 months, they were gradually fed and rehabilitated. Keep in mind that the level of food restriction was not as severe as that of many anorectics. These are some of the changes that occurred in the semi-starved men:

- Overwhelming preoccupation with food, with corresponding decreased interest in sex and activity. The men read about, talked about, and dreamed about food. They developed rituals around eating.

- Episodes of binge eating. During the rehabilitation phase, many men ate large quantities of food, and for a few, this persisted for as long as 5 months after they had free access to food.
- Irritability and anger outbursts were frequent, anxiety increased, and apathy was widespread. Two subjects exhibited psychotic symptoms, and most had episodes of depression. For some of the men, the symptoms persisted or even increased during the period of refeeding. Participants took a standard personality test prior to and after the experiment, so researchers were able to compare personality profiles before and after semi-starvation. They found serious pathological changes and emotional disturbance after the starvation period.
- Social withdrawal and isolation increased.
- Intelligence testing did not find changes in ability, but participants reported problems with concentration, alertness, comprehension, and judgment during the period of restricted food intake (Garner, 1997).

The implications of these results for individuals with eating disorder are clear: Many of the behaviors associated with anorexia nervosa may be the effect of semi-starvation on the system. The fact that these symptoms continued even when normal feeding resumed suggests that treatment for anorexia needs to continue past the point when the client achieves their weight goals. Healthy and realistic weight goals are established with input from a physician.

Bulimia Nervosa

A diagnosis of *bulimia nervosa* requires that the following symptoms are present:

- Recurrent episodes of binge eating: Eating a large amount of food in a discrete period of time along with a sense of loss of control of what and how much one is eating during the episode
- Recurrent compensatory behaviors to prevent weight gain: Self-induced vomiting, abuse of laxatives, diuretics, or other medication, fasting, or excessive exercise
- Binging/purging behaviors: Occurring on an average of once per week for 3 months
- Self-evaluation: Overemphasizing body weight and shape

These behaviors do not occur only during episodes of anorexia nervosa.

As with anorexia nervosa, electrolyte abnormalities are common in bulimia, as are dehydration and constipation (really, problems with the entire digestive system). For those who purge, erosion of the enamel of the teeth is a potential consequence. I (SB) worked with a young woman with bulimia who had needed to have very expensive dental work done, as her frequent purging had destroyed the enamel on her teeth. In fact, she came for treatment only because her parents had refused to pay for any additional dental work. With bulimia, "Russell's sign" is often an early indicator of the purging behavior; it refers to sores or calluses on the hand caused by using the hand to induce vomiting.

Binge-Eating Disorder

A diagnosis of binge-eating disorder requires the following symptoms:

- Recurrent episodes of binge eating: Eating a large amount of food in a discrete period of time along with a sense of loss of control of what and how much one is eating during the episode
- Binging/purging behaviors: Occurring on an average of once per week for 3 months

- Binge episodes: Three or more of the following:
  - Eating rapidly (more than normal)
  - Feeling uncomfortably full
  - Eating large amounts when not really feeling hunger
  - Eating alone because of feeling embarrassed about how much is eaten
  - Feelings of disgust with oneself; depression; guilt

There are no *regular* compensatory behaviors (e.g., purging, dieting, overexercising) as there are with bulimia. As with the other eating disorders, there are significant health complications related to binge eating (e.g., obesity, diabetes, hypertension, and cardiovascular disease). Because this disorder has some important differences from bulimia, treatment approaches need to be adapted to this clientele (Marcus, 1997).

Other Specified Feeding and Eating Disorders

A diagnosis of other specified feeding and eating disorders (OSFED) refers to behavior that meets most, but not all, criteria for one of the other disorders—for example, if the frequency of a behavior does not meet the diagnostic threshold, but all of the other criteria are met for anorexia or the binge-purge cycles do not occur frequently enough to meet criteria for bulimia. In contemporary American society, there are many who do not strictly meet all criteria for any of these diagnoses but whose eating patterns and behaviors around food have many characteristics of eating disorders. For example, a study conducted with Minnesota high school students found disordered eating in 30% of the ninth- and 12th-grade males in their large sample, and 55% of females (Croll et al., 2002). These are shocking figures. Counselors also need to focus on *subclinical* levels of these behaviors, hopefully preventing the progression to the eating disorders.

Avoidant Restrictive Food Intake Disorder

The American Psychiatric Association has only recently defined avoidant restrictive food intake disorder (ARFID) as an eating disorder characterized as a food avoidance (or limited food repertoire = extremely picky eating) that results in a persistent failure to meet nutritional needs. A diagnosis of ARFID requires one or more of the following:

- Significant weight loss or a failure to achieve an expected weight gain for children
- A significant nutritional deficiency
- Reliance on a feeding tube or oral nutrition supplements in order to obtain sufficient nutritional input
- Interference with social functioning (e.g., an inability to eat with others)

Clients with ARFID may report a low appetite or lack of interest in eating. They may avoid foods based on their sensory characteristics (texture, color, smell, appearance). There may be a great deal of anxiety about eating as a result of significant/traumatic past event such as an episode of choking or food poisoning. The client may fear choking (again) or nausea, vomiting, constipation, or an allergic reaction—and therefore avoid or limit themselves to very specific foods. Food avoidance or limiting food repertoire typically develops in childhood, but ARFID does not include what may be considered developmentally normal behavior (e.g., a toddler who is a picky eater). ARFID can start and be present at any age.

Clients with ARFID may suffer from malnutrition. Therefore, some of the same health complications mentioned in the previous eating disorders can be a consequence of ARFID.

It is important to note that clients who may be on the autism spectrum often have rigid eating behaviors and/or sensitivities to sensory input. Although this may seem to appear like ARFID, their behaviors do not necessarily reach the level of impairment for a diagnosis of ARFID—or may not warrant a separate diagnosis.

Pica

Pica is an eating disorder in which a person repeatedly eats non-nutritive substances (things that are not food). The behavior must be present for over 1 month and cause enough distress to warrant clinical attention. Some typical substances ingested with pica include paper, soap, cloth, hair, chalk, metal, pebbles/rocks, charcoal, and clay. Pica is not diagnosed in children under 2 years old, as it is developmentally appropriate for children to put things in their mouths. Pica often occurs along with a diagnosis of autism spectrum disorder or an intellectual disability.

Rumination Disorder

Rumination disorder is the repeated regurgitation of food after eating. Food that has been swallowed is brought back up for rechewing and reswallowing or spat out. A diagnosis of rumination disorder requires that the regurgitation occurs repeatedly over at least a 1-month period—and is not due to another medical or gastrointestinal problem. The disorder can occur in other disorders, such as an intellectual disability, but the behavior must be severe enough to warrant a separate diagnosis or specific clinical attention.

Orthorexia

Although orthorexia is not formally recognized in the DSM, we feel it is worth mentioning as being of at least some clinical importance and of something counselors should be aware. The National Eating Disorders Association (NEDA, 2017b) includes this area of clinical focus in their information about eating disorders. The term *orthorexia nervosa* was first coined in 1997 and is generally defined as an unhealthy obsession with healthy eating, hyperfocusing on concerns regarding food quality and composition (Zagaria et al., 2022). The idea of being aware of and concerned about the food eaten is not a problem in and of itself; however, people who might be considered to have orthorexia become so fixated on healthy eating that they damage their own well-being (NEDA, 2017b).

There are no diagnostic criteria, but the following warning signs and symptoms are provided by NEDA (2017b):

- Compulsive checking of ingredient lists and nutritional labels
- An increase in concern about the health of ingredients
- Cutting out an increasing number of food groups (e.g., all sugar, all carbs, all dairy, all meat, all animal products)
- An inability to eat anything but a narrow group of foods
- Unusual interest in the health of what other people are eating
- Spending an unusual amount of time thinking about what food might be served at upcoming events
- Showing high levels of distress when "safe" or "health" foods are not available

Someone who displays these symptoms may be restricting the amount and variety of foods eaten, and malnutrition is a potential physical consequence of orthorexia. Because of this, orthorexia shares many of the same possible health consequences of anorexia and bulimia.

Zagaria et al. (2021) completed a systematic review and meta-analaysis of research related to orthorexia and found that 36 studies on the clinical issue had already been completed. They found that symptoms of orthorexia are distinct from other eating disorders (and distinct from obsessive-compulsive disorder).

Prevalence

Different studies report different rates of these disorders in the population depending on the source of data and the methods used. For adolescent females, eating disorders are the third most common chronic illness, exceeded by only obesity and asthma (Croll et al., 2002). Silen and Keski-Rahkonen (2022) found that .8% to 6.3% of women (.1% to .3% of men) meet full diagnostic criteria for anorexia, .8% to 2.6% of women (.1% to.2% of men) meet the criteria for bulimia, .6% to 6.1% of women (.3% to.7% of men) meet the criteria for binge-eating disorder, and .6% to 11.5% of women (.2% to.3% of men) meet the criteria for other specified feeding or eating disorder. About one third of individuals diagnosed with bulimia have previously met criteria for anorexia. Rates of eating disorders in males seem to be increasing, which may reflect an actual increase or an increase in males seeking treatment (Kinnaird et al., 2019).

Subclinical: Symptoms that are present but not severe enough to meet diagnostic criteria for a mental disorder

Research suggests that full recovery rates for eating disorders is achieved in about two thirds of clients after 20 years (62.8% of clients with anorexia, 68.2% of clients with bulimia). However, it may take time for some. At a 9-year follow-up, only 31.4% of those with anorexia had recovered (the same number of those with bulimia had recovered at year 9 as had at year 22; Eddy et al., 2017). A startling 6%–20% of those diagnosed with anorexia die from complications of the disorder (starvation, suicide, heart problems; Mitchell et al., 1997). Clients with anorexia are at nine times the risk of death within the first 5 years of the diagnosis, as opposed to those without anorexia (Auger et al., 2021).

Populations that are at high risk for eating disorders include those whose activities or careers are believed to be enhanced by a lean or thin physique. These include professional dancers and many athletes. There is a greater prevalence of eating disorders among athletes than nonathletes. Rates vary from 6% to 45% in female athletes and from 0%–19% in male athletes (Conviser et al., 2018). Athletes who compete in aesthetic, or lean, sports (e.g., gymnastics, diving, rowing, figure skating, cheerleading, long-distance running, wrestling) may be more susceptible to developing an eating disorder compared to those who compete in nonaesthetic/nonlean sports (e.g., volleyball, softball, soccer; Chapa et al., 2022).

Adolescent and young adult women are the largest group with these disorders, but it is important not to rule out the presence of these problems in males, adult women, and seniors. Eating disorders are in all of these groups but may be overlooked because of false assumptions that this disorder is limited to young females. Other conditions are frequently associated with eating disorders. Prominent among these are substance use, depression, anxiety, and personality disorders. This means that in many cases, treatment must address these comorbid conditions along with the eating disorder.

Developmental Influences

In this section, we will review significant developmental events that contribute to the later emergence of eating disorders. The developmental patterns of the three primary eating disorders (anorexia, bulimia, and binge eating) are somewhat different. The onset of anorexia is most often in adolescence, while bulimia emerges in late adolescence or early adulthood. Binge eating, however, often begins at a very early age. All three disorders are more often found in females (Galmiche et al., 2019).

Although interest in a biological origin for the disorders diminished after the 1930s, studies that are more recent explore the contributions of genetics and biology. Using studies of twins, researchers have discovered that there are genetic risk factors for developing both binge eating and obesity (Bulik et al., 2003). Genetic factors contribute to 40% to 60% of the variance in eating disorders (Trace et al., 2013). Relatives of individuals with an eating disorder have been found to be more likely to develop an eating disorder than relatives of individuals without an eating disorder, and researchers are able to pinpoint genome data to estimate heritability (Bulik et al., 2019). Another twin study found that the genetic mechanisms may not activate until puberty, presumably as a result of the biochemical changes that occur during that process (Klump et al., 2003).

Psychodynamic theorists emphasize early mother–child relationships in the development of eating disorders, particularly when the mother is ambivalent about the pregnancy (Farrell, 2000). Object relations theories consider food to be equivalent to "mother" and view disordered eating as a reflection of conflict about separation and individuation.

When an infant is distressed, they feel comfort when fed, not only the satiation of hunger but also the nurturing, physical warmth, and soothing talk that accompany the food served to calm the baby. The infant learns that feeding is comforting, and it is not difficult to understand that adults may seek food, which they link with comfort, when upset. This tendency, along with the intense cultural pressure toward thinness, may set the stage for the vulnerable individual to discover the antidote to excessive eating—purging.

Teasing plays a significant role the development of eating disorders. In one study, individuals with bulimia reported more teasing about weight and size than did those with binge eating disorder. Researchers also found that teasing by significant adult figures (e.g., coaches, instructors) can have a strong influence on later eating disordered behavior. A former client of Sheri Bauman's, a college student, vividly remembers a negative comment about their weight made by a gymnastics coach when they were age 8 or 9 and traces the origin of their disordered attitudes about weight and eating to that event. The woman in our case study remembers how hurtful it was to be called "fatso" when she now realizes she was actually at a normal weight. Experts believe that teasing by parents about weight has a profound effect on children, although problems may not emerge until adolescence.

A model developed by Streigel-Moore and Cachelin (1999) proposed two developmental pathways to eating disorders. The first pathway involves the internalization of the pervasive societal messages about the thinness as the ideal and the standard of beauty, and the second is the result of inadequate nurturing from parents, which leads to low self-esteem. In most cases, both pathways are probably involved. Littleton and Ollendick (2003) identified the following risk factors in children that may predispose them to eating disorders.

Individual factors:

- Temperament: High levels of negative emotions (irritability, inflexibility) and low levels of cooperativeness were risk factors for disordered eating behaviors.
- Early puberty in girls has been link to disordered eating, perhaps due to the accumulation of fat that accompanies this developmental process and the social consequences of early maturity.
- Low self-esteem may include dissatisfaction with one's body image, which in turn leads to disordered eating. Low self-esteem may also involve feelings of ineffectiveness, which results in restrictive eating to enhance feelings of control.

Social factors:

- Exposure to thin media images. The marked rise in eating disordered behaviors among Fijian teenage girls following the introduction of TV in 1995 illustrates this effect. Fijian TV broadcasts American, British, and Australian programming (Becker, 2002).
- Response to media messages about dieting or exercise products encouraging weight loss.
- Social reinforcement by peers for the thin ideal.

Family factors:

- Disordered eating and dieting behavior in parents.
- Parental criticism of child's weight.

There is a strong association between childhood sexual abuse and eating disorders (Solmi et al., 2020). Wonderlich et al. (2000) compared a group of girls aged 10 to 15 who had been sexually abused with a matched control group and found sexually abused girls were more likely to exhibit weight dissatisfaction, food restriction when upset, and purging behaviors. These girls may dislike their own bodies and seek to disappear. They may wish to deny their sexuality, so the increased body fat and development of a womanly shape may be particularly frightening and dangerous to a girl who has been sexually abused.

A personality trait (and processing style) observed in childhood that has been linked to eating disorders for decades is *perfectionism*, particularly the tendency to be overly self-critical and to be concerned that making mistakes will result in a loss of others' approval (Ralph-Nearman et al., 2019). Tyrka et al. (2002) found that perfectionism and low body weight at age 12–16 predicted the development of anorexia in young adulthood, while negative emotional states were associated with young adult development of bulimia. A perfectionistic style of information processing develops prior to the onset of the eating disorder and is a predictor of later development of the disorder.

Digital Media Influences

The visual culture of social media platforms has received much attention from researchers related to eating disorders (Marks et al., 2020). Researchers have been able to establish that social media use is directly related to higher levels of body dissatisfaction and has a significantly harmful effect on body image (Fardouly & Vartanian, 2016; Harriger et al., 2022; Saiphoo & Vahedi, 2019). Although there can be some benefits related to the use of social media (e.g., peer support and information), the influence of these platforms can be toxic related to the development of disordered eating. Marks et al. (2020) indicate that social media platforms are characterized by the following:

- An increase in negative social comparisons (an increased amount of time comparing oneself to others or what may be considered the "ideal," creating psychological distress, dissatisfaction, and shame)
- Increased time "self-presenting" (creating and curating desirable public representations of themselves, which drives a self-objectification and a disconnect from who they are online and in real life. The curated images may be filtered and misrepresent how someone actually appears in real life).
- Increased anxiety about appearance and body image (more exposure to image-based content leads to an internalization of a "thin ideal" and increased dissatisfaction with their own body).

- Misinformation about health and wellness content found online (anyone can create social media content, regardless of education, qualifications, or experience).

Researchers have begun to evaluate interventions designed to disrupt the relationship between social media, appearance comparison, and negative body image (which may lead to disordered eating). Interventions have included psychoeducation in a classroom setting, a single-session meeting challenging social media ideals, social media literacy activities, a writing/journaling task, and self-guided education modules designed to reduce self-criticism and increase self-compassion (de Valle & Wade, 2022). The results of work in this area are promising, but more work needs to be done to address the ever-evolving landscape of social media.

A disturbing trend found online is "pro-ana" (pro-anorexia) and "pro-mia" (pro-bulimia) content. This content promotes anorexic or bulimic behavior and/or mind-sets. The general idea of this (harmful) content is that an eating disorder is a "lifestyle" choice as opposed to being a dangerous, complex disorder typically influenced by multiple factors. The content might promote dangerous eating behaviors and typically falls under what is considered "thinspiration" content: information intended to provide inspiration for losing weight. Many of these websites or content place an extreme value on thinness, and they may attempt to educate people on how to incorporate harmful eating behaviors and how to perhaps hide the behavior from the people in their lives (Within Health, 2022).

The significant problem of the content these days, particularly in social media, is the curation of content that is personalized, displaying videos that the platform has deemed likely that the user/viewer would enjoy. An algorithm is used to predict what is thought the user may want to see, based on what has been viewed previously (but without a moral- or health-related judgment; Gerrard, 2020). If the social media platform thinks you enjoy watching videos about disordered eating behaviors, it will offer you more videos on the topic. The videos could be triggering for someone who has an eating disorder (someone sharing diet tips or purging methods).

Counselors may want to spend some time talking with clients who may have disordered eating behaviors (particularly adolescents) about the content they watch and engage with online. Rather than eliminate using technology altogether, which may be unrealistic for an adolescent, it may be better to work with them on understanding how their social media sites may be collecting information about their content interests. Many sites have options of "not interested" or a "thumbs down" when certain content is presented. Knowing how to use these features will (over time) help them to see more appropriate content for them and reduce the amount of triggering content (Gerrard, 2020).

Assessment

In this section, we will describe how a professional determines whether a client has an eating disorder. For the counselor who does not treat these disorders, they may want to make a referral. For the many clients with other disorders in addition to eating disorders, the counselor must consider the best combination of treatment strategies to address the particular constellation of problems the client has.

In order to decide whether a client meets DSM-5-TR criteria for eating disorders, a structured clinical interview is often used. However, the clinician will want more information about the client's clinical picture so that they can tailor treatment to the client's unique profile. Questions regarding weight and body image are very revealing and should be included in the interview. Crowther and Sherwood (1997) recommend getting highest and lowest weights at current height, range of weight fluctuation, the person's conception of an ideal weight, and their childhood weight (and the presence of obesity and experience of teasing in childhood). Specific information about patterns of binge/purge episodes, dietary "rules," frequency of weighing, and use of compensatory methods to control weight are all important data for the clinician to obtain. Also essential is information about comorbid disorders, previous treatment attempts, and medical status.

Because there is a high rate of comorbidity with eating disorders, clinicians may wish to administer a general measure to clarify the clinical picture, such as the MMPI-3 (which contains a scale that assesses eating concerns) or MCMI-IV (or the MMPI-A-RF or MACI-II for adolescents). Because substance use is specifically associated with eating disorders, the clinician might be well advised to assess for this problem as well.

There are several formal assessment instruments available to assist clinicians in understanding various aspects of the eating disorder, and the clinician will select those that are most useful. In considering which assessments to use, clinicians will want to consider whether the sample on which the scale was normed is similar to the clientele with whom they will use it. They will want to examine the subscales to see if the information provided is comprehensive. They will want to consider the length and readability of the questionnaire and the ease and time involved in administration and scoring.

Self-report questionnaires are typically useful for initial screening, and structured interviews may add more in-depth data. The Eating Disorder Examination (EDE) is a structured interview protocol that is widely used, and there is also a self-report questionnaire version of that inventory. Copies of the EDE (interview and questionnaire versions) are in *Cognitive Behavior Therapy and Eating Disorders*, by Fairburn (2008). The NEDA also has a brief self-report screening tool on their website.

For the reader who would like more information on available instruments, an article by Schaefer et al. (2021) provides a fairly thorough list of psychometrically validated assessments that are available for eating disorders. They provide a listing and summary of assessment in four areas: (a) structured interviews to assess eating disorder symptoms and diagnoses, (b) self-report questionnaires used to assess eating disorder symptoms, (c) self-report questionnaires used to assess features associated with eating disorders, and (d) eating disorder assessments used with specific populations.

Treatment Options and Considerations

In this section, we will discuss in some detail the most empirically supported and widely accepted treatment approaches for eating disorders. Keep in mind that treatment in clinical practice "differs substantially from treatment in research settings with regard to therapist, clients, and treatment components" (Hass & Clopton, 2003, p. 417). Research on the effectiveness of treatment approaches is carefully controlled so that the researchers can be certain that observed differences can be attributed to the type of treatment rather than other factors. That often means that people with comorbid disorders cannot be participants in the study. Practicing therapists, however, say that most clients with eating disorders have comorbid disorders, so they question the applicability of such research. Further, research participants must receive only the treatment component being studied (e.g., group therapy), but in practice clients may need group and individual therapy, and perhaps medication and other components. Clinicians are likely to lack training in using empirically validated treatments. Many therapists depend on reading and occasional continuing education courses for their information but do not get intensive training. A final concern about implementing these treatment approaches is that the manuals may not be flexible enough to allow for the individual needs of a particular client or of particular settings (Haas & Clopton, 2003).

One way to determine what level of treatment is most appropriate in a particular case is to use the decision tree developed by Garner and Needleman (1997). This is a sequential approach to considering the relevant client issues in coming to a treatment decision. Keep in mind that in addition to philosophy and technique, approaches vary in intensity (outpatient, intensive outpatient, and inpatient), intrusiveness, and cost. One should always consider the least intrusive and least costly methods that are appropriate in the situation. The clinician should insist that an evaluation by a physician (if one has not already been done) be included in any treatment plan. Conviser et al. (2018) provide a great summary regarding levels of care with eating disorders (Table 8.1).

TABLE 8.1. Levels of Care for Clients With an Eating Disorder

Levels of Care	Medical Stability	Suicide Risk	Percent of Ideal Body Weight (IBW)	Eating Disorder Behaviors	Motivation	Support System
Inpatient	24-hour medical supervision required	High risk of danger to self	< 85% IBW	Requires 24-hour supervision	Very poor to poor	Lack of support
Residential	Daytime monitoring	High risk of danger to self	< 85% IBW	Requires supervision	Poor to fair	Lack of support
Partial Hospitalization	Medically stable	Monitor as needed	> 80% IBW	Requires structure	Partially motivated	Limited to partial support
Intensive Outpatient	Medically stable	Monitor as needed	> 80% IBW	Uses structure	Fair cooperative	Adequate support

Adapted from Joel Yager, et al., Treatment of Patients with Eating Disorders, p. 500.
Copyright © 2012 by American Psychiatric Association Publishing.

Medication

The mental health professional does not prescribe medication (with the exception of psychologists in a few states) but may recommend that clients seek consultation with a psychiatrist to evaluate the potential usefulness of medication. The clinician will be better able to consult and communicate with prescribing clinicians and clients if they have some familiarity with the use of medication in treating eating disorders.

Although medication may be helpful for many clients with eating disorders, experts caution against relying on it as a first line of defense. Medication alone is almost never an appropriate treatment. There is evidence that medication is helpful for clients with bulimia or binge-eating disorder, but there is limited evidence that it is helpful for anorexia (Davis & Attia, 2017). For bulimia, antidepressant medications, particularly SSRIs, are most commonly used. Because anxiety is sometimes a stimulus for a binge/purge cycle, some experts have considered whether anxiolytics (antianxiety medication) might be useful. One concern with many medications of this type is their potential for abuse, and since substance abuse is often associated with eating disorders, caution is necessary. For binge-eating disorder, the U.S. FDA has indicated that lisdexamfetamine is safe and effective and has approved it for use with binge-eating disorder (Davis & Attia, 2017; Monteleone et al., 2022). Davis and Attia (2017) suggest that second-generation antipsychotic medications, such as olanzapine, may be helpful with weight gain for those clients with anorexia, but they are quick to remind that it is not advised as a stand-alone treatment. Increased appetite may not be the most useful intervention anyway, as clients with eating disorders have not lost their appetite for food—on the contrary, their disorder involves resisting the impulse to eat despite the presence of a normal (or even increased) appetite.

Clients with bulimia may decide to stop taking their medication if side effects are unpleasant or because of their need for control conflicts with the belief that medication can help. Ambivalence about giving up their eating disorders is not unusual, and I (SB) have had clients with bulimia panic when they learn that a possible side effect of some antidepressants is weight gain. It makes sense to defer the decision about medication until CBT is attempted. If it is not successful, medication can be added to the treatment plan. Most of these clients benefit from a 4- to 6-month course of medication, but some will require continued medication to maintain the beneficial effects (Garfinkel & Walsh, 1997).

The use of medication with anorexia nervosa is more controversial. Although symptoms of depression are common in these clients, there may be the effect of semi-starvation, so it is unclear whether prescribing antidepressants prior to weight gain is advisable. Anxiolytics (antianxiety medications) may help with increased anxiety that accompanies weight-gain strategies, but in these cases, experts recommend a low dose for a limited period of time.

Another line of inquiry has been the use of estrogen when decreased bone density is a concern, but it appears that it is the weight gain that has the necessary effect on bone density rather than estrogen therapy. Thus, medication may be helpful as a supplement to other avenues of treatment, and a clinician should be able to discuss these options intelligently with clients and other professionals alike.

CBT and Enhanced CBT

By far, the most widely used treatment for eating disorders is CBT and enhanced cognitive-behavioral therapy (E-CBT). CBT is used for both anorexia and bulimia, with a primary target outcome of symptom reduction. Bulimia is usually addressed within 20 weekly sessions—and anorexia addressed within 40 weekly sessions or more (Hay, 2020). Most clients are appropriate for this approach, with the exception of those with psychotic symptoms, severely depressed or suicidal clients, and substance abusers. These complicating disorders may prevent them benefiting from this type of treatment.

CBT focuses on the present and future, and the focus is on the specific problem, in this case the eating disorder. CBT sessions have a predictable structure: review of self-monitoring, deciding on an agenda, working on the agenda items, summarizing the session, and assigning homework. CBT therapists recognize the importance of a strong therapeutic alliance, and early stages of treatment concentrate on building that relationship. Initial sessions focus on the client/therapist relationship, explaining this form of therapy to the client, providing information about the effects of the eating disorder, introducing weekly weighing, and teaching the importance of regular meals, healthy food choices, and alternative activities. Clients are likely to be ambivalent about change, with worries about weight gain often predominating worries about the harmful consequences of the disorder. CBT therapists anticipate this conflict and use motivational strategies to gain the client's genuine commitment. It is helpful to reassure clients that significant weight gain is unlikely to occur as a result of treatment.

Providing information is an important component of eating disorder treatment. In addition to education within therapy sessions, counselors may require outside reading for additional information. The Resources section later in this chapter will list some of the books you might use for this purpose.

Self-monitoring is an essential technique in this approach. Clients record everything they eat, usually on special forms provided for that purpose. Of course, these days, a lot of clients might be more apt to use a mobile device app for self-monitoring. The website Choosing Therapy has a good list of the top eating disorder apps (Shafir, 2023).

This type of self-monitoring provides the therapist with detailed information about the eating patterns and situational triggers for disordered behaviors. For the client, this practice increases awareness of patterns and leads to a sense of control. Weekly weighing is a firm requirement. Many eating disordered clients weigh far too often, and others may refuse to weigh themselves. This weekly strategy allows the client to gauge the effectiveness of the strategies learned in therapy. Clients do not focus on the absolute weight but on changes they see when they implement the new techniques.

CBT counselors advise eating-disordered clients to eat three healthy meals a day plus two planned snacks every day. This is so that regular eating habits can reduce the urge to binge, and in effect reduce the total number of calories consumed. It may be difficult to get clients to comply with this strategy, but it is essential. A technique to make this plan more manageable is to eliminate binge foods from the house. Another is to ensure that the client prepares a list of alternative behaviors they can use to manage high-risk situations when they are most likely to purge. Clients also learn problem-solving skills to enable them to cope with difficult situations without resorting to disordered eating.

CBT includes a major emphasis on cognitive restructuring, or changing the faulty thinking patterns that perpetuate the eating disorder. Clients learn to identify irrational or illogical thinking, to bring evidence to evaluate and challenge irrational ideas, and to replace them with more accurate beliefs. For example, individuals with eating disorders tend to think in black-and-white terms (e.g., fat = bad), which is a notion to challenge. Counselors should help them develop a more accurate definition of *fat*. In the final stages of treatment, time is devoted to planning for the end of treatment by developing plans to maintain gains attained in therapy.

Anorexics can be difficult to motivate for treatment, as their fear of being fat is so intense and ingrained. People with anorexia are often coerced into treatment by significant others, which means they may not be truly motivated to change. Therapists cannot tell them, as they can bulimic clients, that they will not gain weight, since that is a main goal of treatment. Clients with anorexia need to understand the possible medical consequences of the disorder and need to know that hospitalization will occur if weight falls below a specified minimum. Psychological treatment should always be coordinated with a physician who can assist in evaluating the client's medical status. While CBT treatment for bulimia is relatively brief (20 sessions), treatment for anorexia should be planned in terms of years rather than months. Initial sessions may be held more often than the once-per-week format used with bulimia.

Because treatment for this clientele is rarely voluntary, the therapist must concentrate on developing the therapeutic alliance. This may mean stressing that the counselor is not simply following the instructions of whoever initiated treatment. It also means that the therapist must instill hope that this disorder is treatable.

Weight goals are a major focus of treatment, all the more so in early stages of treatment when the client must gain weight. Each session begins with a weight check, and the results direct the remainder of the session. If the client achieves their weight goals, the counselor and client can address other issues. If not, the weight becomes the focus, with problem solving directed toward resolving the barriers to compliance. As treatment progresses and the client achieves their weight goals, the psychological concerns such as self-esteem, perfectionism, expression of feelings, and dealing with conflict can occupy more of the treatment time.

Clinicians have to modify CBT use with clients with binge-eating disorder. Unlike those with bulimia, these clients do not restrict food intake nor do they overvalue thinness as an ideal. Depression is common in this group (Grilo et al., 2021), and shame and self-consciousness are important themes. Those with other eating disorders often receive praise when they lose weight, while clients who binge eat face scorn and rejection based on their weight. Bulimics overuse exercise to compensate for binge eating, while exercise is typically absent in binge-eating disorder.

Some modifications in the CBT approach with binge-eating disorder clients include providing information about obesity, promoting an exercise regimen, extensive nutrition education, and modification of eating habits. While these clients tend not to have distorted body images, they do have "body image disparagement" and will benefit from accepting and caring for a larger-than-average body. With CBT, at least 50% of clients with binge-eating disorder recover, although many may fail to lose weight (Grilo et al., 2021). CBT treatment tends to be somewhat longer for binge eating than bulimia, and experts recommend individual as opposed to group treatment formats for most clients.

Interpersonal Therapy

Interpersonal therapy for eating disorders (IPT or IPT-ED) is also considered an evidence-based treatment. This approach is intended to address significant interpersonal problems that are thought to maintain the eating disorder (Sivyer et al., 2020). This approach to the treatment of eating disorders is a modification of an IPT model used for depression. IPT is a good alternative to CBT, but IPT is slower than CBT at creating client change, and the response may be less pronounced than CBT (Fairburn et al., 2015).

The following overview of this approach describes Fairburn's (1997) model, designed for 15–20 sessions over 4–5 months and involving three stages. Readers who would like a "cookbook" for this approach will find it in his book or in Murphy et al. (2012).

In the initial stage of treatment, the client becomes familiar with the IPT approach. It is important for the client to realize that the eating disorder per se will *not* be the focus of the therapy; rather, this model emphasizes the primary role of interpersonal relationships in this disorder. Early sessions focus on identifying the client's particular interpersonal problems, by taking extensive histories, assessing the client's current relationships, and determining the interpersonal precipitators of binge/purge behaviors. Problems tend to be in one of four areas: unresolved grief, interpersonal role disputes, role transitions, and interpersonal deficits or difficulty with forming and maintaining relationships.

Once the problems are identified, the therapy moves into the second stage. IPT is a nondirective present-centered approach, with the therapist taking an active role. Sessions focus on the interpersonal issues of the client's choosing, but the therapist helps the client remain focused on the identified issues and clarifies and illuminates important points. The therapist provides a summary at the end of each session and periodically reviews the client's progress. The therapist stresses the importance of change, but the specific changes are the client's choice. In general, IPT counselors avoid behavioral techniques, although some role playing is used to assist the client with interpersonal goals. The final stage of treatment concentrates on preventing relapse, primarily by educating the client about likely challenges they will face in the recovery process after treatment has concluded.

Fairburn (1997) recommends that CBT-E be the first choice of approach with eating disordered clients because of its demonstrated effectiveness. IPT would be a good alternative when CBT does not seem to produce desired results.

Brief Solution-Focused Therapy

Brief solution-focused therapy has received considerable attention over time, perhaps because of the influence of managed care. This is probably the least intensive and most cost-effective approach available, using the minimum number of sessions necessary to accomplish the goals. McFarland (1995) provides excellent guide for this approach to treatment of eating disorders.

Brief solution-focused therapy adheres to a set of principles:

- Focus on the presenting problem.
- When the solution is identified, amplify it.
- Don't persist in ineffective interventions.

This is a strengths-based model based on the belief that the client has the resources to solve their own problems and in fact has already done so in some ways. It is a present- and future-focused model and does not advocate exploration of past or events. The therapeutic relationship is a collaborative one, with the client as the identified expert on their own situation.

In this model, the first session is critical. The counselor needs to learn about previous attempts at treatment and looks for what worked. Early on, the counselor will pose the standard solution-focused query, called the *miracle question*: "If a miracle happened tonight when you were sleeping that solved the problem, and you didn't know that because you were sleeping, what will be the first thing you'll notice tomorrow that will tell you the problem is solved?" The counselor probes for detail in the responses, which helps in developing specific goals. The next strategy is looking for exceptions, times when the problem was absent or less severe. This allows the therapist to learn about strategies that have already been successful. The therapist asks "scaling questions," such as "On a scale of 1 to 10, with 10 being the best ever and 1 being the worst, how would you rate the symptoms today?" Or the therapist might ask the client to identify a time when they were a 10, rate that day, and inquire about what they need to do to get a little closer to the 10. Specific, realistic goals are established. Many solution-focused therapists use a written message to the client from the therapist that are prepared during a short break in the last few minutes of the session. The message includes appropriate compliments, a restatement of counseling goals, and a homework assignment, including the reason for the assignment. Homework is an important component of solution-focused treatment.

In the second session, the counselor assesses the client's motivation to change. The session begins with a question such as "What is better since our last session?" (McFarland, 1995. p. 128.) Subsequent sessions continue to focus on exceptions to the problem, acknowledging the client's efforts and helping the client focus on what is effective.

This approach works in a group context, as well as in individual sessions. McFarland (1995) provides a session-by-session outline for an 8-week psychoeducational body image group. They also advocate the use of aftercare psychotherapy groups for 6 months following termination from individual therapy.

Acceptance and Commitment Therapy

Acceptance and commitment therapy (ACT; Hayes et al., 2011) is a transdiagnostic approach that has also gained quite a bit of attention since it was first introduced. Fogelkvist et al. (2021) describe ACT as being in a "third wave" of CBT. Researchers have found initial support for its application with eating disorder clients (Onnink et al., 2022). As its name implies, ACT focuses on "accepting" unwanted thoughts and feelings rather than attempting to change them while attempting to "commit" to behaviors that are more in alignment with the way a person wishes to live. With ACT, it is believed that attempts to control or avoid the unwanted thoughts and feelings can create additional stress. Clients are encouraged to develop *psychological flexibility*.

Readers interested in this conceptual model are encouraged to check out *ACT Made Simple: An Easy-to-read Primer on Acceptance and Commitment Therapy* by Hayes et al. (2019). The idea of developing psychological flexibility is in achieved in six core processes:

- Acceptance: Accepting the full range of your thoughts and feelings rather than avoiding, denying, or changing them.
- Defusion: Separating yourself from, and changing the way you react to, those negative thoughts and feelings.
- Present moment awareness: Being mindful in the present moment.
- Self as context: Taking a role of a more objective observer to let go of unhelpful self-concepts
- Values clarification: Choosing the values you wish to have, not values of others
- Committed action: Taking steps to make and incorporate changes that align with your values.

Self-Help Approaches

In some cases, counselors may use self-help via bibliotherapy if the client's symptoms are not severe. Self-help is unlikely to be useful with those who are anorexic and is more likely an option for clients with bulimia or binge-eating disorder. Self-help is clearly more economical than other forms of treatment and may provide assistance to clients who cannot or will not enroll in treatment programs. Some of the books available, however, are by authors with dubious credentials in the field of eating disorders and may contain inaccurate information. There have been very few research studies examining the impact of self-help books, but no clear evidence has emerged.

We like the book *Transforming Body Image: Learning to Love the Body You Have* both to recommend to motivated clients and to use as a source of material and exercises for education and outreach. Although there are numerous self-help books on the market, and clinicians have their own preferences, the ones we find most useful are Peter Cooper's (2021) Overcoming *Bulimia Nervosa and Binge Eating* and Gregory Jantz and Ann McMurray's (2010) *Hope, Help, & Healing for Eating Disorders: A Whole-person Approach to Treatment of Anorexia, Bulimia, and Disordered Eating*. These books are also helpful for parents and family members of clients with eating disorders.

Another self-help approach is sometimes helpful for bulimia or binge-eating disorders is the 12-step program Overeaters Anonymous. This is a nonprofessional support program led by members and follows the same structure as other 12-step programs. One of the positive aspects of this approach is the reduction of isolation and the sense of commonality of concerns. Meeting locations can be found on their website, www.oa.org. Many therapists advocate these self-help strategies in addition to rather than in place of professional treatment.

In addition to the approaches described, which reflect different beliefs about the causes and nature of eating disorders and beliefs about the change process, there are several different formats or contexts in which treatment can be provided. Most commonly used with eating disorders are individual, group, and family therapy. Because of the complexity of these disorders, a treatment team approach is often used. We will briefly review each of these modalities as they apply to eating disorders.

Group Therapy

Group therapy is common in treatment for eating disorders, although outcomes seem to be better with bulimia than anorexia. Groups are efficient formats for providing education, which is an essential component of treatment for eating disorders. Using the group format to provide essential information allows individual therapy to focus on more personal, individual concerns.

As with any group, screening and preparation of group members will ensure a better-functioning group. Clients who should not be in a group include those with psychotic symptoms, anger management problems, and so on. Setting expectations and formulating goals in presession meetings with clients will prepare clients for the experience and reduce uncertainty.

Group therapy might be one component of treatment, usually paired with individual therapy, but it also may at times be the only therapy a client receives. The curative factors that operate in most groups certainly influence eating disorders groups, but there are several features of the disorder that make groups particularly useful. For eating disordered clients, for whom secrecy maintains the disorder, disclosing to a supportive, nonjudgmental group is an important step in breaking that pattern of secrecy. Also, because these clients tend to be isolated and socially withdrawn, groups provide an opportunity for interpersonal interaction that may be lacking in their lives. Groups also demonstrate to clients that they are not alone in their struggle; the shame and secrecy that surround the behavior often keep the client from the awareness that others do this too.

Despite the widespread inclusion of group therapy in treatment programs for eating disorders, experts are not unanimous in their endorsement of this format. Claude-Pierre (1998) worries about *iatrogenic* potential and urges caution about using groups for this population. They point out that the group may become a vehicle for clients to reinforce each other's distorted thinking patterns and promote the tendency to share "trade secrets" about their disordered behaviors. For this reason, they advise against placing eating disordered clients in groups that are homogenous for that disorder. In an eating disorder group I (SB), one of the members was a binge eater who had never purged. Their intense interest in the bulimic behaviors of other members was not a good sign.

Iatrogenic: Negative outcomes caused by treatment

Counselors need to think about several questions when considering groups for eating disorders. One is whether the groups will include both anorexic and bulimic members. There are valid arguments for both positions. One major concern about groups for only anorexic clients is the tendency for them to imitate and reinforce each other's disorder. With only the leader(s) to model healthy behaviors, the interpersonal power of the group may be detrimental. However, mixed groups also present challenges. Clients may learn weight-loss techniques from each other, and those with bulimia who are normal weight may want to emulate the thinner image of the anorexics. Like other issue-specific groups, there is a danger that clients will see themselves as only able to relate to others with their problem, and this may exacerbate their feelings of social ostracism. Since anorexics tend to require longer term therapy, they are probably not best included in time-limited groups. If they are included in open groups with bulimic clients who exit more quickly, there may be a tendency to see themselves as hopeless. Each therapist will have to decide the heterogeneous versus homogeneous question based on the context of the particular group.

The leaders can structure an eating disorders group to prevent some of the unwanted behaviors from occurring. It is important to actively work to keep the group from reinforcing or teaching unhealthy behaviors. In setting ground rules, leaders can insist that members do not discuss any specific behaviors in the group. That is, members may not discuss *how* they purge but should focus on *what* behaviors the member would like support. For the same reason, discussion of specific weight gains or losses should also be discouraged, as it may engender unwanted competitiveness. Another behavior that should be discouraged is venting without accepting feedback. In order to keep the group from deteriorating into a litany of complaints, which can be contagious, leaders can model how to frame concerns in a way that will produce growth. For example, instead of saying "Therapy sucks," the therapist can reframe the concern as "I'm frustrated that I am not making more progress," or "It's hard for me to practice new behaviors and sometimes I wonder if I will ever recover." It is also important not to allow the group to normalize or glamorize the eating disorder (Costin, 1999). Seeing that everyone else in the group has the same behavior may suggest that it is normal, which is something the leader needs to actively guard against. It is also important to keep the group from providing extra attention to the clients with the worst symptoms.

Concerns that are more practical may also drive the composition of the group. Although eating disorders are common in adolescents, they are not exclusive to that age group. A group composed of members with a wide age range and varied life circumstances may have difficulty becoming cohesive. The questions of leadership and open versus closed groups may need to defer to circumstance. For example, in some settings with changing populations, such as inpatient facilities, open groups are necessary. Leaders may not always have suitable coleaders available with whom to work.

Family Therapy

A number of pioneers in the field of family therapy did seminal work on families of clients with anorexia, so family therapy has a tradition with eating disorders. Costin (1999) proclaimed that for youthful clients, "family therapy is necessary for recovery" (p. 173). Family-based treatment (FBT) achieves greater weight gain and higher remission rates than individual treatment for

Enmeshment: An unhealthy extreme of family involvement, characterized by excessive closeness. Boundaries between individuals are blurred, and family members are emotionally overreactive to one another.

clients with anorexia (and remission rates for clients with bulimia; Couturier et al., 2020). Although the various schools of family therapy differ in some theoretical and technical aspects, there are features that are widely accepted as characteristic of families in which eating disorders emerge: enmeshment, overprotectiveness, rigidity, and absence of conflict resolution. Some experts believe that the symptoms of the eating disordered client actually help the family avoid other conflict (Dare & Eisler, 1997). However, the areas of family malfunctioning can vary in terms of family structure and dysfunctional patterns. In general, an integrated approach is appropriate for conceptualizing the family from a systemic perspective (Erriu et al., 2020).

Family therapists see eating disorders as a symptom of dysfunction in the family system, so treating the whole system is the logical approach. Family therapists can be highly active and directive. The general design of family therapy proceeds in phases. In the first and essential phase, the therapist must gain the family's involvement and cooperation. This is sometimes difficult, because the person with the eating disorder is the "identified client" and others in the family may resist examining their own role in the problem. Education about the potential medical complications from the disorder may assist in winning the family's participation.

The next phase of family therapy involves assessing the structure and organization of the family, seeking to understand the role of the eating disorder in the system. This can be a very complex process, determined by multiple factors (Erriu et al., 2020). It is only after these tasks that the family therapist can implement interventions designed to change the system so that the member with eating disorder can give up the symptom.

Family therapy interventions may need to disrupt the dysfunctional organization in the family and change the structure, often by encouraging a stronger united parental unit with clearer boundaries. One technique is for the therapist to attend a family meal, with the parents encouraged to take charge. Some schools of family therapy favor paradoxical interventions, such as prescribing "no change for now," expecting the family to defy the instructions and change (Dare & Eisler, 1997).

Costin (1999) indicated that in many families in which individuals develop eating disorders, there is a pattern of equating self-worth with achievement. They observed alternating patterns of enmeshment and disengagement in many of the families they had treated. They see the tasks of family therapy to be educating the family about the eating disorder, examining the impact of the eating disorder on all family members, reducing blame, understanding parental expectations for the children, elucidating the client's role in the family, addressing any abuse issues, adjusting the structure of the family (e.g., by strengthening the parental alliance), and pointing out and changing destructive interaction patterns within the family.

Disengagement: Family members do not show concern for each other and live very separate lives. This is the opposite end of the continuum from *enmeshment.*

Some treatment programs incorporate multifamily therapy (MFT) groups into the treatment plan. This format provides support for parents, an opportunity to observe how other families respond, and the experience of learning from others. There has been some empirical support for the use of MFT (in comparison to single-family therapy; Couturier et al., 2020).

Multidisciplinary Team Approaches

The *Best Practice Guidelines*, fourth edition, published in 2023 by the American Psychiatric Association recommends collaboration by clinicians implementing components of treatment for eating disorders (medical, psychiatric, psychological, and nutritional expertise). Given the medical dangers that accompany this disorder, a physician is an important member of the team who can thoroughly assess the client's medical condition and assist in decision-making regarding the need for hospitalization. In many cases of bulimia, it may be necessary to have a dental evaluation as well. Because medication can be used along with other therapies, a psychiatrist who can prescribe and monitor the effectiveness of medication is also important. Individual and/or group therapists are most likely to provide the psychological treatment to the client, but if family therapy is added, treatment outcomes may improve. A nutritionist is an essential member of the team. Nutritional rehabilitation is an essential goal in treatment of eating disorders, and a specialist in nutrition makes a valuable contribution to the overall treatment program.

Issues of Diversity

At one time, the conventional view of eating disorders was that it is a disease of young White women. We now know that is no longer the case, if it ever was. We will now discuss issues related to males with eating disorders and then look at racial and ethnic differences, sexual orientation, and disabilities as they relate to this issue.

The NEDA (2017a) reports that one in three people with an eating disorder is male, with subclinical disordered eating (not qualifying for an ED diagnosis) being nearly as common among men as they are with women. Men who participate in certain sports for which weight is a perceived factor in performance may be especially prone to the disorder. Sports such as wrestling, gymnastics, swimming, horse racing, and running, for example, all promote the notion of low weight as a performance advantage. There are several ways experts agree that males differ from females with the disorder: (a) They are less likely to have *anorexia nervosa*, and (b) they are less likely to seek treatment for the disorder. Physicians may overlook the possibility of eating disorders in their male patients, while they are more alert to the symptoms in females.

Studies have found that men with eating disorders are more likely to have been obese as children and teased by peers. For example, in Abou-Saleh et al.'s (1998) report of five cases of anorexia in Arab clients, both males were adolescent, and both had been obese at one time and subject to teasing as a result. The weight of males with eating disorders fluctuates more than the weight of women. Although relatively few men are diagnosed with anorexia, the medical complications tend to be more severe in males. Like many females with eating disorders, males who were sexually abused as children may wish to reverse signs of sexual maturity through weight loss. Decreased levels of testosterone and sexual desire can be consequences of weight loss in males, equivalent to the cessation of menstrual periods in women. The age of onset of eating disorders seems to be later in males than females; as puberty also occurs later in males, the increased risk at that time may explain the difference in timing.

Researchers consider it crucial to pinpoint cultural elements that could distinguish eating disorders across various racial and ethnic groups (Rodgers et al., 2018). However, it seems empirical information on racial and ethnic representation in eating disorders is limited. Ethnic and racial differences in eating disorders are difficult to quantify, as different studies use different methods of assessment—and some don't report on the race or ethnicity of the study participants (Egbert et al., 2022). In a review conducted by Egbert et al. in 2022, they examined research conducted over a 2-decade span. Their findings revealed that among studies that included information on race and ethnicity, 70% of the participants were White, while 10% were of Hispanic/Latinx descent. Participants from all other racial and ethnic backgrounds each comprised less than 5% of the total.

Rodgers et al. (2018) reviewed literature published between 2015 to 2018 in order to provide an update of the current understanding of eating disorders across race and ethnicity.

Asian and Asian American

- May have an increased likelihood of engaging in disordered eating and unhealthy weight control behaviors, compared to people from all other racial/ethnic groups. Adolescent girls report the highest rates of disordered eating, and adolescent boys report the highest rates of dieting, unhealthy weight control behaviors, and overeating.
- Asian American, college-aged men endorse higher concerns regarding body image, a desire for more muscularity, and internalization of an "ideal male body"—in comparison to college-aged White and Black men.
- Asian men who reported binge-eating behaviors also reported higher rates of compulsive exercise.

Hispanic/Latinx

- Lower prevalence rates of anorexia (compared to non-Hispanic Whites) but comparable rates of bulimia and binge-eating disorder.
- Higher prevalence of recurrent overeating (compared to non-Hispanic Whites) and higher reports of being upset and more fearful of weight gain due to binge-eating.
- Some research suggests fewer weight concerns, less dieting, and fewer exercise behaviors than all other racial/ethnic groups. However, eating disorder symptoms may be a concern for those who have a higher BMI.

Black/African American

- Findings on the prevalence of disordered eating are mixed.
- There is a higher average BMI among Black/African American men compared to White or Asian American men, but they report higher body satisfaction. There is a lower prevalence of negative feelings about binge eating and a lower prevalence of being fearful of weight gain due to binge eating.
- Prevalence of dieting was lowest among Black girls, compared to all other racial/ethnic groups.
- Black girls endorsed the lowest prevalence of unhealthy weight-control behaviors among all groups studied. However, when weight status was considered, the risk of unhealthy weight-control behaviors was higher for Black girls than any other racial or ethnic identity.
- College-aged Black women endorsed lower levels of eating disorders.

There has been a longstanding assumption that only those of higher SES display or endorse eating disorders. This assumption is false, as eating disorders are present across all levels of SES (Burke et al., 2023). Burke et al. (2023) found that people with lower SES had a greater prevalence of eating disorders than those of higher SES, particularly those with multiple minority identities. They recommend that it is highly important to consider the multiple layers of identity constructs (race/ethnicity, gender identity, sexual orientation) when working with clients and attempting to identify risk.

Body dissatisfaction, eating disorders, and disordered eating behaviors are common among sexual and gender minority populations (Nagata et al., 2020). Nagata et al. (2020) found that the lifetime prevalence of eating disorder diagnoses are higher among sexual minority adults when compared to cisgender, heterosexual adults—and are even higher for transgender men and transgender women. They posit that body dissatisfaction may be a core stressor experienced by transgender people—which may perpetuate disordered eating behaviors.

Persons who are from non-Westernized cultures may have different cultural practices regarding food and different idealized body images (Abou-Saleh et al., 1998; Krentz & Arthur, 2001), and therefore eating disorders may be less prevalent.

Asceticism: Practice of self-discipline and self-denial as a route to spiritual growth

For example, among some religious groups in Southeast Asia, asceticism (including severe food restriction) is considered a route to spiritual growth. The Muslim tradition includes fasting during the holy month of Ramadan, which must not be seen as an example of disordered eating. An interesting observation of the impact of cultural context on eating disorders is found in Abou-Saleh et al.'s (1998) report of cases of anorexia nervosa in the United Arab Emirates. These researchers cite the previous work of Nasser, who found disordered eating attitudes in twice as many Arab female students in a London university than in a matched sample attending a Cairo university. They describe five cases of anorexia, three in females and two in males. They speculate that as the country becomes more Westernized, the incidence of the disorder will increase.

Persons With Disabilities

There are few population-based studies that examined the incidence of eating disorders in persons with disabilities. Emerson (2003) analyzed data from 10, 438 children ages 5–15 in England and found no significant differences in the prevalence of eating disorders in children with and without intellectual disabilities. In contrast, Gravestock (2003) reviewed the literature and found studies demonstrating an association between eating disorders and several syndromes and disorders (e.g., Down's, Kleine-Levin, Kluver-Bucy, Turner and Williams syndromes, phenylketonuria, and autism). Gravestock (2003) observed that due to the complicated diagnostic profiles or both eating disorders and intellectual disabilities, it is likely that many cases of eating disorders are not appropriately diagnosed in this population. The lack of expressive language can interfere with the clinician's attempts to gather needed information for a diagnosis of eating disorders. Gravestock also noted that when the concept of eating disorder is expanded to include *abnormal eating behaviors* (AEBs), there are many cases of eating disorders in individuals with intellectual

Abnormal Eating Behaviors

Pica: Eating non-nutritive substances (e.g., clay, plaster, sand) on a persistent basis

Rumination/regurgitation: Repeated regurgitation and rechewing of food without accompanying nausea or intestinal disorder

Food faddiness/refusal: An obsession with eating only certain types of food/strict avoidance of certain foods or categories of food

impairments. AEBs are defined as food faddiness/refusal, rumination/regurgitation, and pica. It is notable that these disorders are diagnosed in infancy or early childhood, but in adults with severe or profound intellectual disabilities, they may emerge or persist.

Some intellectual disabilities are genetic and may involve biological impairments that manifest as AEBs. In other cases for which brain damage exists (including epilepsy), there may be neurological involvement or mineral deficiencies that increase the risk for both AEBs and eating disorders (Gravestock, 2003). Some disabilities have physical complications, such as dental problems, hernias, and constipation or diarrhea, that can make eating unpleasant or painful and thus might contribute to eating disorders.

It seems logical that since the development of eating disorders requires a distorted body image, those who do not have the ability to create visual images—those who are blind or visually impaired—would be less likely to develop these disorders (Krentz & Arthur, 2001; van de Wege & Vandereycken, 1995). Research has not supported this position; eating disorders do occur in this population, and a distorted body image is not a prerequisite. Krentz and Arthur suggest that eating disorders may arise from the efforts of blind or visually impaired persons to gain some control in their lives. Among deaf and hearing-impaired persons, binge eating was reported less frequently than by those without hearing impairments, but twice as many deaf women (21%) as deaf men did report disordered eating behaviors. One possible explanation for these findings is that deaf and visually impaired people are aware of cultural ideals of thinness and attempt to cope with their disabilities by having perfect, unimpaired, bodies.

Clients with type 1 diabetes have a higher prevalence of eating disorders than the general population, and having diabetes increases the risk of displaying or developing disordered eating behaviors (Albaladejo et al., 2023; Hanlan et al., 2013; Scheuing et al., 2014). Treatment of diabetes (whether type 1 or type 2) typically involves (and encourages) a major focus of food, what is consumed on a daily basis (i.e., eating patterns), the importance of weight control, and exercise. In addition, during the initial diagnosis of diabetes, there is usually an episode of weight loss as a result of the disease. If an insulin regimen is applied, there is usually an increase in body weight as a result. Those clients who use an insulin pump (or daily injections) may misuse their insulin (up to 39% of those clients) in an effort to lose weight (Albaladejo et al., 2023). Children with type 1 diabetes may perceive their parents as overprotective or controlling, a similar perception of younger people with eating disorders. Both situations may result in in the client displaying acts of rebellion or acts of independence related to problematic eating behaviors (ANRED, n.d.b.). The development of disordered eating, or an actual eating disorder, is atypical in comparison to other populations—and can increase the risk of diabetes-related health complications.

An additional issue worthy of mention is that many psychoactive medications that are commonly prescribed to persons with intellectual or psychiatric disabilities have side effects of increased appetite and weight gain. This may be an additional risk factor for eating disorders in individuals with disabilities.

What this information means for the counselor is that when working with clients with disabilities, regardless of the presenting issues, screening and frank discussion of eating disorders will ensure that this problem is not overlooked. In addition, it is helpful for a mental health provider to communicate with physicians who provide care for the disability to ensure that possible interactions are identified.

Counselor Issues

Counselors' own beliefs and attitudes about a topic, along with their personal experiences, cannot help but affect the way they relate to clients. Eating disorders are not an exception to this challenge. In fact, it is particularly important for counselors to recognize that the same media and societal pressures that affect their clients affect them, and they must be alert to how their own concerns about weight and food affect their clients.

Therapists may need to consider the impact of their appearance on clients. What message is your body giving to clients? For the thin or average-weight therapist, clients may wonder (and ask) whether you have an eating disorder or how you keep weight at that level. If you are overweight, how do you present yourself? Are you confident with a positive self-image, or embarrassed and concerned about your weight? Just as parents' attitudes and behaviors affect children, the modeling by therapists has a considerable impact on clients, particularly those with eating disorders, and the clinician needs to be mindful of this.

A decision about self-disclosure when the therapist does have a history of eating disorders is not an easy one. One group of researchers found that recovery self-disclosures may increase recovery motivation for clients with an eating disorder (Wasil et al., 2019). An interesting article about one clinician's struggle to decide whether or not to disclose to their group and later to an individual client (Bloomgarden, 2000) concludes with some useful questions counselors might ask themselves about self-disclosure that would apply to any issue. Two important ones relate to boundaries—if one withholds relevant personal information, are the boundaries too close so that the therapist is detached from the clients, and if one chooses to self-disclose too easily, are the boundaries too diffuse, so there is no distinction between therapist and client? What are the risks in telling clients about your history? Readers who are struggling with these concerns may wish to read the article in its entirety.

Clients with anorexia are especially difficult to treat. Their fears of gaining weight are so intense, and their self-image so dependent on their weight, that they are likely to resist the counselors' best efforts to help. Counselors who work with these clients need to consider their own tolerance for frustration and how they will balance their own need to be helpful against a clientele that does not want to be helped, despite their severe condition. In addition, this disorder has the highest mortality rate of any psychiatric disorder, other than opioid use disorder (American Psychiatric Association, n.d.; Auger et al., 2021). Thus, there is the distinct possibility that a counselor will have to deal with the death of a client. Counselors who work with this clientele should seek consultation and supervision from other professionals with whom they can process their own reactions and responses to their work.

A NOTE TO SCHOOL COUNSELORS

What is the best approach for school counselors in addressing this problem? As school leaders, school counselors might begin by assessing the ways in which the school climate promotes an unhealthy emphasis on thinness. Examining the practices related to weight in athletics and cheerleading, taking an active stance against weight- and shape-related teasing, and noting how healthy eating habits are, or are not, promoted in the school are the first steps in making positive changes in the overall school climate.

Because school counselors have regular contact with the vulnerable population (young adolescents and adolescents), they are in a position to "identify at-risk individuals, implement effective school-based prevention programs, make appropriate referrals, and provide support for recovering individuals" (Bardick et al., 2004, p. 168). Youth who are close to puberty are prime targets for prevention programming (Omizo & Omizo, 1992). Note that providing treatment is not appropriate or possible in the school setting, but the school counselor may be the first professional to recognize the need for further assessment and treatment, and in so doing may be the first line of defense. Eating disorders, like many of the issues discussed in this book, have the best outcomes when detected and treated early.

Prevention is an important strategy to reduce the harmful consequences of eating disorders. However, Schiele et al. (2020) observed that many school mental health professions lack training and confidence in their ability to conduct prevention activities related to eating disorders. Research evaluating the effects of prevention programs for eating disorders has found moderate positive effects, but programs that utilize testimonials from recovering celebrities or peers are discouraged, as they may glamorize the behaviors the program hopes to discourage (Yager & O'Dea, 2005). Likewise, Bardick et al. (2004) caution that providing information to students that includes a list of specific eating disordered behaviors may cause some vulnerable youth to experiment with such behaviors. The experts stress the need for school counselors to obtain training in order to ensure they are well prepared to deliver such programs and to collaborate with other professionals both within the school environment (health instructors, school nurses) and in the community (physicians, nutritionists) to design a prevention strategy.

Identifying at-risk individuals begins with educating all staff about eating disorders and enlisting their cooperation. A brief in-service presentation to faculty and staff, followed by some printed material, can alert them to danger signs. Faculty involved with students in high-risk activities (cheerleaders, gymnasts, wrestlers, dancers, etc.) should

(Continued)

be particularly vigilant for signs of incipient disordered eating behaviors. Your job is to take a closer look at those children and determine whether further intervention is appropriate.

Once a student has been identified as at risk, talking with them is a first step, but denial of a problem is often the response. The skilled school counselor will use empathy, observation, and skillful questioning to get a sense of whether this student needs further intervention. It is important to share, in a nonjudgmental manner, your observations and concerns with the student honestly and directly. If the school counselor believes the concern is warranted, parents must be notified. This, too, is a process that must be handled sensitively; the counselor should express concern for the student's well-being and suggest that the family seek an assessment from a specialist in eating disorders to evaluate the situation. School counselors are well aware of how referrals to outside agencies must be made to avoid financial liability, but having a list of resources in the community is very helpful.

When students receive outside treatment for eating disorders, the school counselor can provide support at school either during or after treatment. Schiele et al. (2020) suggest that this level of support from school mental health providers can decrease the prevalence of disordered eating among students, shorten the time span between identification of problems and intervention, and decrease the likelihood of relapse. Omizo and Omize (1992) suggest that support groups at school for students with eating disorders can be very helpful. We urge school counselors who are considering such groups to reread the section on group therapy to be aware of the potential pitfalls in such groups.

School counselors, although they may not provide treatment, provide many services that assist students with eating disorders. They are in a unique position, having both contact and awareness, to influence the school climate with respect to the ways an emphasis on appearance and bodily perfection can be promoted.

Ethical Concerns

Perhaps the most common dilemma for counselors is that of client competence to consent to treatment. As discussed, there are cognitive effects of eating disorders that may impair the client's ability to make informed decisions about treatment. However, the clinician should not assume that the client is incompetent to consent to treatment simply by virtue of the diagnosis. Rather, the clinician must carefully assess the client's capacity to understand the nature of treatment, why it is necessary, and what the consequences might be of not receiving treatment. Unfortunately, there are no clear standards by which to determine this competency, and the clinicians must rely on professional judgment to make these decisions. Informed consent should be an ongoing process, not something only discussed at the beginning of treatment. Clients' capacities may improve or deteriorate, circumstances may change, and clients may need frequent reminders of their choices. These decisions are even more complex when the client is a child. Although the parent may give consent, it is essential that the child also understand the decisions to the fullest extent possible.

In addition, there are situations in which the clinician may recommend involuntary treatment or hospitalization, which impinges on client autonomy. Making an ethically sound decision involves considering whether less intrusive methods have been tried, whether there is a medical emergency, and the likely effect on the therapeutic alliance. If the client is at substantial risk and is unwilling to consent to treatment, the clinician may want to involve a treatment team to consider involuntary treatment. Client safety is the most important consideration, and the team should consider and evaluate all possible alternatives. The goal should be to empower the client to make informed decisions on their own behalf. It is important that decisions regarding involuntary treatment be made compassionately, with concern for feelings of both client and significant others, and with the certainty that the decision is made for the client's welfare rather than the convenience of treatment team or family members. Note that researchers have found no significant differences in the short-term response to treatment between voluntary and involuntary patients (Watson et al., 2000).

Summary

- Eating disorders are widespread in Western cultures and are found in males and females from all racial and ethnic groups.
- The following diagnoses are used to describe eating disorders: anorexia nervosa, bulimia nervosa, binge eating disorders, OSFED, ARFID, pica, and rumination disorder. Orthorexia may also be an issue of clinical concern, but it is not currently a DSM-5 disorder.
- Although eating disorders are considered mental disorders, there are serious physical and medical complications that may develop.
- Many people who do not meet criteria for diagnosis engage in disordered eating behaviors.
- Childhood experiences contribute to later development of eating disorders. Perfectionism has been linked to eating disorders, and childhood teasing about weight, especially by parents, is also a common precursor.
- A variety of formal assessment instruments are available for determining if eating disorders are present.
- Cognitive behavioral approaches have the most empirical support for treating eating disorders, but interpersonal therapy and brief-solution focused therapy may also be helpful.
- Treatment includes individual, group, and family therapy. Clinicians should be familiar with advantages and disadvantages of each modality and know for which clients each is most likely to be helpful.
- A multidisciplinary team approach to treatment is advised due to the many aspects of these disorders.
- Self-help programs and reading are often useful adjuncts to professional treatment.
- Counselors must be aware of the effect of their own attitudes and appearance on clients with eating disorders.
- This population is difficult to treat, and clinicians need a high frustration tolerance to work with this clientele.
- Ethical concerns about involuntary hospitalization may be confronted, especially with anorexia. Clinicians need clear guidelines for making ethical decisions.

Additional Resources

On the Web

- https://www.nationaleatingdisorders.org/ is NEDA's website, a nonprofit organization dedicated to supporting individuals and families affected by eating disorders. They have an online screening tool in addition to information, forums, and a database of treatment providers.
- www.anred.com is the website for Anorexia Nervosa and Related Eating Disorders, Inc. and has a wealth of excellent information and links. Information is clear and succinct, which makes it a good site to recommend to clients.
- www.EDreferral.com is also one that clients might find helpful. It has good information on research, and even has contact information for clients who might like to be subjects in

research studies on eating disorders. There is an electronic mailing list clients can subscribe to via this site that provides monthly updates on the latest research and events of interest.
- https://anad.org/ is the site of the National Association of Anorexia Nervosa and Associated Disorders and has a variety of information on referrals, including support groups.
- www.nedic.ca is the Canadian National Eating Disorders Information Centre site, which has the advantage of having both reading lists and links include excellent summaries so the user can get an idea of what they will find in those further resources. In addition, this site has an active EDTalk Discussion list, which might be useful for both practitioners and clients. For school counselors, there is a terrific website hosted by the U.S. Department of Health and Human Resources that has material the counselor can use immediately and distribute to teachers or parents:
- http://www.eatingdisorderresources.com/ is an excellent source of movies and videos useful for psychoeducational groups and/or for presentations.
- https://www.choosingtherapy.com/best-eating-disorder-recovery-apps/ is Choosing Therapy's list of top eating disorder apps.

In Print for Counselors

- *Handbook of Treatment for Eating Disorders* by Garner and Garfinkel is thorough, comprehensive, well researched, and highly readable.
- *Handbook of Eating Disorders* by Brownell and Foreyt is an excellent edited volume, although it is a little dated. It includes obesity as an eating disorder.
- *Eating Disorders Sourcebook* by Costin is a less technical volume with considerable useful information that is palatable for professionals and consumers alike and may be particularly helpful for family members of clients with eating disorders. The second edition includes detailed information about many treatment programs around the country.
- *When Dieting Becomes Dangerous: A Guide to Understanding and Treating Anorexia and Bulimia* by Michel and Willard is very useful and readable for both professionals and family members.
- *The Body Betrayed* by Kathryn Zerbe is less treatment focused but provides an excellent background on all aspects of eating disorders. It is well researched but not dense, so would make a good addition to a clinician's bookshelf.
- *Brief Therapy and Eating Disorders* by McFarland describes brief solution-focused approach in cookbook-type fashion for the novice therapist to follow.
- *Practice Guideline for the Treatment of Patients With Eating Disorders* (fourth edition) has an extraordinary amount of information in a small volume. It is available in a print version and for download from the association's website. This is an essential reference for any helping professional who provides services for this disorder.

In Print for Clients

- *The Intuitive Eating Workbook: Ten Principles for Nourishing a Healthy Relationship With Food* by Evelyn Tribole and Elyse Resch.
- *Sick Enough: A Guide to the Medical Complications of Eating Disorders* by Jennifer Gaudiani.
- *The Brain Over Binge Recovery Guide: A Simple and Personalized Plan for Ending Bulimia and Binge Eating Disorder* by Kathryn Hansen and Amy Johnson.
- *The Eating Disorder Recovery Journal* by Cara Lisette and Victoria Barron.
- *The Body Keeps the Score: Brain, Mind, and Body in the Healing of Trauma* by Bessel van der Kolk.

- *Overcoming Binge Eating* by Fairburn is great for clients with bulimia or binge-eating disorder. The author is a respected expert in the field and has published empirical support for the approach. The book is in two parts, with the first providing background information and the second presenting a specific self-help approach to stopping binge eating. It is reads easily, and the format is user friendly.
- *Bulimia Nervosa and Binge Eating: A Guide to Recovery* by Peter J. Cooper. The format is similar to that of Fairburn's book, in that part one provides background information and education about the disorders, while part two is a self-help manual complete with useful worksheets and examples.
- *Dying to Be Thin* by Sacker and Zimmer is quite popular. The strength and weakness of the book are the numerous case histories, which illustrate the points but may take space from the necessary information. It includes advice sections for parents, friends, and teachers of those with eating disorders.
- *Hope, Help, & Healing for Eating Disorders* by Gregory Jantz is another popular self-book book based on what he calls his "whole person" approach that addresses physical, emotional, relational, and spiritual domains. He suggests that the book as a companion to therapy. One strong reservation I have is the exclusively Christian interpretation of spirituality. Not all clients will share that perspective.
- *Anorexia Nervosa: A Survival Guide for Families, Friends, and Sufferers* by Treasure could be suggested to clients and family members. Given the dangers of anorexia, I am leery of relying on bibliotherapy alone but do think some reading can be appropriate in conjunction with treatment. This book does offer many specific and practical suggestions for families, and even has sections for teachers and family physicians.
- *Helping Your Teenager Beat an Eating Disorder* by James Lock and Daniel Le Grange is a recent book to recommend to parents.

Novels for Counselors and Clients

- *The Best Little Girl in the* World by Steven Levenkron is almost a classic on this topic.
- *Wasted* by Marya Hornbacher is a memoir of a bright and articulate young woman's struggle with eating disorders. The author is one of the women featured in the video *Perfect Illusions*.
- *My Sister's Bones* by Cathi Hanauer is a novel about two sisters' battles with eating disorders.
- *Second Star to the Right* by Deborah Hautzig is written from the perspective of the person with an eating disorder.
- *Stick Figure* by Lori Gottlieb aid the clinician in gaining insight into eating disorders.
- *Unglamored* by Jessie Cheng is a story about a Chinese American fictional pop star.
- *The Girls at 17 Swann Street* by Yara Zgheib is a novel about a young woman's struggle with anorexia.

Film and Television

- A commercial film, *Real Women Have Curves* is one of the only popular media productions in which a female protagonist has a healthy body image despite immense pressures to be thin. I strongly recommend this film, which would also be wonderful for adolescent girls to view.
- A PBS special called *Perfect Illusion: Eating Disorders and the Family* is also an outstanding program for clients and for general presentations for which the goal is to raise awareness of eating disorders.
- *Dumplin* is a film not necessarily about eating disorders—but about body acceptance and positivity.

Exercises

1. Reflect on your personal body image and level of body satisfaction. Go to www.halls.md/body-mass-index/bmi.htm and calculate your BMI. Think about your results and discuss or write about your reactions. Then consider how your feelings about your own appearance and weight might impact your work with a client with an eating disorder.

2. Assume you have an adult client with anorexia nervosa who needs hospitalization due to their unwillingness to cooperate with weight gain goals. How will you proceed?

3. Assume you have been working with a client with anorexia nervosa. They have attained their weight goal and resumed regular menstrual cycles. The client proclaims that they are cured and wishes to terminate treatment. How will you evaluate the appropriate of termination? If you decide termination is not yet appropriate, how will you present that to the client?

4. You have a client you are treating for depression, but you realize they also have an eating disorder. How will you approach this situation?

5. Assume you have a male client who has an eating disorder. You require all your clients to attend a group, and all other group members are female. How might you proceed?

6. Assume you are working with a 10-year-old girl whom you believe is at high risk for later development of an eating disorder. She has been sexually abused, which is the reason for referral. She exhibits many perfectionistic traits. She describes her family as "too busy" to do many things together. How will you attempt to implement preventive strategies to shield her from eating disorders?

7. If you don't treat clients with eating disorders, how will you go about making a referral to someone who discloses this problem to you after several sessions?

8. Assume you accept an invitation to a middle-school class to talk about body image. What will you cover? What videos, if any, will you show? What activities might you include?

9. Watch *Real Women Have Curves*. Pay attention to your reaction to the scene in which the women work in the underclothes. Discuss your reactions with your classmates. Talk or write about your impression of the protagonist and the family dynamics. How is it that Ana is able to resist all the pressure to lose weight and to value herself based on her appearance?

10. Watch *Perfect Illusions*. Discuss or write about your responses to the many negative statements that were made about therapists and treatment.

11. Use a jigsaw activity to share responses to the novels recommended in this chapter. Form groups of four students, each of whom reads one of the novels. In the group, share what you learned as a clinician from the novel and what you learned about yourself. As a group, create a list of cogent points summarizing your learning. The group might then compile a list of do's and don'ts for working with clients with eating disorders and their families, based on insights gained from their reading.

CHAPTER 9

Self-Harm

F ew mental health professionals will have careers that do not include at least one client who self-harms. The goal of this chapter is to provide readers with sufficient information to be able to respond to these clients in a helpful way. For readers who decide not to treat these clients, we hope the increased knowledge will allow them to make referrals without suggesting that clients are hopeless. We will begin with a case study of someone who self-harms in order to place the concepts in a context.

CASE STUDY

Renee is a 37-year-old Black woman who has been self-injuring for most of the last 20 years. She is one of seven children in a military family who presented a well-functioning face to the community but whose private world was dysfunctional. Her father was an alcoholic, and her mother was highly critical of the children, often making cruel comments and using physical methods of discipline. As a child, Renee was convinced that her mother did not like her.

Like many self-injurers, Renee has expressed her pain via other symptoms in addition to self-injuring. She has abused drugs, made several suicide attempts, and has exhibited disordered eating. Also, like many others with this problem, Renee is a victim of childhood sexual abuse. She had repressed her memories of the abuse by her father for many years, but then began having flashbacks and eventually recovered those memories. The abuse occurred when she was very young, and if her mother knew, she did nothing to protect Renee or stop the abuse.

Although she did some scratching of names on her arm as a young teen, Renee's first serious act of self-harm occurred when she was a 17-year-old inpatient in a psychiatric facility. She felt overwhelmed with anger and rage that she was unable to contain and needed to do something to relieve the tension. She saw a nail on the floor and plunged it into her arm. It worked—the tension subsided, which set the stage for a pattern that continued for several decades.

During the worst periods of self-harm, Renee would engage in self-harming behaviors several times a day. Her preferred method was puncture, using scissors, knives, pens, and pencils, because that would do serious damage and cause more suffering, which she believed she deserved. She mutilated her arms, which allowed her to easily see the scars as a reminder. At times, Renee would conceal the evidence of her behavior under her sleeves, but at other times she would self-injure openly, in front of others—friends, therapists, her father. She felt rewarded by their shocked reactions and by the solicitous responses that sometimes followed. When her father would learn that

(Continued)

she had self-harmed, he would take her shopping for new clothes; she got a reward for her self-harming behaviors! Renee used this behavior to express what she was unable at that time to express in words: "I want you to know my pain, how much I hurt."

For Renee, self-harming was an attempt to stop feeling intense emotional pain. Physical pain has a known source, while emotional pain seems endless and hopeless. The sight of blood running down from the wound was reinforcing: She was watching the pain and hurt flow out of her. She felt almost intoxicated by the smell of the blood, which made her want to cut more. Sometimes she would avoid cleaning it up, and when she later would see the stains on the floor, she would want to cut again.

Sometimes, Renee felt "cut off" from herself or numb, and the self-harming and bleeding was a way to feel alive. She says she did not feel the pain from the punctures, so she would often leave objects in the open wound (staples, paper clips) so that the wound would become infected—and then she would finally feel the pain. On three occasions, surgery was required to remove the objects from her arm.

Renee has seen many therapists over the years but credits her current therapist with helping her to finally stop self-harming. The clear boundaries that were set in early sessions have removed the rewards for self-harm. In the past, therapists would offer extra sessions when she hurt herself, which encouraged the behavior. Her present therapist made it clear that he would not accept emergency calls or have extra sessions in response to self-harming behavior. He continues to see her for regularly scheduled appointments but does not bring his dogs (whom she loves to see) when she has been hurting herself. She finds these behavioral methods to be extremely effective. She also values the list she and her therapist created for alternatives to self-harming behavior when she feels the urge to do so. She keeps it with her and can access it when needed. The list includes permission to call the therapist instead of hurting herself, and she has done this with good success. With these strategies to control the self-harming behavior, Renee has been able to work in therapy to deal with the many traumas she has experienced and to create hope for her future. Learning to express feelings directly, in words, has been extremely difficult for Renee, but she believes her therapist has encouraged her and supported her efforts to do so. She believes she no longer needs to self-harm to express her feelings and that she will be able to continue to resist the impulse to do so when she notices it.

Definitions and Description of Problem

Self-harm is a baffling behavior because it appears so contrary to the innate human desire to avoid pain. Other terms are sometimes used to describe this behavior (self-injury, nonsuicidal self-injury, self-wounding, and self-mutilation), but self-harming is the most widely used and the most precise. Self-harm is not a separate mental disorder, but it is a symptom of several disorders; borderline personality disorder is probably most commonly diagnosed, but posttraumatic stress disorder and dissociative disorder are also used. This behavior also occurs in individuals with bipolar disorder, major depression, anxiety disorders, and schizophrenia.

Self-harm refers to intentional, nonlethal, repetitive bodily harm or disfigurement that is socially unacceptable. Self-harming behaviors include cutting, carving, burning or scalding, preventing the healing of wounds, punching oneself, breaking bones. Those who self-harm often conceal evidence of this activity under clothing and/or explain it away ("The dog scratched me, I burned myself while cooking dinner"). It is important to distinguish deliberate self-harm from unintentional or related behaviors with which it might be confused. It is also sometimes referred to as "nonsuicidal self-injury"

Self-Harm: Self-inflicted bodily harm that is nonlethal and socially unacceptable

(NSSI), for which the American Psychiatric Association has noted as a condition in need of further study (Wilson & Ougrin, 2021). Unlike suicide attempts, the intent of these behaviors is *not* to cause death, although those who self-harm are 100 times more likely to commit suicide within a year of an act of self-harm than the general population (Whotton, 2002). Unlike the widespread practices of tattooing and piercing, self-harming behaviors are more generally socially unacceptable. Unlike other unintentional or risky and harmful behaviors, deliberate self-harm is intentional and direct. Self-harm usually begins in late childhood or early adolescence and may continue for 10 or 15 years or more.

Categories of Self-Harm

Armando Favazza (2011), a leading expert in this field, describes three types of self-harming behaviors:

1. *Major* self-harm refers to extreme acts that occur suddenly and cause considerable damage. These actions are usually associated with a psychotic state or acute intoxication and may be a response to religious or sexual delusions and/or command hallucinations. Readers of the popular novel *I Know This Much Is True* (Lamb, 1998) will remember their horror and shock at just such an act. Many readers will be aware of Vincent van Gogh's well-known act of self-mutilation. Both are examples of this type.

2. *Stereotypic* self-harm refers to the repetitive, often rhythmic self-injurious behaviors found in autistic and intellectually disabled individuals and in about a third of individuals with Tourette's syndrome. This type is usually not secretive and seems to have a strong biological component. The most common such behavior is head banging.

3. *Moderate or superficial* self-harm is the type that mental health professionals are most likely to encounter. Behaviors in this category include hair pulling, skin scratching, picking, cutting, burning, and carving. Favazza (2011) further divides this category into three groups: compulsive, episodic, or repetitive.

   · *Compulsive* self-harm involves repetitive, ritualistic behavior that occurs many times in a day. The two most common forms of this are hair pulling (*trichotillomania*) and various forms of insults to the skin (scratching, picking, or digging) that are often motivated by attempts to remove imagined blemishes or toxic organisms. Clients who do this will usually be treated by a family physician or dermatologist at first, rather than by a mental health professional.

   Trichotillomania: Recurrent pulling of one's own hair that results in hair loss

   · *Episodic* self-harm refers to behaviors that occur periodically but that do not preoccupy the individual or result in a "cutter" identity. This type of self-harm can occur as a symptom or feature of a number of disorders, including anxiety and depression. It appears in clients with personality disorders, most commonly borderline personality disorder.

   · In contrast, in *repetitive* self-harm, the behavior is a major preoccupation, and the person assumes a self-identity of a "cutter" or "burner." These individuals generally describe their behavior as an addiction that they cannot stop. Favazza (2011) argues that this type of self-harm should be a separate mental disorder within the group of impulse control disorders "not otherwise specified." He would call this disorder "repetitive self-harm syndrome." This suggested syndrome generally first appears in late childhood or early adolescence, is more common in females, and may persist for many years.

Prevalence

Anecdotal reports from school counselors and other educators strongly suggest that this practice is on the rise, particularly among young adolescents in middle schools. Several factors that may be related to the perceived increase in self-harm in adolescents are the increased public awareness of this behavior and the dramatic increase in the number of internet message boards and chat rooms devoted to this topic. It was the mid-1990s when self-injury began to appear in the media, and in the early 2000s when websites on self-injury began to flourish (Chaney, 2019). Message boards and social media may have a particular appeal to adolescents who do not have highly developed social skills, as they can practice their skills anonymously in these contexts (Whitlock et al., 2006a). Aredndt et al. (2019) found that exposure to (i.e., viewing) self-harm content on social media was directly linked to suicidal ideation, self-harm, and emotional disturbance.

The frequency of deliberate self-harming behavior in the general population is difficult to determine for a number of reasons. Different attempts to determine the prevalence of self-harm find different results, due partially to differences in the definition of self-harm and how the data are collected. When researchers do not distinguish between nonsuicidal self-injury and suicide attempts that involve self-harm, accurate prevalence rates are impossible to determine (Ross & Heath, 2002). In addition, many, if not most, episodes of self-injury will not be noted in medical records, since treatment may not be needed or sought—or it is not known for certain if it was a deliberate act. However, prevalence rates are sometimes calculated from such records. Recent researchers (Daukantaitė et al., 2020) have obtained findings that question the reliability and validity of lifetime frequencies of self-reported self-harm.

From the available data it is possible to make some estimates, with the caveat that they are only estimates. McManus et al. (2019) used data collected at three different times across 14 years (in England). They found that self-reported nonsuicidal self-harm had increased over time, and increases in prevalence were found in all genders and across age groups. In 2014, 6.4% of the population surveyed reported nonsuicidal self-harm; yet younger people (ages 16–24) had higher reports of nonsuicidal self-harm than any other age group (11.2%; McManus et al., 2019). Favazza's (2011) own research also suggests that the behavior is not uncommon. In a study of university students, he found that 13.8% admitted to at least one act of self-harm. Other research reports that 17% of adolescents engage in nonsuicidal self-injury at least once (Buelens et al., 2020). The DSM-5 indicates that NSSI is a distinct clinical phenomenon and included a diagnosis of nonsuicidal self-injury disorder (NSSI-D) as a condition that requires further research (American Psychiatric Association, 2022).

Buelens et al. (2020) studied the NSSI-D rates in a sample of over 2,000 adolescents. They found an overall prevalence rate to be 7.6%, with females (11.7%) reporting higher rates than males (2.9%). A study in the United States surveyed students in an urban and a suburban high school. The urban school was quite diverse in terms of race and ethnicity, while the suburban school students were largely White upper middle class. Data collection included an initial screening questionnaire followed by a semi-structured interview that clarified that the individual met criteria for self-harm. Of 440 participants, 13% of students in the urban school and 14.8% in the suburban school were self-harmers. The overall prevalence rate was 13.9%, with females significantly more likely to be doing so than males. An online survey of college students in two northeastern universities found that 17% of the 8,300 participants had engaged in a self-injurious behavior in their lifetime, and of those, 75% had done so more than once (Whitlock et al., 2006b). Additional findings of note were that those who self-injured were more likely to be female, bisexual, or actively questioning their sexual orientation. Further, 36% indicated that they had told no one about this practice.

These researchers also asked the students about specific practices. The most commonly reported method of self-harm was skin cutting (41%), followed by self-hitting (32.8%). Another 3.3% favored burning. Another important finding was that 13% of the group reported engaging in this behavior more than once per day, while 18% had done so on only one occasion.

College campuses are encountering more and more students who are self-harming and completing suicide. Lin et al. (2021) were concerned about the health and well-being of college students, specifically related to self-harm and suicidality. They used data from the National College Health Assessment to find groups of college students who were displaying signs of emotional exhaustion and multiple psychiatric symptoms. Those students of color who displayed higher levels of exhaustion and symptoms had increased odds of self-harm and suicidal intent (Lin et al., 2021).

There are two environments in which self-harm occurs at particularly high rates: prisons and inpatient facilities. In prison, self-harm may provide *secondary gains*, over and above the psychological functions it serves. The inmate may feel a measure of control that is lacking in the prison setting. For example, an injured inmate may avoid being moved to a less desirable unit or facility due to the need for medical supervision. It may also provide attention in the form of medical intervention.

In inpatient psychiatric settings, *contagion* may influence the rate of this behavior. Patients may observe that those who self-harm receive attention or medication and begin self-harming in order to obtain the perceived benefits for themselves. More recently, contagion has been suggested as an explanation for the recent rise in self-harm observed in schools (Khasawneh et al., 2020; Seong et al., 2021). Associating with others who engage in self-harm has been found to increase risk in adolescents. In some settings, there is one powerful individual ("alpha male/female") whose behaviors, including self-harm, peers imitate.

Secondary Gain: Interpersonal or social advantages that one gets due to an illness

Contagion: Imitation of behaviors by others in an environment

Self-harm often appears along with other disorders. It is most often associated with eating disorders, substance abuse, and personality disorders. Self-harm and eating disorders also may be replacements for the other (Hodge & Baker, 2021; Lavis et al., 2022; Warne et al., 2021). These symptoms may also represent different ineffective coping strategies.

We would be remiss to discuss self-harm without mentioning borderline personality disorder, as self-injurers frequently receive this diagnosis. We want to stress that while this is often the diagnosis, it is not the only correct one for clients who self-harm. Also, many self-injurers are adolescents, and we believe labeling a youth with a personality disorder diagnosis is premature. The DSM-V-TR notes that personality disorders can be diagnosed in children or adolescents in certain unusual circumstances, and we urge counselors to be very cautious and judicious in making such diagnoses. We have both treated adolescents with no other characteristics of borderline personality disorder who confess to briefly experimenting with self-harm. It is important to keep in mind the distinction between personality traits, which everyone has, and personality disorders, which tend to be inflexible and enduring patterns of behavior that interfere with one's functioning. Box 9.1 explains personality disorders for readers who may have not yet studied mental disorders and then lists the criteria for borderline personality disorder (American Pscyhiatric Association, 2022; Sharp, 2022).

Developmental Influences

Self-harming behaviors often begin in late childhood or early adolescence (Jung et al., 2018). Experts believe that the roots of this behavior are in early childhood experiences. Some (e.g., Tao et al., 2020) look to infant attachment disorders as setting the stage for later self-harm. Others focus on difficulties encountered by toddlers as they attempt to differentiate from parents and become more independent. Erik Erikson might surmise that those who self-harm did not successfully resolve the developmental crises of earlier stages. Most experts agree that the childhood experiences of

BOX 9.1 **Definition and Criteria for Diagnosis**

What is a personality disorder?

- An enduring pattern of behavior and inner experience that begins in adolescence or early adulthood
- A deviation from cultural norms (what is a personality disorder in one culture may be normative, accepted behavior in another)
- An inflexible pattern that is apparent in a variety of situations
- A pattern that interferes with one's personal, social, or occupational functioning

How is a personality disorder exhibited?

Manifested in at least two of the following:

- Emotions (appropriateness, intensity, changeability, and range)
- Thoughts (how one interprets and perceives events, people, and the world)
- Behaviors (impulse control)
- Interpersonal relationships

What is borderline personality disorder?

The most obvious characteristics include the following:

- A pattern of instability
- Frequent crises and mood swings
- Unstable relationships

What are the criteria for a diagnosis of borderline personality disorder?

By early adulthood, the individual exhibits at least five of the following in a variety of situations:

- Desperate attempts to prevent real or imagined abandonment
- Unstable relationships, alternating between putting someone on a pedestal and devaluing the person
- Unstable self-image
- Dangerous impulsiveness (substance abuse, sexual acting out, overspending, excessive risk taking)
- Self-mutilation or suicide attempts
- Severe mood swings
- Severe problems with anger management
- Brief periods of paranoia or dissociation in stressful situations
- Chronic feelings of emptiness

self-injurers were unhappy at best, and often include trauma from sexual abuse, loss of a parent, or illness or surgery.

Rahman et al. (2021), as well as the Australian Institute of Health and Welfare (2023), cite that several childhood events and circumstances are risk factors and are highly correlated with self-harm in adolescents. The loss of a parent via divorce or an out-of-home placement was common in self-harming adolescents. Loss of a parent in these ways, as opposed to the finality of death, make it more difficult to heal. A history of serious childhood illness and/or surgery was also more common among self-harmers. Medical trauma may lead to hatred of one's body and/or alienation from the body. Or, it may be that the child then has a body image of weakness and deformity, so self-harm seems appropriate. Some experts suggest another link between early medical problems and self-harm: A child, particularly one who is abused in the home, may experience a secondary gain (attention, regular meals, toys to play with) in the hospital or medical environment and then come to associate the injury with welcome nurturance. The self-cutting may be an imperfect attempt to re-create the medical context in order to gain attention and nurturance. The experience of physical and sexual abuse in childhood often leads victims to believe their bodies are defective and/or dirty. There may feel betrayed by the body, particularly in the case of sexual abuse. This alienated part of the self then deserves the punishment of self-harm. Children who witness family violence are also more likely to self-harm than children who do not. Observing impulsive self-destructive behavior may provide an early template for self-harm.

While these events in childhood may not lead directly to self-harm, the entry into adolescence may intensify these feelings. Puberty brings about changes in the body, which the youth may already despise. Now the increase in size and especially the emergence of secondary sex characteristics may increase self-loathing. Pubertal changes may trigger the development of self-harming behaviors since self-harmers have been found to have higher rates of eating disorders and high levels of distress about sexual or gender identity, and to be less attentive to personal hygiene and grooming than their nonself-harming peers.

As difficult as it may be to grasp, self-harming appears to serve an important function for those who engage in this behavior, and it serves as an effective coping mechanism when other strategies are not present (Chakraborti et al., 2021). Self-harmers typically lack the ability to effectively self-regulate or control their emotions (Faradiba et al., 2022). They may discover that cutting serves as a release of pressure (Yip, 2006), akin to bursting a balloon that is stretched too thin. In a family environment in which normal emotional expression is discouraged or even punished, children do not learn to develop tolerance for strong emotions. Instead, they learn emotional restraint by observing constricted parents or other adult models. They may even observe others using self-harming as a coping technique. In any case, when feeling intense emotions such as isolation, perceived abandonment, discouragement or depression, and the level of tension or anxiety becomes unbearable, cutting relieves the tension. For other self-harmers, the physical pain of a self-inflicted wound, which has a specific source and is under the control of the individual, is a way to refocus attention away from unbearable emotional pain that seems to be boundless and over which the individual feels a lack of control.

People who are the victims of childhood abuse sometimes learn to dissociate as a way to disconnect from the intense physical or emotional pain they experience (Talmon & Ginzburg, 2021). This strategy of dissociating, while useful during abuse, may become frequent and problematic, so the person feels detached from reality. Self-harming serves to increase awareness of and attention to the body, which ends the dissociative experience. Cutting, for example, may appear to be a way to feel something, anything.

Self-harming may increase the level of *endorphins* in the system and this positive state (akin to an opiate "high") can

Endorphin: Hormone found mainly in the brain that reduces the feeling of pain

become addictive. Once the person experiences the euphoria that is the effect of endorphins released by the body to ameliorate the pain, they may seek this experience over and over again. For others, cutting and burning are ways to express emotional pain that seems inexpressible in words (Zila & Kiselica, 2001). Expressing pain externally is tangible evidence of the internal suffering. In fact, it may be a way to communicate to others the depths of the suffering. Another perceived benefit of self-harming is the self-care that follows. For many who feel unloved and isolated, cutting or burning allows them to care for and nurture themselves in ways they do not feel are attainable from others. Others use self-harming as way to establish and express control over their bodies, when everything else in their lives appears out of control. For those who were unable to stop the abuse they suffered as young children, the fact that they can stop this abuse may provide a comforting sense of control.

Self-harm has sometimes been described as a compulsive, rather than impulsive, behavior. The person who repetitively self-harms may experience powerful mental/emotional and physical urges, which are satisfied by the self-harming behavior (Miller et al., 2021). It may feel much like an addictive urge and a compulsion to self-harm in order to continue to survive. The behavior serves as a way to regulate powerful emotions and urges.

Given the abuse history of many self-harmers, the acts of self-harm may serve as punishment when they hold the mistaken belief that they somehow caused the abuse or that they are flawed to a degree that justified the abuse. Others with similar histories may hurt themselves as a way to reenact the earlier trauma. These individuals will likely have other symptoms of PTSD as well. For other victims of abuse, self-harm is a way to disfigure and make less desirable the body that was appropriated by their abuser.

For some self-harmers, ritual and symbolism are important elements of the acts. Many explanations given by self-harmers for their behavior have religious overtones, such as atoning for sins or a ritual for purification (Hodge & Baker, 2021). This is not unlike the self-flagellation practiced by some religious sects. Blood also has important symbolic connotations. For some self-harmers the sight of blood is soothing because it is evidence of being alive. Other cutters find the blood to be symbolic of the "evil" flowing away (as in "bad blood"). The adolescent female may view this blood flow as within her control, in contrast to the mysterious and uncontrollable monthly flows she now experiences. Strong (1998) describes a young woman who left the dried blood on her arm as a reminder to herself of her secret act, which meant to her that she was in control of this pain.

The purpose of this discussion of functions of self-harming is to impress upon clinicians that despite the apparent dysfunction exhibited in this behavior, counselors need to recognize that to self-harmers, their actions provide important benefits that they do not know how to obtain any other way—and different people may have different reasons for self-harm. Thus, advising or encouraging someone to give up this behavior before they have developed effective strategies to meet these needs is quite dangerous because there is no replacement strategy for dealing with distress. Counselors should explore the functions of self-harm with each respective client, understand that self-harm may serve more than one function, and develop a personalized approach to self-harm care (Mughal et al., 2023).

Theoretical Views

Different theories seek to explain the origin and dynamics of self-harming behaviors. At this point, there is no single widely accepted theory that all experts agree on. Because these theories lead to the treatment approaches described later in the chapter, we will provide an overview here first.

Biological Theories

Biological explanations implicate low levels of serotonin in the brains of those who self-harm. Although the evidence is indirect and hardly conclusive, scientists found that medications that increase serotonin in the brain result in decreases in self-harm behaviors (Nock, 2014; Turner et al., 2014). Endorphins in the brain may also contribute to an understanding of this behavior. Endorphins are neurotransmitters that relieve pain and control emotions. When endorphins are produced,

Classical Conditioning: the best-known example is Pavlov's dog experiment. When a neutral stimulus (a bell) is repeatedly paired with an unconditioned stimulus (food), the neutral stimulus comes to elicit the unconditioned response (salivating) by itself.

the person experiences pleasurable feelings. When someone is injured (as they are in self-harm behaviors), endorphins are produced by the brain to reduce the pain. After several such experiences, the person associates cutting or burning with a pleasurable sensation that is the result of increased endorphins. This is what is called *classical conditioning*. The expectation of the "high" encourages the individual to seek out the experience again.

Favazza (1996) noted that one problem with this theory is that the vast majority of those who self-harm report experiencing little or no pain when doing the cutting or burning. Researchers know that abused children, who experience trauma and injury on a regular basis, may actually become less sensitive to pain, due perhaps to the increased production of endorphins. They may become accustomed to these high levels of endorphins in the system, so when they are alone, they may experience a "withdrawal" phenomenon that causes them to self-harm to return to the higher level of endorphins. This explanation is consistent with data that show a strong relationship between childhood abuse and self-harm behaviors.

Psychodynamic Theories

Psychodynamic theories trace their roots to Freud and his followers (Nock, 2014; Persano, 2022). Although psychoanalysts interpret self-harming behaviors in several ways (e.g., the conflict between the life and death instincts, a symbolic castration, an attempt to merge with the menstruating mother), they agree that real or anticipated loss is a significant antecedent to the self-harming behavior. Self-harm is seen as a sequence of events: the experience or perception of loss, the resultant increase in tension that cannot be expressed verbally, a state of dissociation or depersonalization, an irresistible urge to harm oneself, the act of self-harm, and the tension relief and return to pre-incident state.

A lesser-known developmental theory of Freud's sets the stage for this sequence to occur. The theory proposes three stages in an infant's development; the first, autoeroticism, is the earliest period. In this stage, the infant's sensations and impulses are fragmented and without cohesion or any sense of self; the next is the stage of normal narcissism, in which the infant recognizes that they are a unit or distinct identity with impulses, sensations, movements, and so forth integrated in one functional organism. The final infant phase is that of object love, when the infant recognizes not only itself as a distinct entity, but also the mother. The infant now possesses the beginning of the ability to form an intimate relationship with another.

When these stages are somehow disrupted, the seeds of the self-harming pattern are sown. Psychoanalysts view the self-harm as a regression (return) to the early infant state, in that they lack the capacity for object love due to loss or abandonment (real or felt) by the parent. When a person experiences a loss later in life, the loss revisits the pain and triggers the sequence. The regressive nature of the experience is evident in the inability to verbalize the emotional pain re-created by the present loss. The self-harm occurs because the individual reacts to the threat with aggression, which is turned inward. They blame themselves for the loss and believe they deserve punishment. A further dynamic of this sequence is that when the individual dissociates and experiences the body as alien or fragmented, they may panic because they fear disintegration. Thus, self-harm paradoxically assures the individual that the body is one unit. Interestingly, many of those who self-harm describe the event as painless, which gives support to the notion of dissociation as a component of the sequence.

Another view from the psychodynamic tradition is that of Connors (2000), who also sees self-harm as rooted in childhood trauma and loss. She suggests the skin is a metaphor for the boundary of the self. The process of attachment and separation in early childhood ordinarily results in a child's sense of self, which is usually achieved at age 3 or 4. When there is a trauma or loss at this time, there are long-term consequences to the sense of self. The sense of self depends on a boundary between "me" and "not-me." It allows the individual to discern their own thoughts, and beliefs from those of powerful others. It serves as a kind of "home base" from which the person perceives and relates to the world. Early in the formation of the self, the caregiver (usually mother) regulates emotions for the child. When upset, caregivers soothe and comfort, frequently providing tactile, verbal, and physical reassurance. As the self becomes increasingly defined and bounded, the regulator role is assumed by the individual. Connors (2000) believes this ideally occurs by 3 years and 6 months. As the child continues to develop, it gains more practice in self-regulation. When this process does not proceed apace, due to a trauma of some kind, the result may be an inability to self-regulate and a tendency to be overwhelmed by intense emotions along with low frustration tolerance. To compensate for the inadequate self-boundary, the person resorts to cutting the skin, the metaphoric boundary, and that reassures the individual that the boundary is still there.

When a person has a fragile self-boundary, and then feels emotions that are reminiscent of the 2-year-old self, they may be unable to integrate those feelings with the adult self. Connors thinks a diagnosis of PTSD is more appropriate than borderline personality disorder because it acknowledges the childhood trauma at the root of self-harming behaviors.

CBT

CBT also offers a way to think about self-harm (Nock, 2014). Cognitive behaviorists see this behavior as a specific symptom and are not concerned with underlying issues. This approach gravitates toward four faulty beliefs that lead to self-harming behaviors:

- Self-harming behaviors are acceptable, necessary, or advantageous.
- One's body and self are disgusting and deserving of punishment.
- Some type of physical action is necessary to reduce unpleasant feelings and bring relief.
- Overt action is necessary to communicate feelings to others. If others do not see visible signs, they will not understand how much the individual hurts.

These "illogical thoughts" stem from a negative self-image and low self-esteem. Cognitive theorists believe that negative emotional states and self-defeating behaviors are the result of thinking errors, which can be corrected. Behaviorists believe that all behavior, including self-harm, is learned and can be unlearned (or extinguished). When an individual associates a pleasurable feeling (relief) with a behavior (cutting or burning) over a period of time, the behavior is conditioned. That is, the person has learned that cutting brings relief from intolerable feelings. Operant conditioning focuses on the manner in which a particular behavior gets reinforced. The release of tension and anxiety that occurs with the self-harming act serves as negative reinforcement for the behavior. That is, self-harm removes or reduces an unpleasant stimulus (tension and anxiety). This reinforcement strengthens the behavior. In some instances, negative reinforcement can come from others, as when others' anger or rejection stops when they see the self-harm. Positive reinforcement also may come from the reaction of others, who may express sympathy or concern, and provide attention. Medical and mental health professionals also provide positive reinforcement via their caring and nurturing behaviors. The fact that both positive and negative reinforcement results from this behavior, from both internal and external sources, suggests that this behavior will be very difficult to eliminate.

Narrative Theory

Miller (1996) bases her theory of self-harming behavior on her experience with survivors of childhood trauma. While she accepts that self-harming serves important coping functions for the individuals, she focuses on the "physical and psychological *reenactments* of childhood trauma expressed in self-harmful behavior" (p. 214). Miller believes that those who self-harm are reenacting the interpersonal violence they experienced as children and proving that they are incapable of self-protection because they were not protected as children. Actions committed by those who self-harm are symbolic of what was done to them as children. When the self-harm continues despite intervention, the client and the clinician may both become discouraged, which Miller believes is yet another replication of harmful childhood dynamics.

According to Miller (1996), four themes are common in those who self-harm:

- A hatred of one's own body is central to the self-concept of the individual.
- Secrecy is an organizing principle, as it was in childhood
- The behavior pattern is rooted in "the inability to self-protect and a fragmented sense of self" (p. 218). The person has not learned how to stay safe, or soothe oneself, and may have used dissociation as a way to manage distress. The *internalized abuser* becomes the bad part of oneself, the *nonprotecting bystander* is the internalized lack of protection the individual experienced, and the *victim* is the "wounded child within." They lack an internalized *protective presence*. The internal dynamic is replayed with every episode of self-harm and is the internal abuser hurting the victim while the bystander does nothing.
- Relationship problems are frequent, as most of those who self-harm have a core feeling of loneliness.

Treatment Options and Considerations

As theories differ on the causes and function of self-harming behavior, they also differ on recommended treatment. In this section, we review what is currently known about treatment but caution the reader that there is not unanimity on the best course to take.

There is insufficient research evidence to make any clear judgments about the efficacy of the various treatment approaches. There are few empirically supported interventions for self-harming behavior (Nock, 2014). Although research is ongoing, it is challenging to compare, due to the different definitions of self-harming behavior (most studies include suicide attempters as well) and the differences in outcome measures (repetition of self-harm, elapsed time to self-harm episode, reduction in other symptoms, etc.). It is difficult for researchers to obtain sufficient sample sizes in randomized trials to meet the requirements for many statistical tests. Although readers will note that there is not a shortage of approaches to treatment, there is no one method that has been shown to be superior to any other, leaving the clinician without a standard of practice to adhere to.

The first treatment consideration that clinicians must ponder is whether to make the self-harming behavior the focus of treatment. This has been a subject of considerable controversy among treatment professionals (Strong, 1998). Temporary increases in the self-harming behavior may be a consequence of more intensive therapy that delves into childhood trauma, but this is less likely to happen with short-term cognitive behavioral treatment. However, some clinicians may initially use a cognitive behavioral approach, to which they then add more intensive approaches when the client is ready.

In an age of managed care and restricted access to mental health services, long-term intensive psychotherapy is not often available. Residential treatment is also a luxury available to only a few. Self-harm is often associated with serious psychological disorders, such as borderline personality disorder or PTSD, that are not effectively treated with short-term interventions. The clinician may be in a position of choosing the best alternative based on practical issues rather than therapeutic factors. Some online interventions have been tested and may help to overcome limited availability of other interventions (Kaess et al., 2019).

Another consideration is whether treatment for self-harming behaviors can be effective when the individual does not want to give up this practice. As noted earlier, this behavior serves a variety of important functions for individuals who do not have other internal resources and then is reinforced with repeated action, strengthening the behavior. Clinicians must consider whether working with someone who does not want to change is something they want to do. Favazza (2011), a leading expert on this behavior, cautioned against working with very many of these clients concurrently, as the emotional drain on the clinician is considerable. Given the high incidence of childhood trauma and loss in individuals who self-harm, the clinician must be prepared to address those issues in treatment.

Medication

Medication is often used in conjunction with psychological treatment (Nock, 2014). SSRIs (e.g., Prozac, Paxil, Luvox, etc.) reduce self-harming behaviors in some clients. Given the intractability of this behavior, a referral to a physician or psychiatrist for a trial course of medication would be a reasonable plan. However, it is important to consider medication as an adjunct to psychological treatment rather than as a substitute. Favazza (2011) recommends using medication to quickly reduce the self-harming behavior while other elements of treatment are implemented.

SSRI (selective-serotonin reuptake inhibitor): A class of drug that works by making more serotonin available in the brain

Dialectical Behavioral Therapy

Because self-harming behaviors are often associated with a diagnosis of borderline personality disorder, the dialectical behavioral approach developed and popularized by Marsha Linehan may be useful (Nock, 2014). Linehan's program is specifically designed for clients who engage in what she calls "parasuicidal" behavior (self-harm and suicide attempts). Research provides some support for the effectiveness of this approach. However, the research studied women with borderline personality disorder, and there are no data supporting the efficacy of dialectical behavioral therapy (DBT) in men who self-harm. The underlying premise of DBT is that self-harm is due to a lack of skills for coping with intense emotion. Typically, the program is delivered on an outpatient basis and includes 1 hour weekly of individual therapy and 2 and a half hours of weekly group therapy, both of which continue for a year. DBT training includes instruction in mindfulness, interpersonal effectiveness, emotion regulation, and distress tolerance. Therapy uses a team approach, and services typically include phone consultation for the client between sessions. Proponents of DBT state that this comprehensive treatment enhances the behavioral repertoire of clients, increases their motivation to change, and ensures that new behaviors are applied in the clients' world outside treatment. The program is highly structured for both clients and providers. A manual outlining this approach is available to clinicians, as is training in this method. The manual (Linehan, 2015) provides lessons, handouts, and homework assignments for teaching these skills. A series of training videos for use with clients is available, as are professional development videos.

Although the DBT approach appears useful, it is also impractical for many clients due to the intensity of the treatment (Nock, 2014). Both finances and time may be a barrier that keeps clients from entering this type of treatment. Further, this approach is most likely to work with highly motivated clients. There are guidelines that indicate that if a client misses four consecutive sessions, they are discharged (Linehan, 2015). Individuals who self-harm are often ambivalent about treatment, and one study found that borderline patients could manage up to 18 sessions with good results. The year-long treatment may not attract the very clients who need it, so shorter treatment may be a useful alternative.

Manual-Assisted Cognitive Behavior Therapy

Manual-assisted cognitive behavior therapy (MACT) incorporates many of the principles of DBT but is delivered in a maximum of six sessions (Evans et al., 1999; Nock, 2014). In fact, some clients opt to receive the treatment entirely via bibliotherapy (reading the six booklets designed for the program). Participants in a pilot study of this approach were 34 patients between 16 and 50 who were recruited immediately following an episode of self-harm. Of the 34 participants, 18 received the MACT treatment and 16 received treatment as usual (serving as a comparison group). Patients were not part of the study if their primary diagnosis was organic brain damage, substance dependence, or schizophrenia. Although the numbers were small, results were somewhat encouraging: Rate of self-harm at discharge and at follow-up (4–6 months post-treatment) was lower for the MACT group, although the difference was not statistically significant. However, a statistically significant difference was detected between the two groups on depressive symptoms, with the MACT group having fewer symptoms.

Cognitive Analytic Therapy

Another approach developed in England is cognitive analytic therapy (Nock, 2014; Sheard et al., 2000), designed for use with repeat self-harmers and taking into account their ambivalence about therapy. The intervention can be done in one session if necessary and can be used by counselors without extensive additional training. The essential elements of this approach are a problem-solving focus and analysis of reciprocal role relationships (patterns of relating to others and ourselves). The intervention includes a self-harm self-help file for the client and an assessor's response file for the clinician, both completed prior to the initial session. These assessments provide a structure and focus for the sessions. This model was pilot tested with optimistic results, although the originators of the approach recognize the need for future research to evaluate its effectiveness.

Cowmeadow (1994) outlined the steps of therapy using this approach:

- Assist the client to understand the self-harming behavior so that it makes sense to them and is less shameful.

- Identify the "target problem procedures" (p. 137), the recurrent maladaptive patterns that contribute to the self-harming behavior. These include thoughts, emotions, and actions that trigger the episodes.
- The third task is to help the client find alternatives to those maladaptive patterns, using a menu of ways the client might deal with stress other than self-harming. This element is a part of many of the approaches covered here.

Both of MACT and CAT approaches have been developed and tested with different groups in England (e.g., Taylor et al., 2017). We hope that these theories will be imported and tested in the United States, as there is a great need for brief, effective treatment for self-harm in this country as well. In an environment in which brief therapy is optimal, both for economic reasons and client compliance, these approaches offer definite advantages.

Narrative Therapy

Since Miller (1996) sees the origins of the symptoms in the childhood trauma, she does not advocate separate approaches for clients with substance abuse, eating disorders, or self-harming behaviors. These symptoms are all examples of self-abusive patterns stemming from childhood trauma. Miller's approach to treatment draws on both narrative theory and DBT. The self-harming behavior is an attempt to deal with a negative environment. Symptoms are "stories" in the narrative tradition, in which the problem is located outside the individual. The treatment model proposed by Miller involves three stages, or circles.

The *outer* circle is the focus of the initial stage of treatment. The counselor inquires about the context of the client's life, collecting stories that can be used later to construct a more helpful narrative. During this stage, Miller (1996) does not allow the discussion to focus on the trauma or symptoms, including self-harm. She believes that it is important to establish a strong therapeutic alliance before such topics come up. In the *middle* stage or circle, the stories more directly consider the trauma and symptoms. In addition, a major effort in this stage is encouraging the client to build a support system. The *inner* stage or circle is focused on identifying, understanding, and integrating the fragmented aspects of self that were internalized as a way to cope with the trauma or abuse. The most important work here, according to Miller, is to help the client replace the nonprotecting bystander with a protective presence. This process unfolds with the therapist first serving in the role of protective presence, with the client gradually incorporating this construct into the self.

Group Therapy

Group therapy is often used in conjunction with individual therapy to treat self-harmers. Many of the approaches described incorporate group therapy as part of a broader intervention program. Homogenous groups for those clients who self-harm provide safety and a sense that the client is not alone in this problem. However, there are some particular challenges in groups that include those who self-harm, which lead the Self-Injury Institute (2014) to recommend against group therapy for that population. In groups with any members who engage in self-harm, there are several potential problems:

- Some group members may feel invisible, which may have been an initial reason for self-injury.
- Feeling lost or invisible in the group may trigger self-harming episodes.
- Self-harm may be used as a way to communicate within a group.
- Self-harm may be used in a group to manipulate other members or the therapist.
- Members may achieve status in the group, or membership, via their self-harming behaviors.

Strategies to minimize these problems include labeling self-harming behaviors as such and clearly explaining this to the group. This will avoid the life-and-death crisis mentality that could emerge after an episode and inadvertently reinforce the behavior. Others in the group may enjoy the drama and the role of rescuer, so it is essential to correctly characterize the behaviors and distinguish it from suicidal behavior. The Self-Injury Institute (2014) suggests that there be strict rules and expectations that may restrict any kind of sharing about self-harming behavior, if group therapy is attempted

Walsh and Rosen (1988) also suggest that therapists, knowing the repetitive nature of this behavior, predict the repetition in advance. This prediction sometimes has a paradoxical intention but also can enhance the credibility of the therapist if it does occur. The therapist might even predict that some contagion will occur, with other members observing the positive aspects of the behavior and trying it out for themselves. In order to avoid the manipulative effect of a self-harm episode, these experts suggest reframing the "helpful" behaviors of group members (nurturing, attending, etc.) as "harmful" to the person they wish to help.

However, there is the potential for group therapy to benefit the self-harmer. The group is an excellent opportunity to teach, model, and reinforce alternative methods of coping with and communicating about distress. Group members can practice skills within the group, try them outside the group, and get feedback from the group on their performance. Preparation for termination is particularly important for those who self-harm so that they can anticipate and deal with the loss in advance of the actual event.

Inpatient Treatment

In extreme situations, there are inpatient programs that specialize in treatment for self-harming behaviors. Information about the nationally recognized SAFE (Self-Abuse Finally Ends) Alternatives program can be found at http://selfinjury.com/treatment. Such a program is an option if the behavior is escalating and outpatient treatment is not effective.

Do's and Don'ts

Not only is there no consensus on the best method of treating self-harming behaviors, there is also debate about whether to use specific techniques. Of greatest concern are strategies that might be damaging rather than helpful. Solomon and Farrand (1996) emphasized the importance of not demanding that the self-harm stop completely once the client enters therapy. It is important to help the client develop and practice alternative strategies for dealing with impulses to hurt themselves before insisting they stop. Therapy that focuses exclusively on the self-harming behavior is unlikely to progress because underlying issues are not addressed. One suggestion is to make an agreement with clients to contact the therapist when they feel the urge to harm themselves. That encourages the client to use an alternative strategy (seeking help or support, and verbalizing the pain). The agreement would also restrict contact with the therapist for 24 hours after an event if self-injury does occur. The therapist helps clients have a plan for receiving good care for their wounds from medical personnel who are nonjudgmental. This strategy stresses the importance of behavior change but does not set up a failure scenario.

As with other issues in treatment of self-harming, the SAFE Alternatives program disagrees with this strategy. It requires clients to sign a contract that explicitly forbids self-harm while in the program. Conterio and Lader (1998) describe counseling strategies and techniques that are likely to be harmful or damaging to treatment. However, it is important to remember that there is disagreement about many of these points, with other experts recommending the same interventions.

The reader will need to reflect on these ideas and make a personal decision about what is helpful and what is not. Conterio and Lader discourage the following practices:

- Displaying wounds or scars, or encouraging detailed verbal descriptions of the self-harming act. They believe such practices serve to glorify the behavior and focus attention away from the underlying painful emotional issues.
- Prescribing substitute behaviors, such as holding ice cubes, writing on arms rather than cutting, and breaking eggs on the arm to create the feeling of bleeding. While behavioral therapists may recommend exactly such techniques, these authors contend that such strategies reinforce the faulty notion that tension must be discharged by "doing" something.
- Anger release techniques, such as punching pillows. They believe the message in such actions is that violent behavior is the only way to discharge feelings of anger rather than encouraging verbal expression.
- Physical activity. Although counselors often prescribe running or engaging in high levels of exertion as anger management techniques, these authors are concerned that high levels of physical arousal often increase, rather than decrease, the likelihood of self-harm.
- Hypnosis. Conterio and Lader are adamantly opposed to this method and report that clients can suffer serious negative consequences from this treatment.
- Heroic rescue. Therapist behaviors, such as taking potentially dangerous objects away from clients, arranging for someone to "babysit" the client, or responding to self-injurious acts with excessive sympathy and nurturing behaviors, actually reinforce the behavior.

On the personal website of a self-harmer, one client's perception of what is helpful provides a comparison with the professional recommendations:

- Show that you are interested in and care about the person behind the self-injury.
- Show concern for the injuries and offer compassion.
- Communicate that you are willing to talk about self-harm.
- Help the client recognize and understand the function and origins of the behavior.
- Recognize and acknowledge the ambivalence about stopping the behavior.
- Encourage the client to use the urge to self-harm as a signal of difficult and painful feelings, memories, or needs. Help the client learn other ways of expressing these feelings and to ask for support when needed.
- Encourage the client to create and strengthen support systems in order to reduce the isolation and shame that perpetuates the behavior.
- Recognize that clients can make progress in therapy even if they don't give up the behavior, especially early in therapy. Realize the behavior may even increase as painful issues are talked about.
- Encourage and acknowledge small gains, recognizing that small steps are important and lead to bigger ones.

It is interesting to note that this client does support the use of expressive techniques, such as hitting pillows, which is discouraged by Conterio and Lader (1998). This difference of opinion highlights the current state of affairs in that no approach has emerged as superior.

For the clinician faced with a client who self-harms, what is the best approach? While DBT may have many positive aspects, the disadvantage is the long-term commitment and the intensity of the program. These disadvantages may be particularly problematic in a managed care environment. Clinicians who are interested in working with these clients might do well to utilize certain elements of DBT (especially the manual) and to stay abreast of developments of the newer approaches.

It is also important to consider that it may turn out that certain treatment characteristics, rather than the specific model, are the critical elements in effective treatment. Cowmeadow (1994) suggests the following essential ingredients: flexibility to deal with a wide range of client difficulties; relevance to client needs, which encourages compliance; rapid engagement to facilitate the development of a strong therapeutic alliance; and inclusion of a specific problem-solving component.

Issues of Diversity

There is very little about race, ethnicity, or socio-economic class as they relate to self-harm. Lieberman and Poland (2006) assert that the behavior crosses the lines of culture, race, and socioeconomic status. One dissertation study (Mesirow, 1999) found no significant differences by race in incarcerated adult males who self-injured and a matched group who did not. Weinz (1977) obtained similar results in a large sample in a northern metropolitan area. However, Weinz included self-harming whether or not there was suicidal intent, and Mesirow does not specify their definition.

In Ross and Heath's (2002) study, 77% of the students who were identified as having self-harmed at least one time were Caucasian, 5% African American, 6.5% Asian, 3.3% Hispanic, and 8.2% were other minority. These researchers noted the large percentage of students identified as engaging in self-harming were White, even in the urban school which was quite diverse.

Several studies suggest that in terms of gender differences, females self-harm at a higher rate than males at all age levels. However, that is not an unequivocal fact, as other studies have found equal rates for males and females (e.g., Briere & Gil, 1998). It may be that females are more likely to seek treatment, and thus there are proportionately more females in samples taken from inpatient or emergency room records. Whitlock et al. (2006a) found that college students who admitted to repeated self-harming behaviors were more likely to be female, bisexual, or questioning their sexual orientation.

The American Psychological Association said in 2015 that people self-harm regardless of race or SES. However, having LGBTQIA+ status may put younger people more at risk than those who are not LGBTQIA+. Males who identify as gay or bisexual report higher rates of self-harming behavior than heterosexual, cisgender males. For females, 47% of those who identify as bisexual have endorsed self-harming behavior (DeAngelis, 2015).

Persons With Disabilities

Self-harming, or self-injurious behavior, is a common form of destructive behavior exhibited by individuals with developmental disabilities, found in 2%–4% of community-residing adults and as many as 39% with multiple disabilities (cerebral palsy, epilepsy, and learning disabilities; Martin & Guth, 2005). In this population, the behavior is most often of the *stereotypic* type (Kress, 2003) described earlier in the chapter. The strongest risk factor for self-injurious behavior is the degree of intellectual impairment, with those persons with severe or profound disabilities exhibiting more than four times the self-harming behavior those with mild or moderate disabilities (McClintock et al., 2003). Oliver et al. list the following risk factors for self-injurious behavior: intellectual disability, poor expressive communication skills, and the presence of stereotyped or compulsive behaviors.

Stereotypic Behavior: A repetitive, usually rhythmic behavior pattern with no purpose or goal

Stereotypic self-harming behavior is often associated with cognitive/intellectual disabilities and developmental delays and appears to have an organic cause. These behaviors can cause tissue damage, ranging from mild to severe. Major self-harming behaviors are seen in individuals with severe psychoses and may be prompted by hallucinations or delusions. People who engage in this type of behavior may report an absence of pain and a feeling of calm associated with the self-harming behavior. Treatment for self-injurious behaviors in persons with disabilities is similar to that used with other populations, although medication and behavior modifications programs may be preferred.

Influence of Digital Media

The use of digital media is a complex issue, as there are both positive and negative outcomes with respect to self-harm (Lavis et al., 2022). Digital media may have some positive and helpful social or networking effects for those people who may identify as someone who self-harms. Getting connected with others (through technology) may reduce feelings of social isolation and provide a sense of community. Some interactions may be encouraging in terms of reduction or recovery. The connection may reduce or lessen urges to self-harm. However, as mentioned previously in this chapter, exposure to self-harm content on social media has been found to trigger imitative behavior (Arendt et al., 2019). These researchers found that nearly one third (32%) of individuals studied performed the same self-harming behavior that they viewed on a social media platform.

Some efforts to create forums or communities for those who self-harm have also led to paradoxical effects (Pirkis et al., 2017). Online interactions between peers in the community were found to normalize self-harming behaviors, with the community seeing the behaviors as routine and acceptable responses to life's stressors. Counselors should be wary of recommending digital media connections for their clients. It may prove to be nearly impossible to minimize the risk without filtering out potentially all helpful content (House, 2020).

Assessment

There have been a few attempts to develop formal assessments of self-harming behavior: Functional Assessment of Self-Mutilation (FASM), the Deliberate Self-harm Inventory (DSHI), the Suicide Attempt Self-Injury Interview (SASII), and the Self-Injurious Thoughts and Behaviors Interview (SITBI), just to name a few. Many self-report inventories (e.g., Trauma Symptom Inventory) include items that address this concern. Observation and direct questioning about signs may be the most effective way to discover whether self-harming is occurring with a particular client, but such strategies are likely to be effective only when there is a solid therapeutic alliance. What is probably more important for the clinician is to remember that when self-harming behaviors are recognized, it is unlikely to be the only symptom or focus of clinical attention. Thus, given the array of diagnoses and problems that may accompany this behavior, it is essential that the clinician do a thorough assessment to detect any other conditions that may be present. This will provide a basis for a more complete and coherent treatment plan. Kress (2003) emphasizes that inquiring about self-harming behavior should be part of initial or intake interviews, and when it is acknowledged, more in-depth questioning should follow. They also note that a medical assessment is almost always recommended. In cases of severe self-harming behavior, the physician will need to check for infection and other medical consequences. In cases of mild self-harming behavior, the medical examination should include advice to avoid sharing blades and other instruments of self-harm to avoid transmitting disease.

Counselor Issues

Probably the most difficult aspect of working with clients who engage in self-harm is keeping one's reactions from interfering with the treatment. It is not easy to witness the effects of self-injury without having a strong reaction (Azalia Novoa, 2021; Kress, 2003). Alderman (1997) described their own intense desire to make a client stop hurting themselves and their frustration at the inability to do so. A counselor needs to remember that this behavior serves important purposes for clients, and they may not be willing or ready to give it up just because they enter treatment. The counselor must also realize that they do not have the power to change this individual and recognize the difficulty of changing this behavior. One needs to somehow avoid open displays of revulsion on seeing the evidence of self-harm, or clients will be sure to keep it hidden. Alderman makes an important distinction between sympathy and empathy for these clients; while empathy is helpful, sympathy can be a barrier. Sympathy and excessive concern by a clinician reinforce the behavior and may impede progress. One can empathize with the disappointment, fear, or other precipitating emotion the client experienced as the trigger for self-injury, but treating them with solicitous attention because of the wounds is not therapeutic.

Another issue that counselors must recognize is that despite the unpleasant nature of the wounds, self-harming does not usually require hospitalization. These wounds are unlikely to be life-threatening, and many do not even require medical attention. It is important that the counselor not over-react and seek unnecessary medical intervention. For one, this kind of attention serves to reinforce the behavior. For another, it may unnecessarily breach confidentiality and undermine the therapeutic alliance. Counselors need to assess suicidal risk and reserve extreme measures for appropriate situations.

Clients who engage in self-harm are likely to have frequent crises and require more "emergency" responses than other clients. This may involve telephone consultation, urgent appointments, and so on. Counselors need to consider whether they are willing to make the kind of commitment that is generally called for in this population.

Some therapists use "no harm contracts" as a way to reduce self-harming behavior. There has not been any empirical support, that we are aware of, for the use of no-harm contracts. In reality, these contracts are not binding and may put the counselor and the client in a "no-win" situation. Rudd et al. (2006) provide a case against using no harm contracts. What might be more productive is for the counselor to spell out in advance a "safety plan" or how they will respond to incidents of self-harm. If a safety plan is developed, it should include specific actions (or options) that the client can take in different situations. Options can include what to do in minor or major crisis circumstances. Whisenhunt et al. (2016) suggest that safety plans include a discussion of warning signs, (internal) coping strategies, positive distractions, and people to ask for help when needed. It is recommended that if a client contacts the counselor following a self-injury episode, the counselor should make an assessment of the client's need for medical intervention. No other interaction should occur outside the session. If a client attends a session with fresh injuries, the counselor should focus on the medical needs, insisting on medical examination in lieu of the therapy session, if warranted. These behaviors, while not rejecting the client, do not reinforce episodes of self-harm.

It is important to recognize when the counselor's frustration and fear becomes an impediment to progress. Some time ago, a website for those who self-harm included the following comments about therapists:

> I almost lost my first [psychotherapist]. She tried to use my cutting as a boundary. She told me if I cut again she would not see me anymore. She did not see me for a few weeks till I called feeling very out of control. It was out of her frustration with me. *(Female, age 27, 3 years self-injurious behavior)*

The first time I cut myself, I called my therapist because I was scared that I couldn't/ wouldn't stop. She seemed ok and calm with the situation that night. I always had difficulty expressing myself and I was totally intimidated by her, so for me to even call her and admit to my foolishness was a big step for me. Unfortunately, she "dumped" me the next evening by saying that she couldn't give me the help she felt I needed. I now know that she was somewhat panic-stricken, but I felt even more worthless than ever. … I'M SO SCREWED UP THAT EVEN A THERAPIST CAN'T HELP ME! I still feel that she was a coward about the whole thing. *(Female, age 34 who self-harmed for 2.5 years)*

Thank God, I found my present therapist 16 years ago and she has been my therapist through periods of self-injury and periods without it (9 years until this one). She would never threaten me or give me an ultimatum over the behavior. MANY previous therapists completely freaked out about it, and ended up traumatizing me one way or another *(Female, 39 years old, who had been engaging in self-harming behaviors on and off for 27 years)*

It's important for counselors to be self-aware and recognize their own limits and boundaries of competence. It may be that this issue (feeling incompetent or significantly frustrated with a client), once known, is a signal to the counselor that a referral is in order to a counselor who is more prepared to deal with such clients.

Counselors who are not well informed about self-harm may not be aware that a client is doing this behavior. They may come for treatment on other issues, often testing the counselor to determine whether they are aware or prepared to address the issue. One way a counselor can indicate to clients that they are knowledgeable about this symptom is to ask about it directly at intake. Although the client may not admit it at that point, bringing up the subject gives a message that the counselor is approachable. Counselors providing services to any client should be alert to the possibility of self-harm and inquire about bruises, cuts, or burns they notice. Although clients may not immediately admit the source of the wounds, they will be aware of your concern, and if there is repeated new evidence, the counselor has established a foundation from which to discuss the issue.

A NOTE TO SCHOOL COUNSELORS

We note that self-harm has become a common adolescent problem (Te Maro et al., 2019; Townsend et al., 2022). As such, self-harming behavior is a phenomenon addressed almost daily by school counselors. While the causes of this behavior are varied and complex, episodes in adolescents are often precipitated by the breakup of romantic relationships or conflict with parents. Regardless of the trigger, school counselors may be the first professional to discover the behavior, and their actions and decisions are important. Froeschle and Moyer (2004) recommend consulting with other professionals and make referrals to community providers when that is indicated.

In addition to educating staff and providing individual support and group counseling as appropriate, there are difficult ethical issues to be faced (Kotsopoulou & Melis, 2015). Probably the most difficult decision the school counselor will make is whether to notify the student's parents once self-harming behaviors have been detected. The duty to warn when there is the potential for serious harm has been upheld in court, and the counselor may be liable if they do not report and the parent later learns that the school counselor withheld this information. There are no specific definitions of what constitutes "serious harm," and the school counselor might well decide that superficial cuts do not qualify. On the other hand, there are arguments to support maintaining confidentiality: The student's feelings of alienation could be exacerbated by breach of confidentiality, and the willingness of students to disclose personal material could be compromised. The best solution, according to Froeschle and Moyer, (2004) is to persuade the student of the importance of telling parents and to offer to be present as a support when the student does so. Kress et al. (2006) recommend that the school counselor conduct a thorough assessment of both self-injury and suicide as a way to decide whether the student is in danger. They also point out that, given the increasing frequency of self-harming among students, a school policy should be developed that specifies the roles of various personnel (including the school counselors) and includes guidelines for parental notification. Because school counselors, unlike other mental health professionals, have multiple constituencies (students, school administrators, and parents), their roles are quite complex. It might be prudent to consult with legal experts in drafting a policy and to establish a network of colleagues who agree to stay current and to be available for consultation in challenging cases of self-harm in the school.

Ethical Concerns

A mental health professional's ethical obligation regarding suicide, homicide, and child abuse are quite straightforward. Every mental health professional is familiar with the duty to warn and duty to protect, and clinicians know they must provide informed consent that include telling potential clients of the limits of confidentiality.

Dealing with self-injury is not quite as clear and therefore may be even more troubling to clinicians who feel ethical and legal guidelines aren't available to guide their decision-making (Alderman, 1997; Whisenhunt et al., 2016). In one of the earlier articles that discuss the ethical dilemmas associated with this behavior, Vesper (1996) discussed the question of boundaries of competence. The American Counseling Association (2014) standard states, "Counselors practice only within the boundaries of their competence, based on their education, training, supervised experience, state and national professional credentials, and appropriate professional experience" (p. 8). Because there are no empirically validated treatments that are standard practice for treating self-harm, many clinicians have developed untested personal theories. Vesper suggests this strategy borders on the unethical, as such treatment might be unhelpful at best, or detrimental in the worst cases. One specific issue she raises is over-reaction: Because of their own fears, counselors may determine that the very act of self-harm is evidence of serious psychopathology and take steps to hospitalize the client who is neither suicidal nor lethal. Some counselors simply refuse to treat clients who self-harm, which is unethical unless they make appropriate referrals and/or assure client safety.

Because self-harm can become lethal, it is important to monitor the client, as would be the case for any client with severe depression or other factors that place them at risk. One potentially difficult situation is that of the client who, perhaps because they are discussing painful issues, begins to self-harm (cut or burn) during a session. How should an ethical counselor respond to a client who is scratching or cutting her arm in session, assuming the gesture is not lethal? There are several inappropriate strategies; to focus on the behavior and discontinue the psychological work is an impediment to the therapeutic process. However, it is appropriate to acknowledge the behavior but not interrupt the work. The counselor might say, "I know this is very painful to talk about, and I notice you are cutting your arm to help you cope." To physically intercede, attempt to remove the instrument of cutting, is to violate the client and perhaps reenact childhood trauma. Thus, it is ethical to observe the behavior without actively intervening when the action is clearly nonlethal. What if the client's behavior escalates to a level that serious harm is possible? Again, physically intervening is not appropriate, nor is touching the client in this case. In this case, the counselor should change the focus of the discussion from the issues to the cutting itself (Vesper, 1996).

Without specific training, what is a well-intentioned counselor to do without going beyond the boundaries of competence? An ethical professional will actively seek information, and most important, seek supervision and consultation from a colleague who has experience with this issue (Whisenhunt et al., 2016). Clinicians should attempt to distinguish those acts of self-injury that are life-threatening from the more commonly encountered acts that may not even require medical attention. Including questions about self-harm in intake interviews may alert the counselor to the need for vigilance, and informed consent must be very clear, particularly so with self-harming clients. Informed consent should include information about the therapist's competence and willingness to work with clients who self-harm. Ultimately, the most ethical course for clinicians who treat this clientele is to stay informed and utilize all available resources to do so.

Summary

- Self-harm, self-injury, and NSSI refer to intentional, nonlethal, repetitive bodily harm or disfigurement that is socially unacceptable.
- Those who self-harm are much more likely to eventually commit suicide than people who do not engage in this behavior.
- As difficult as it may be to grasp, self-harming appears to serve an important function for those who engage in this behavior and serves as an effective coping mechanism when other strategies are not present.
- This behavior is frequently associated with borderline personality disorder, but self-harming behaviors exist in adolescents or individuals with other diagnoses.
- There is no treatment approach that is clearly superior to others for this behavior.
- It is important not to demand that clients give up this behavior before they have learned other coping strategies.
- Dialectical behavior therapy is a well-known treatment for this behavior, but it is costly and time-intensive. Briefer therapies are available, along with medication to control the behavior.
- It is important that mental health professionals not directly or indirectly reinforce the behavior.

Additional Resources

On the Web

- http://www.acat.org.uk/ is an outstanding and very complete resource for counselors who are interested in cognitive analytic therapy, with links to many other useful sites and a list of books and other resources.
- https://www.selfinjury.bctr.cornell.edu/resources.html is Cornell University's Self-Injury and Recovery Resources Center, which contains links to resources, websites, books and articles.
- https://www.crisistextline.org/help-for-self-harm/ is a crisis response center for those who self-harm. Assistance can be provided through text messaging 24 hours per day.
- https://selfinjury.com/ is the SAFE Alternatives program's website.
- http://www.recoveryourlife.com/ is the website for a self-harm support community (please see section in the chapter about the impact of digital media before recommending a site like this to a client).

In Print

- *Cut* by Patricia McCormick. Intended for young adults. An excellent opportunity for a clinician unfamiliar with this behavior to get in the head of an adolescent who self-harms, without having to respond to a client. A very quick read and a good first introduction for clinicians.
- *The Scarred Soul* by Tracy Alderman. Useful for both counselors and clients.
- *Bodily Harm* by Karen Conterio and Wendy Lader. Both this and *The Scarred Soul* include sections for therapists.
- *A Bright Red Scream* by M. Strong. Written for the lay audience, this provides excellent, in-depth information about self-harm and belongs on every professional's reference shelf.
- *Bodies Under Siege* by A. R. Favassa. The most complete and scholarly coverage of this topic.
- *The Oxford Handbook of Suicide and Self-Injury* by Matthew Nock. A fairly thorough edited text related to self-harm.
- *Girl in Pieces* by Kathleen Glasgow. Fictional story of 17-year-old who self-harms.

Films and Television

- *Sharp Objects* (2018), starring Amy Adams, based on Gillian Flynn's (2006) book of the same name. The main character displays symptoms of addiction and self-harming behaviors.
- *Girl, Interrupted* (1999), staring Winona Ryder and Angelina Jolie, follows a young woman who spends time in a psychiatric hospital following a suicide attempt. Borderline personality disorder, as well as self-harming behavior, are portrayed.

Exercises

1. Go to www.selfinjury.bctr.cornell.edu/resources.html#tab6 and watch some of the videos. Pay attention to content that is "difficult" for you to absorb. Monitor your own reactions as you imagine working with one of these contributors. Are you disgusted, angry, afraid? Discuss or write about your own awareness about working with this clientele.

2. Read *Cut*. Discuss what work remains to be done in therapy with this client and how you would proceed as the clinician.

3. After reading *Cut*, which is advertised as a young adult book, decide if you would recommend or assign it to an adolescent cutter. Explain your decision.

4. Imagine you are working with a client on another problem and you become aware that the client is self-harming. After careful consideration, you decide that you are not the best person to work with this, but you also now know that abandonment and loss are often major issues for these individuals. How will you handle a referral to minimize the damage?

5. A client comes to you for treatment, and you discover early on that the client is a cutter. You feel you are competent to work with this client and arrange for consultation with a colleague. Given the approaches to therapy described, decide which approach you think is most appropriate and most compatible with your personal style. Then, develop a conceptualization and treatment plan for the client that is grounded in the theory you selected. Explain your choice, including reasons you rejected other approaches.

6. Imagine you work with young adolescents in a school or community setting. Discuss the special ethical considerations that you would have to consider if you learned that one of your clients is self-harming. Decide how you would resolve the ethical issues, giving reasons for your decisions.

7. Interview a clinician in your area who has worked with clients who self-harm. Find out how they take care of themselves when working with this clientele.

8. Termination is particularly important with this clientele. Consider what you might do to prepare and effectively terminate with a client who self-harms. Discuss or write about your plan.

9. After reading the case study, consider how you would proceed with this client. She is not currently hurting herself. Would you consider termination? What other indicators of progress will you use?

10. List three questions you would ask Renee if you had the opportunity.

PART IV

FINAL
THOUGHTS

CHAPTER 10
Reflections

We have covered a lot of ground in the previous chapters and hope you have found them useful. In this chapter we want to emphasize some points and provide some additional food for thought.

Our most important message to readers is that this book does not provide expertise in any of the topics we include. Think of the book as a primer, or introduction to important areas that may not be covered in graduate programs. Each chapter could easily be expanded into a book or course, but that is not our purpose. We want readers to have a starting point, a basic understanding, that will allow you to make decisions about particular cases (Do you need to seek consultation? Do you need to refer? How do you refer a client respectfully and with the interests of the client at the center of the process?).

The book provides a primer, and the responsibility rests on your shoulders to practice within the scope of your competence (we refer you to section C of the 2014 ACA code of ethics). Most, if not all, of the topics covered in this text are complex and challenging issues in which a majority of counselors are obligated, at the least, to consult with other mental health professionals to ensure the competence of their work and protect others from possible harm (ACA, 2014). Regarding the topics in this text, we believe in the idea that "two heads are better than one" with respect to most of them. Seek out assistance, supervision, and/or consultation when necessary, and refer when necessary. Know that you are not alone when you encounter a new or difficult issue with a client. For a beginning counselor who is just starting to gain experience, all client issues are new issues that you most likely don't have any prior experience addressing. Supervision and consultation will be mandatory. However, even a seasoned counselor will benefit from consultation regarding a good number of these topics (e.g., a suicidal client).

We noted at the beginning of the book, and stress again, that these issues rarely occur in isolation. Clients struggling with any of one of these issues may actually be struggling with two or more. People seeking counseling may believe that if they can just stop self-harming, they will have fulfilling lives with minimal stress. However, we know that self-harm is a way to manage psychological pain. The root of that pain may be trauma, abuse, complicated grief, and so forth. Even as a specialist, the mental health professional must have sufficient general knowledge to recognize the many layers of their disordered behavior. The same principle applies to theory: You might find that CBT fits well with your beliefs about change, and you obtain additional training in that approach. However, there may be cases when recognizing the historical origins may improve the treatment, or you have a psychodynamic perspective but have only a few sessions to work with this client (bully, victim) and decide that BSFT would be more appropriate under the circumstances. From any theoretical framework, knowing how much families have to contribute, you might choose one of the family approaches and/or incorporate play or art therapy with young children. Continue to advance your knowledge and experience with marginalized groups to ensure equity in mental health services (Tambling et al., 2023).

Know that mental health professionals are sorely needed. As you look for your professional home, we encourage you to be very deliberate about the kind of environment where you would be able to flourish. Some group practices have philosophical underpinnings that may or may not be consistent with your world view. Ask probing questions, spend time in the setting, and pay attention to your reactions. Will you have a good balance between autonomy and support? Do the providers seem congenial? Does the available space reflect the ambiance that reflects your personal style? Are staff efficient and pleasant with clients? Mental health counseling is a challenging job, and having a soothing environment and amiable colleagues has a definite impact on your stress level. Choose wisely.

We also want to encourage professionals to join and become involved in professional organizations. In addition to accessing new information from associated journals and newsletters, professionals have an opportunity to build a network of professionals with similar interests, which expands their options of collaboration, consultation, and supervision. Not only do the publications and conference presentations keep you up-to-date with new developments, they are also powerful voices advocating for important legislative and policy initiatives. ACA has a model for developing advocacy competences (Toporek & Daniels, 2018) that could be incorporated into counselor education curricula. For example, the National Board of Certified Counselors (NBCC) portability proposal (https://www.nbcc.org/portability) would be a sensible and beneficial advance for counselors and clients. Without such an agreement, relocating is a costly, time-consuming process that delays the continuation of services. In the era of telehealth, this is highly salient.

Another important task in which professional organizations and clinicians must engage is reducing the stigma that prevents people from seeking mental health counseling. Doing outreach, engaging in promotional activities (e.g., community fairs) are steps in that direction. Advocacy to make mental health treatment more accessible, equitable, and affordable is equally important.

The speed at which technology has affected every aspect of our lives means that it will continue to do so. Counselors will undoubtedly have to use telemental health at some point and must recognize that there are critical differences in that modality from a traditional face-to-face context (Lattie et al., 2022; Maldonado et al., 2022). In addition to getting some specialized training in this new mode of service delivery (some programs required this during COVID, and hopefully will continue to offer it for students and new professionals), counselors must become savvy about what the internet has to offer both counselors and clients. We will need to decide how to best incorporate those options into their treatment and to raise questions about clients' engagement in technology prior to or during treatment. There are wonderful tools that can enhance growth, but also dangerous and deceptive options that can do considerable harm, especially to vulnerable individuals. The case of Michelle Carter, convicted of using technology (primarily texts) to urge her boyfriend to commit suicide (giving instructions and listening while he died), is a horrific example of what can happen (McNamara, 2020).

The other field in which new developments are likely to be rapid and relevant to mental health is neuroscience. The rapidly increasing pool of knowledge regarding the role of the brain in mental health disorders may lead to new diagnostic methods and/or new treatments. We are learning more and more about how biology, as well as lived experiences and events impact the physical makeup, development, structure, and processes of our brain—and we are learning more and more about how the physical makeup, development, structure, and processes of our brain impacts our thoughts, feelings, and behavior. It behooves us to keep informed about these important advances.

Finally, we are in this field because we believe that change and healing are possible and that mental health professionals have much to contribute to the well-being of people across the life span. We are excited about adding new professional counselors to a field in which there is so much need.

References

Preface

American Counseling Association. (2014). *2014 ACA code of ethics*.

Reinert, M., Fritze, D., & Nguyen, T. (2021, October). *The state of mental health in America*. Mental Health America.

Rich, R. (2013). *The great recession*. Federal Reserve History. https://www.federalreservehistory.org/essays/great-recession-of-200709

Introduction

Carroll, A. E., & Hayes, D. (2023). The US mental health system is so broken that even money can't fix it. *JAMA Pediatrics*, 177(1), 8–10. https://doi.org/10.1001/jamapediatrics.2022.4416

Elflein, J. (2023, January 16). *Mental health treatment or counseling 2002-2021*. Statista. https://www.statista.com/statistics/794027/mental-health-treatment-counseling-past-year-us-adults/

Lattie, E. G., Stiles-Shields, C., & Graham, A. K. (2022). An overview of and recommendations for more accessible digital mental health services. *Nature Reviews Psychology*, 1(2). https://doi.org/10.1038/s44159-021-00003-1

Posluns, K., & Gall, T. L. (2020). Dear mental health practitioners, take care of yourselves: A literature review on self-care. *International Journal for the Advancement of Counseling*, 42(1), 1–20. https://doi.org/10.1007/s10447-019-09382-w

Samji, H., Wu, J., Ladak, A., Vossen, C., Stewart, E., Dove, N., Long, D., & Snell, G. (2022). Review: Mental health impacts of the COVID-19 pandemic on children and youth—a systematic review. *Child and Adolescent Mental Health*, 27(2), 173–189. https://doi.org/10.1111/camh.12501

Thomeer, M. B., Moody, M. D., & Yahirun, J. (2023). Racial and ethnic disparities in mental health and mental health care during the COVID-19 pandemic. *Journal of Racial and Ethnic Health Disparities*, 10(2), 961–976. https://doi.org/10.1007/s40615-022-01284-9

Chapter 2: COVID-19

Abdalla, S. M., Cohen, G. H., Tamrakar, S., Koya, S. F., & Galea, S. (2021). Media exposure and the risk of post-traumatic stress disorder following a mass traumatic event: An *in-silico* experiment. *Frontiers in Psychiatry*, 12, 1-6. https://doi.org/10.3389/fpsyt.2021.674263

Al-Alawi, M., McCall, R. K., Sultan, A., Al Balushi, N., Al-Mahrouqi, T., Al Ghailani, A., ... & Al Sinawi, H. (2021). Efficacy of a six-week-long therapist-guided online therapy versus self-help internet-based therapy for COVID-19–induced anxiety and depression: Open-label, pragmatic, randomized controlled trial. *JMIR Mental Health*, 8(2), e26683.

Alexander, E. R., Savitz-Romer, M., Nicola, T. P., Rowan-Kenyon, H. T., & Carroll, S. (2022). "We are the heartbeat of the school": How school counselors supported student mental health during the COVID-19 pandemic. *Professional School Counseling*, 26(1b), https://doi.org/10.1177/2156759X221105557221105557.

Alvarez, J. M., Saunders, R., Neubauer, E., & Brown, C. H. (2022). School counselors implementing a trauma-informed approach through evidence-based practices. *Professional School Counseling, 26*(1a), 1-8. https://doi-org.ezproxy2.library.arizona.edu/10.1177/2156759X221086742

American Counseling Association. (n.d.). *Top 4 things to know about the counseling compact.* https://www.counseling.org/docs/default-source/government-affairs/top4things2knowaboutcounselingcompact.pdf?sfvrsn=514d352c_2

Andersson, G. (2022). Internet-delivered psychological treatments. *Annual Review of Clinical Psychology 12,* 157–179.

Baik, S. H., Fox, R. S., Mills, S. D., Roesch, S. C., Sadler, G. R., Klonoff, E. A., & Malcarne, V. L. (2019). Reliability and validity of the Perceived Stress Scale-10 in Hispanic Americans with English or Spanish language preference. *Journal of Health Psychology, 24*(5), 628–639.

Blanchflower, D. G., & Bryson, A. (2022). Covid and mental health in America. *PloS One, 17*(7), e0269855.

Bleiberg, L. (n.d.). *How virtual reality is transforming caregiving for seniors.* AARP. https://www.aarp.org/caregiving/home-care/info-2018/virtual-reality-triggers-memory.html

Bunkall, A. (2020, April 19). *Coronavirus: Doctor "has nightmares" as his patients die alone.* Sky News. https://news.sky.com/story/coronavirus-doctors-heartbreak-at-seeing-covid-19-patients-die-alone-11972105

Chatterjee, D. S. (2021, January 25). Understanding COVID-19's traumatic effects and emerging consequences on mental health. Presentation at the GCCA 27th Annual Conference. https://gacollegecounseling.org/wp-content/uploads/2021/01/GCCA-Understanding-COVID-19s-Mental-Health-Consequences-shuba.pdf

Chatterjee, R. (2022). Nearly 8 million kids lost a parent or primary caregiver to the pandemic. NPR Morning Edition. https://www.npr.org/sections/goatsandsoda/2022/09/06/1121254016/nearly-8-million-kids-lost-a-parent-or-primary-caregiver-to-the-pandemic

Chenneville, T., & Schwartz-Mette, R. (2020). Ethical considerations for psychologists in the time of COVID-19. *American Psychologist, 75*(5), 644–744.

Chopik, W. J. (2016). The benefits of social technology use among older adults are mediated by reduced loneliness. *Cyberpsychology, Behavior, and Social Networking, 19*(9), 551–556.

Correia, T. S. P., Martins, M. M. F., Barroso, F. F., Pinho, L. G., Fonseca, C., Valentim, O., & Lopes, M. (2022). The implications of family members' absence from hospital visits during the COVID-19 pandemic: Nurses' perceptions. *International Journal of Environmental Research and Public Health, 19*(15), 1-14. DOI:10.3390/ijerph19158991

Czeisler, M. É. (2020). Mental health, substance use, and suicidal ideation during the COVID-19 pandemic. MMWR. *Morbidity and Mortality Weekly Report, 69*(32).

de Hoog, N., & Verboon, P. (2020). Is the news making us unhappy? The influence of daily news exposure on emotional states. *British Journal of Psychology, 111*(2), 157–173.

Depoux, A., Martin, S., Karafillakis, E., Preet, R., Wilder-Smith, A., & Larson, H. (2020). The pandemic of social media panic travels faster than the COVID-19 outbreak. *Journal of Travel Medicine, 27*(3), 1-2. doi: 10/1093/jtm/taaa031

Dick, A. S., and Comer, J. S. (2022). Disaster news can trigger post-traumatic stress in kids thousands of miles away. *The Washington Post.* https://www.washingtonpost.com/health/2022/02/20/children-disasters-mental-health/

Dollarhide, C. T. (2003). School counselors as program leaders: Applying leadership contexts to school counseling. *Professional School Counseling, 6*(5), 304–308. http://www.jstor.org/stable/42732447

Dueweke, A. R., Wallace, M. M., Nicasio, A. V., Villalobos, B. T., Hernandez Rodriguez, J., and Stewart, R. W. (2020). Resources and recommendations for engaging children and adolescents in telemental health interventions during COVID-19 and beyond. *The Behavior Therapist, 43*(5), 171–176.

Firth, J., Torous, J., Nicholas, J., Carney, R., Rosenbaum, S., & Sarris, J. (2017). Can smartphone mental health interventions reduce symptoms of anxiety? A meta-analysis of randomized controlled trials. *Journal of Affective Disorders, 218,* 15–22.

Fitzgerald, D. A., Nunn, K., & Isaacs, D. (2021). What we have learnt about trauma, loss and grief for children in response to COVID-19. *Paediatric Respiratory Reviews, 39,* 16–21.

Fitzpatrick, K. M., Drawve, G., & Harris, C. (2020). Facing new fears during the COVID-19 pandemic: The state of America's mental health. *Journal of Anxiety Disorders, 75,* 1-7. https://doi.org/10.1016/j.janxdis.2020.102291

Fitzpatrick, N. (2022). No news is not good news: The implications of news fatigue and news avoidance in a pandemic world. *Athens Journal of Mass Media and Communications, 8*(3), 145–160.

Garagiola, E. R., Lam, Q., Wachsmuth, L. S., Tan, T. Y., Ghali, S., Asafo, S., & Swarna, M. (2022). Adolescent resilience during the COVID-19 pandemic: A review of the impact of the pandemic on developmental milestones. *Behavioral Sciences*, 12(7), 220. doi: 10.3390/bs12070220

González-Sanguino, C., Ausín, B., Castellanos, M. Á., Saiz, J., López-Gómez, A., Ugidos, C., and Muñoz, M. (2020). Mental health consequences during the initial stage of the 2020 Coronavirus pandemic (COVID-19), *Spain. Brain Behav Immun.* 87, 172–176.

Hermida, Alfred & Mellado, Claudia. (2020). Dimensions of social media logics: Mapping forms of journalistic norms and practices on twitter and instagram. *Digital Journalism*, 8, 1–21. 10.1080/21670811.2020.1805779.

Hirschberger, G. (2018, August 10). Collective trauma and the social construction of meaning. *Frontiers in Psychology*, 9, 1–14. https://doi.org/10.3389/fpsyg.2018.01441

Holman, E. A., Garfin, D. R., Lubens, P., & Silver, R. C. (2020). Media exposure to collective trauma, mental health, and functioning: Does it matter what you see? *Clinical Psychological Science*, 8(1), 111–124.

Hull, T. D., & Mahan, K. (2017). A study of asynchronous mobile-enabled SMS text psychotherapy. *Telemedicine and e-Health*, 23(3), 240–247.

Manav, A., & Simsek, N. (2019). The effect of reminiscence therapy with internet-based videos on cognitive status and apathy of older people with mild dementia. *Journal of Geriatric Psychiatry and Neurology*, 32(2), 104–113.

Jolliff, A. F., Moreno, M. A., & D'Angelo, J. (2020). The mediating role of depressive and anxiety symptoms in the association between obesity and problematic social media use in young adults. *Obesity Science & Practice*, 6(5), 454–459.

Jones, E. A., Mitra, A. K., & Bhuiyan, A. R. (2021). Impact of COVID-19 on mental health in adolescents: A systematic review. *International Journal of Environmental Research and Public Health*, 18(5), 1-9. https://doi.org/10.3390/ijerph18052470

Keib, K., Espina, C., Lee, Y. I., Wojdynski, B. W., Choi, D., & Bang, H. (2018). Picture this: The influence of emotionally valenced images, on attention, selection, and sharing of social media news. *Media Psychology*, 21(2), 202–221.

Kellerman, J., Hamilton, J., Selby E., Kleiman, E. (2022). The mental health impact of daily news exposure during the COVID-19 pandemic: Ecological momentary assessment study. *JMIR Mental Health*, 9(5). https://mental.jmir.org/2022/5/e36966

Klaiber, P., Wen, J. H., DeLongis, A., and Sin, N. L. (2021). The ups and downs of daily life during COVID-19: Age differences in affect, stress, and positive events. *Journal of Gerontology B*, 76(2), e30–e37.

Koltai, J., Raifman, J., Bor, J., McKee, M., & Stuckler, D. (2022). COVID-19 vaccination and mental health: A difference-in-difference analysis of the understanding America study. *American Journal of Preventive Medicine*, 62(5), 679–687.

Lazarus, R. S., and Folkman, S. (1984). *Stress, Appraisal and Coping*. New York: Springer.

Li, Z., Ge, J., Yang, M., Feng, J., Qiao, M., Jiang, R. Bi, j., Zhan, G., Xu, X., Waang, L., Zhou, Q., Zhou, C., Pan, Y., Liu, S., Zhang, H., Yang, J., Zhu, B., Hu, Y., Hashimoto, K., Jia, Y., & Yang, C. (2020). Vicarious traumatization in the general public, members, and non-members of medical teams aiding in COVID-19 control. *Brain, Behavior, and Immunity*, 88, 916–919.

Litam, S. D. A., Ausloos, C. D., & Harrichand, J. J. (2021). Stress and resilience among professional counselors during the COVID-19 pandemic. *Journal of Counseling & Development*, 99(4), 384–395.

Magson, N. R., Freeman, J. Y., Rapee, R. M., Richardson, C. E., Oar, E. L., & Fardouly, J. (2021). Risk and protective factors for prospective changes in adolescent mental health during the COVID-19 pandemic. *Journal of Youth and Adolescence*, 50, 44–57.

Mahoney, A., Li, I., Haskelberg, H., Millard, M., Newby, J. M. (2021). The uptake and effectiveness of online cognitive behaviour therapy for symptoms of anxiety and depression during COVID-19. *Journal of Affective Disorder*, 292, 197–203.

Manav, A. I., and Simsek, N. (2019). The effect of reminiscence therapy with internet-based videos on cognitive status and apathy of older people with mild dementia. *Journal of Geriatric Psychiatry and Neurology*, 32(2), 104–113.

Marciano, L., Ostroumova, M., Schulz, P. J., & Camerini, A. L. (2022). Digital media use and adolescents' mental health during the COVID-19 pandemic: A systematic review and meta-analysis. *Frontiers in Public Health*, 9, 1-28. https://doi.org/10.3389/fpubh.2021.793868

Mark, J. (2021). California couple die of covid, leaving five kids behind. Their newborn is 3 weeks old. *The Washington Post*. https://www.washingtonpost.com/nation/2021/09/13/davy-daniel-macias-covid-19/

Martinez-Martin, N., Dasgupta, I., Carter, A., Chandler, J. A., Kellmeyer, P., Kreitmair, K., Weiss, A. & Cabrera, L. Y. (2020). Ethics of digital mental health during COVID-19: Crisis and opportunities. *JMIR Mental Health*, 7(12), 1-9. https://doi.org/10.2196/23776

Masiero, M., Mazzocco, K., Harnois, C., Cropley, M., & Pravettoni, G. (2020). From individual to social trauma: Sources of everyday trauma in Italy, the US and UK during the COVID-19 pandemic. *Journal of Trauma & Dissociation*, 21(5), 513–519.

Maxfield, M., & Pituch, K. A. (2021). COVID-19 worry, mental health indicators, and preparedness for future care needs across the adult lifespan. *Aging & Mental Health*, 25(7), 1273–1280.

Mendes-Santos, C., Nunes, F., Weiderpass, E., Santana, R., & Andersson, G. (2022). Understanding mental health professionals' perspectives and practices regarding the implementation of digital mental health: Qualitative study. *JMIR Formative Research*, 6(4)1-20. doi: 10.2196/32558

Mifsud, A., & Herlihy, B. (2022). Ethical standards for a post-COVID-19 world. *Journal of Mental Health Counseling*, 44(1), 82–96.

Moreno, M. A., and Jolliff, A. F. (2022). Depression and Anxiety in the Context of Digital Media, in Nesi, Jacqueline, Eva H. Telzer, and Mitchell J. Prinstein, eds. *Handbook of Adolescent Digital Media Use and Mental Health*. Cambridge: Cambridge University Press, pp. 217–241.

Neale, R. (2021, August 12). A 30-year-old Florida woman gave birth, took 2 photos with her baby and died days later of COVID-19. *USA Today*.

Ortiz, A. (2020, July 13). Kristin Urquiza's obituary blames politicians for her father's death. *The New York Times*. https://www.nytimes.com/2020/07/13/us/arizona-coronavirus-mark-anthony-urquiza.html

Osofsky, J. D., Osofsky, H. J., & Mamon, L. Y. (2020). Psychological and social impact of COVID-19. *Psychological Trauma: Theory, Research, Practice, and Policy*, 12(5), 468–469.

Overstreet, S., & Chafouleas, S. M. (2016). Trauma-informed schools: Introduction to the special issue. *School Mental Health*, 8, 1–6.

Pfefferbaum, B., & North, C. S. (2020). Mental health and the Covid-19 pandemic. *New England Journal of Medicine*, 383(6), 510–512.

Pincus, R., Hannor-Walker, T., Wright, L., & Justice, J. (2020). COVID-19's effect on students: How school counselors rise to the rescue. *NASSP Bulletin*, 104(4), 241–256.

Racine, N., Killam, T., & Madigan, S. (2020). Trauma-informed care as a universal precaution: beyond the adverse childhood experiences questionnaire. *JAMA Pediatrics*, 174(1), 5–6.

Rauschenberg, C., Schick, A., Hirjak, D., Seidler, A., Paetzold, I., Apfelbacher, C., ... & Reininghaus, U. (2021). Evidence synthesis of digital interventions to mitigate the negative impact of the COVID-19 pandemic on public mental health: rapid meta-review. *Journal of Medical Internet Research*, 23(3), 1–14. doi:10.2196/32558

Rizvi, S. L., Finkelstein, J., Wacha-Montes, A., Yeager, A. L., Ruork, A. K., Yin, Q., ... & Kleiman, E. M. (2022). Randomized clinical trial of a brief, scalable intervention for mental health sequelae in college students during the COVID-19 pandemic. *Behaviour Research and Therapy*, 149, 1–10. https://doi.org/10.1016/j.brat.2021.104015 https://doi.org/10.1016/j.brat.2021.104015

Rodriguez-Cayro, K. (2018, June 28). *Here's how to tell if you have headline stress disorder—and how to protect yourself from it.* Bustle. https://www.bustle.com/p/what-is-headline-stress-disorder-heres-how-to-protect-yourselffrom-anxiety-about-the-news-cycle-9611772

Ruwaard, J. J. (2013). The efficacy and effectiveness of online CBT. [Thesis, externally prepared, Universiteit van Amsterdam].

Schuppe, J. (2020). "I gave this to my dad": COVID-19 survivors grapple with guilt of infecting family. NBC News. https://www.nbcnews.com/news/us-news/i-gave-my-dad-covid-19-survivors-grapple-guilt-infecting-n1207921

Shore, R., Strauss, C., Cavanagh, K., Hayward, M., & Ellett, L. (2018). A randomised controlled trial of a brief online mindfulness-based intervention on paranoia in a non-clinical sample. *Mindfulness*, 9, 294–302.

Silver, R. C. (2020). Surviving the trauma of COVID-19. *Science*, 369(6499), 11.

Silver, R. C., Holman, E. A., & Garfin, D. R. (2021). Coping with cascading collective traumas in the United States. *Nature Human Behaviour*, 5(1), 4–6.

Sparks, S. D. (2023). National panel: Kids who lost a caregiver to covid need more support. *Education Week*. https://www.edweek.org/leadership/national-panel-kids-who-lost-a-caregiver-to-covid-need-more-support/2023/03

Stewart, S. E., Best, J. Selles, R., Naqqash, Z., Lin, B., Lu, C., Au, A., Snell, G., Westwell-Roper, C., Vallani, T., Ewing, E., Dogra, K., Doan, Q., & Samji, H. (2023). Age-specific determinants of psychiatric outcomes after the first COVID-19 wave: Baseline findings from a Canadian online cohort study. *Child and Adolescent Psychiatry and Mental Health*, 17(1), 1–14.

Stosny, S. (2017, February 6). Most people get their news online—but many are switching off altogether: Here's why. *The Washington Post*. https://www.washingtonpost.com/news/inspired-life/wp/2017/02/06/suffering-from-headline-stress-disorder-since-trumps-win-youre-definitely-not-alone/

Sweeney, G. M., Donovan, C. L., March, S., & Forbes, Y. (2019). Logging into therapy: Adolescent perceptions of online therapies for mental health problems. *Internet Interventions*, 15, 93–99.

Taylor, M. (2020). Collective trauma and the relational field. *The Humanistic Psychologist*, 48(4), 382–388.

Thomeer, M. B., Moody, M. D., and Yahirun, J. (2023). Racial and ethnic disparities in mental health and mental health care during the COVID 19 pandemic. *Journal of Racial and Ethnic Health Disparities*, 10(2), 961–976.

Treglia, D., Cutuli, J. J., Arasteh, K., J. Bridgeland, J.M., Edson, G., Phillips, S., Balakrishna, A. (2022). Hidden pain: Children who lost a parent or caregiver to COVID-19 and what the nation can do to help them. *COVID Collaborative*. 1–79.

Vahia, I. V., Jeste, D. V., & Reynolds, C. F. (2020). Older adults and the mental health effects of COVID-19. *JAMA*, 324(22), 2253–2254.

van Tilburg, T. G., Steinmetz, S., Stolte, E., van der Roest, H., and de Vries, D. H. (2021). Loneliness and mental health during the COVID-19 pandemic: A study among dutch older adults. *Journal of Gerontology B*, 76(7), e249–e255.

The Washington Post. (2023, April 10). America's teens are in crisis. states are racing to respond. *Columbia Missourian*. https://www.columbiamissourian.com/opinion/guest_commentaries/americas-teens-are-in-crisis-states-are-racing-to-respond/article_b9481082-d3bc-11ed-ba2b-c3ae4f85375a.htmlhttps://www.columbiamissourian.com/opinion/guest_commentaries/americas-teens-are-in-crisis-states-are-racing-to-respond/article_b9481082-d3bc-11ed-ba2b-c3ae4f85375a.html

Williamson, J. N., and Williamson, D. G. (2020). *Distance Counseling and Supervision: A Guide for Mental Health Clinicians*. American Counseling Association.

World Health Organization. (2020, October 12). *Coronavirus disease (COVID-19)*. https://www.who.int/docs/default-source/coronaviruse/situation-reports/20201012-weekly-epi-update-9.pdf

World Health Organization. (2022, January 19). *Coronavirus (COVID-19) disease advice for the public: Mythbusters*. https://www.who.int/emergencies/diseases/novel-coronavirus-2019/advice-for-public/myth-busters

World Health Organization. (2023, March 16). *COVID-19 weekly epidemiological update, edition 134*. https://www.who.int/publications/m/item/weekly-epidemiological-update-on-covid-19---16-march-2023

Xie, T. (2021, February 15). I came home from college for break and gave my dad Covid-19. *HuffPost*. https://www.huffpost.com/entry/college-students-travel-covid-19_n_6026bfb8c5b6591becd870e1

Zhao, N., & Zhou, G. (2020). Social media use and mental health during the COVID-19 pandemic: Moderator role of disaster stressor and mediator role of negative affect. *Applied Psychology: Health and Well-Being*, 12(4), 1019–1038.

Chapter 3: LGBTQIA

Abreu, R. L., Kenny, M. C., Hall, J. G., & Huff, J. (2020). Supporting transgender students: School counselors' preparedness, training efforts, and necessary support. *Journal of LGBT Youth*, 17(1), 107–122.

American Academy of Pediatrics. (1993). Homosexuality and adolescence. *Pediatrics*, 92, 631–634.

American Counseling Association. (2014). *2014 ACA Code of Ethics*.

American Psychological Association. (2005). *Just the facts about sexual orientation and youth: A primer for principals, educators, and school personnel*. https://www.apa.org/pi/lgbt/resources/just-the-facts.pdf

American Psychological Association. (2015). Guidelines for psychological practice with transgender and gender nonconforming people. *American Psychologist*, 70(9), 832–864 .

American Psychological Association. (2021). APA guidelines for psychological practice with sexual minority persons. Author.

American School Counselor Association. (2022). *The school counselor and LGBTQ+ youth*. https://www.schoolcounselor.org/Standards-Positions/Position-Statements/ASCA-Position-Statements/The-School-Counselor-and-LGBTQ-Youth

Anderson, J. D. (1994). School climate for gay and lesbian students and staff members. *Phi Delta Kappan*, 76, 151–154.

Appleby, Y. (1994). Out in the margins. *Disability & Society*, 9, 19–32.

Appleby, G. A., & Anastas, J. W. (1998). *Not just a passing phase: Social work with gay, lesbian, and bisexual people.* Columbia University Press.

Baker, J. M. (2002). *How homophobia hurts children: Nurturing diversity at home, at school, and in the community.* Harrington Park Press.

Bauman, S., & Sachs-Kapp, P. (1998). A school takes a stand: Promotion of sexual orientation workshops by counselors. *Professional School Counseling, 1,* 42–45.

Besner, H. F., & Spungin, C. I. (1995). *Gay and lesbian students: Understanding their needs.* Taylor & Francis.

Boden, R. (1992). Psychotherapy with disabled lesbians. In S. H. Dworkin & F. J. Gutierrez (Eds.), *Counseling gay men and lesbians: Journey to the end of the rainbow* (pp. 157–187). American Association for Counseling and Development.

Bontempo, D. E., & D'Augelli, A. R. (2002). Effects of at-school victimization and sexual orientation on lesbian, gay, or bisexual youths' health risk behavior. *Journal of Adolescent Health, 30,* 364–374.

Cass, V. C. (1979). Homosexual identity formation: A theoretical model. *Journal of Homosexuality, 4,* 219–235.

Chan, C. S. (1995). Issues of sexual identity in an ethnic minority: The case of Chinese American lesbians, gay men, and bisexual people. In A. R. D'Augelli, & C. J. Patterson (Eds.), *Lesbians, gays, and bisexual identities over the life span* (pp. 87–101). Oxford University Press.

Cochran, S. D. (2001). Emerging issues in research on lesbians' and gay men's' mental health: Does sexual orientation really matter? *American Psychologist, 56,* 932–947.

Coleman, E. (1982). Developmental stages of the coming out process. *Journal of Homosexuality, 8,* 31–43.

County of San Mateo. (n.d.). *LGBTQ glossary.* https://www.smcgov.org/lgbtq/lgbtq-glossary

Crisp, C. (2006). The Gay Affirmative Practice Scale (GAP): A new measure for assessing cultural competence with gay and lesbian clients. *Social Work, 51*(2), 115–126.

Dworkin, S. H. (1997). Female, lesbian, and Jewish: Complex and invisible. In B. Greene (Ed.), *Ethnic and cultural diversity among lesbians and gay men* (pp. 63–87). Sage.

Fontaine, J. H. (1998). Evidencing a need: School counselors' experiences with gay and lesbian students. *Professional School Counseling, 1,* 8–14.

Friend, R. (1991). Older lesbian and gay people: A theory of successful aging. *Journal of Homosexuality, 20,* 99–118.

Garnets, L. (2002). Sexual orientations in perspective. *Cultural Diversity and Ethnic Minority Psychology, 8,* 115–129.

GLSEN. (n.d.a.). *Gender terminology: Discussion guide.* https://www.glsen.org/activity/gender-terminology

GLSEN. (2022). *The 2021 National School Climate Survey.* https://www.glsen.org/research/2021-national-school-climate-survey

Greene, B. (1997). Ethnic minority lesbians and gay men: Mental health and treatment issues. In B. Greene (Ed.), *Ethnic and cultural diversity among lesbians and gay men* (pp. 216–239). SAGESAGE.

Hart, R. (2023, March 6). Kids raised by same-sex parents fare same as—or better than—kids of straight couples, research finds. *Forbes.* https://www.forbes.com/sites/roberthart/2023/03/06/kids-raised-by-same-sex-parents-fare-same-as-or-better-than-kids-of-straight-couples-research-finds/

Hays, M. (2001, August 2). Visible queer. *Montreal Mirror.* http://www.montrealmirror.com/ARCHIVES/2001/080201/cover.html

Herr, K. (1997). Learning lessons from school: Homophobia, heterosexism, and the construction of failure. In M. B. Harris (Ed.), *School experiences of gay and lesbian youth: The invisible minority.* Harrington Park Press.

Hetrick, E., & Martin, A. (1987). Developmental issues and their resolution for gay and lesbian adolescents. *Journal of Homosexuality, 14,* 25–42.

Human Rights Campaign. (2019). *Black and African American LGBTQ Youth Report.* Human Rights Campaign Foundation.

Human Rights Watch. (2001). *Hatred in the hallways: Violence and discrimination against lesbian, gay, bisexual, and transgender students in U.S. schools.*

Hunt, B., Matthews, C., Milsom, A., & Lammel, J. A. (2006). Lesbians with physical disabilities: A qualitative study of their experiences with counseling. *Journal of Counseling & Development, 84,* 163–173.

Hunter, J. (1990). Violence against lesbian and gay male youths. *Journal of Interpersonal Violence, 5,* 295–300.

Jacobs, S., Thoman, W., & Lang, S. (1997). *Introduction.* In S. Jacobs, W. Thomas, & S. Lang (Eds.), *Two-spirit people* (pp. 1–18). University of Illinois Press.

Jones, J. M. (2022, February 17). *LGBT identification in U.S. ticks up to 7.1%.* Gallup. https://news.gallup.com/poll/389792/lgbt-identification-ticks-up.aspx

Kimmel, D. C., & Sang, B. E. (1995). Lesbians and gay men in midlife. In A. R. D'Augelli, & C. J. Patterson (Eds.), *Lesbians, gays, and bisexual identities over the life span* (pp. 190–214). Oxford University Press.

Kinsey, A., Pomeroy, W., & Martin, C. (1948). *Sexual behavior in the human male.* W.B. Saunders.

Kinsey, A., Pomeroy, W., Martin, C., & Gebhard, P. (1953). *Sexual behavior in the human female.* W.B. Saunders.

LaSala, M. C. (2000). Lesbians, gay men, and their parents: Family therapy for the coming-out crisis. *Family Process, 39*(1), 67–81.

Lawson, W. (2005). *Sex, sexuality and the autism spectrum.* Jessica Kingsley.

Luk, J. W., Goldstein, R. B., Yu, J., Haynie, D. L., & Gilman, S. E. (2021). Sexual minority status and age of adolescent suicide ideation and behavior. *Pediatrics, 148*(4). https://doi.org/10.1542/peds.2020-034900

Marans, S. R., & Cohen, D. J. (1991). Child psychoanalytic theories of development. In M. Lewis (Ed.), *Child and adolescent psychiatry: A comprehensive textbook* (pp. 129–144). Williams & Wilkins.

Martin, A. (1998). Clinical issues in psychotherapy with lesbian-, gay-, and bisexual-parented families. In A. R. D'Augelli', & C. J. Patterson (Eds.), *Lesbians, gays, and bisexual identities over the life span* (pp. 270–291). Oxford University Press.

Monier, S. S., & Lewis, A. C. (2000). School counselors and sexual minority students. *Q: The Online Journal, 1*(1), 1–16.

Morales, E. S. (1992). Counseling Latino gays and Latina lesbians. In S. H. Dworkin & F. J. Gutierrez (Eds.), *Counseling gay men and lesbians: Journey to the end of the rainbow* (pp. 125–140). American Association for Counseling and Development.

Morrison, L. L., & L'Heureux, J. (2001). Suicide and gay/lesbian/bisexual youth: Implications for clinicians. *Journal of Adolescence, 24,* 39–49.

Morrow, D. (1993). Social work with gay and lesbian adolescents. *Social Work, 38,* 655–660.

Muller, L. E., & Hartman, J. (1998). Group Counseling for Sexual Minority Youth. *Professional School Counseling, 1*(3), 38–41.

National Board for Certified Counselors. (2023a, May). Legislation impacting transgender clients and communities. *NBCC Visions, 38*(5). https://www.nbcc.org/govtaffairs/newsroom/legislation-impacting-transgender-clients-and-communities

National Board for Certified Counselors. (2023b, May). Q&A: Kylie Madhav, senior directors of diversity, equity, and inclusioni at SAGE. *NBCC Visions, 38*(5). https://www.nbcc.org/resources/nccs/newsletter/qa-kylie-madhav-sage

NPR. (2021, June 12). What's changed since the Pulse nightclub shooting. *All Things Considered.* https://www.npr.org/2021/06/12/1005937089/whats-changed-since-the-pulse-nightclub-shooting

O'Conor, A. (1994). Who gets called queer in school? Lesbian, gay, and bisexual teenagers, homophobia and high school. *The High School Journal, 77,* 7–12.

O'Toole, C. J., & Bregante, J. (1992). Lesbians with disabilities. *Sexuality and Disability, 10*(3), 163–172.

Peplau, L. A., Cochran, S. D., & Mays, V. M. (1997). A national survey of the intimate relationships of African American lesbians and gay men: A look at commitment, satisfaction, sexual behavior, and HIV disease. In B. Greene (Ed.), *Ethnic and cultural diversity among lesbians and gay men* (pp. 11–38). Thousand Oaks, CA: Sage

Pilkington, N. W., & D'Augelli, A. R. (1995). Victimization of lesbian, gay, and bisexual youth in community settings. *Journal of Community Psychology, 23,* 33–55.

Puckett, J. A., Kimball, D., Glozier, W. K., Wertz, M., Dunn, T., Lash, B. R., Ralston, A. L., Holt, N. R., Huit, T. Z., Volk, S. A., Hope, D., Mocarski, R., & DuBois, L. Z. (2023). Transgender and gender diverse clients' experiences in therapy: Responses to sociopolitical events and helpful and unhelpful experiences. *Professional Psychology: Research and Practice, 54*(4), 265–274. https://doi.org/10.1037/pro0000513

Reid, J. (1973). *The best little boy in the world.* Ballantine.

Reynolds, A. L., & Koski, M. J. (1994). Lesbian, gay, and bisexual teens and the school counselor: Building alliances. *The High School Journal, 77,* 88–94.

Rostosky, S. S., & Riggle, EB. (2002). "Out" at work: The relation of actor and partner workplace policy and internalized homophobia to disclosure status. *Journal of Counseling Psychology, 49*(4), 411–419.

Russell, S. T., & Truong, N. L. (2001). Adolescent sexual orientation, race and ethnicity, and school environments: A national study of sexual minority youth of color. In K. Kumashiro (Ed.), *Troubling intersections of race and sexuality: Queer students of color and anti-oppressive education* (pp. 113–130). Rowman & Littlefield.

Sadowski, M. (2001, September/October). *Sexual minority students benefit from school-based support-where it exists.* Harvard Education Letter.

Sang, B. E. (1992). Counseling and psychotherapy with midlife and older lesbians, In S. H. Dworkin & F. J. Gutierrez (Eds.), *Counseling gay men and lesbians: Journey to the end of the rainbow* (pp. 35–48). American Association for Counseling and Development.

Savin-Williams, R. (1998). *"... And. A then I became gay": Young men's stories.* Routledge.

Schumm, W., & Crawford, D. (2019). Scientific consensu on whether LGBTQ parents are more likely (or notn) to have LGBTQ children: An analysis of 72 social science reviews of the literature published between 2001 and 2017. *Journal of International Women's Studies, 20*(7), 1–12.

Sears, J. T. (1992). Educators, homosexuality, and homosexual students: Are personal feelings related to professional beliefs? In K. M. Harbeck (Ed.), *Coming out of the classroom closet: Gay and lesbian students, teachers, and curricula* (pp. 29–70). Haworth Press.

Shakespeare, T. (1999). Coming out and coming home. *Journal of Gay, Lesbian, and Bisexual Identity, 4,* 39–51.

Shapiro, J. (2020). The law governing LGBTQ-parent families in the United States. In A. E. Goldberg & K. R. Allen (Eds.), *LGBTQ-parent families: Innovations in research and implications for practice* (pp. 365–382). Springer. https://doi.org/10.1007/978-3-030-35610-1_23

Shi, Q., & Doud, S. (2017). An examination of school counselors' competency working with lesbian, gay and bisexual transgender (LGBT) students. *Journal of LGBT Issues in Counseling, 11*(1), 2–17.

Siecus. (2001, April/May). Fact sheet: Lesbian, gay, bisexual, and transgendered youth issues. *Siecus Report Supplement, 29,* 1–5.

Simons, J. D. (2018). Middle and high school counselor advocates for lesbian, gay, and bisexual students. *Journal of LGBT Issues in Counseling, 12*(3), 158–175.

Swartz, D. B. (1993). A comparative study of sex knowledge among hearing and deaf college freshmen. *Sexuality and Disability, 11,* 129–147.

Tafoya, T. (1997). Native gay and lesbian issues: The two-spirited. In B. Greene (Ed.), *Ethnic and cultural diversity among lesbians and gay men* (pp. 1–9). SAGE.

Tharinger, D., & Wells, G. (2000). An attachment perspective on the developmental challenges of gay and lesbian adolescents: The need for continuity of caregiving from family and schools. *The School Psychology Review, 29,* 158–172.

Thompson, S. A., Bryson, M., & De Castell, S. (2001). Prospects for identity formation for gay, lesbian, and bisexual persons with developmental disabilities. *International Journal of Disability, Development, and Education, 48,* 53–65.

Troiden, R. R. (1989). The formation of homosexual identities. *Journal of Homosexuality, 17,* 43–73.

University of California Davis, LGBTQIA Resource Center. (2023, July 21). *LGBTQIA Resource Center Glossary.* https://lgbtqia.ucdavis.edu/educated/glossary

U.S. Census Bureau. (2023, June).June *LGBTQIA+ Pride month: June 2023.* https://www.census.gov/newsroom/stories/lgbt-pride-month.html

Wildman, S. (2000, October). Coming out early. *The Advocate.*

Chapter 4: People Experiencing Homelessness

A Dream Denied: The Criminalization of Homelessness in U.S. Cities. National Coalition for the homeless. (2008, June). https://www.issuelab.org/resources/1221/1221.pdf

Abdul Rahman, M., Fidel Turner, J., & Elbedour, S. (2015, October). The US homeless student population: Homeless youth education, review of research classifications and typologies, and the US federal legislative response. In *Child & Youth Care Forum* (Vol. 44), pp. 687–709.

American School Counselor Association (ASCA). (2018). *The school counselor and children experiencing homelessness.* https://www.schoolcounselor.org/Standards-Positions/Position-Statements/ASCA-Position-Statements/The-School-Counselor-and-Children-Experiencing-Hom

Baggerly, J., & Borkowski, T. (2004). Applying the ASCA national model to elementary school students who are homeless: A case study. *Professional School Counseling, 8*(2), 116–123.

Bauman, S., & Rivers, I. (2023). *Mental health in the digital age* (2nd ed.) Springer Nature.

Belcher, J. R., Scholler-Jaquish, A., & Drummond, M. (1991). Three stages of homelessness: A conceptual model for social workers in health care. *Health & Social Work*, 16(2), 87–93. https://doi.org/10.1093/hsw/16.2.87

Campaign for Children. (2017). *The homeless children and youth act of 2017.* https://campaignforchildren.org/wp-content/uploads/sites/2/2017/03/HCYA-Fact-Sheet-March-2017-FINAL-.pdf

Carlson, J. L., Sugano, E., Millstein, S. G., & Auerswald, C. L. (2006). Service utilization and the life cycle of youth homelessness. *Journal of Adolescent Health*, 38(5), 624–627.

Daniels, J., D'andrea, M., Omizo, M., & Pier, P. (1999). Group work with homeless youngsters and their mothers. *Journal for Specialists in Group Work*, 24(2), 164–185.

Daniels, J., Pier, P., & D'Andrea, M. (1997). Homeless students' perceptions of school counselors: Iimplications for practice. [ERIC Research Report] ED 411 486.

De Sousa, T., Andrichik, A, Cuellar, M., Marson, J., Rush, K. (2023). *The 2022 annual homelessness assessment report (AHAR) to Ccongress.* U.S. Department of Housing and Urban Development. https://www.huduser.gov/portal/sites/default/files/pdf/2022-AHAR-Part-1.pdf

DiBiase, R., & Waddell, S. (1995). Some effects of homelessness on the psychological functioning of preschoolers. *Journal of Abnormal Child Psychology*, 23(6), 783–792.

Eichenbaum, M., & Nichols, M. (2023, June 9). *Opinion: How Houston's homelessness breakthrough could be a national game-changer.* CNN. https://www.cnn.com/2023/06/08/opinions/homelessness-solutions-houston-model-eichenbaum-nichols/index.html

Gargiulo, R. M. (2006). Homeless and disabled: Rights, responsibilities, and recommendations for serving young children with special needs. *Early Childhood Education Journal*, 33, 357–362.

Goodman, L. A., Saxe, L., & Harvey, M. (1991). Homelessness as psychological trauma: Broadening perspectives. *American Psychologist*, 46(11), 1219.

Haber, M. G., & Toro, P. A. (2004). Homelessness among families, children, and adolescents: An ecological–developmental perspective. *Clinical Child and Family Psychology Review*, 7, 123–164.

Havlik, S. A., Rowley, P., Pucket, J., Wilson, G., & Neason, E. (2017–2018). "Do whatever you can to try to support that kid": School counselors' experiencing addressing student homelessness. *Professional School Counseling*, 21, 1, 47–59. https://doi.org/10.5330/1096-2409-21.1.47

Heaslip, V., Richer, S., Simkhada, B., Dogan, H., & Green, S. (2021). Use of technology to promote health and wellbeing of people who are homeless: A systematic review. *International Journal of Environmental Research and Public Health*, 18(13), 6845.1-18. https://doi-org.ezproxy4.library.arizona.edu/10.3390%2Fijerph18136845

Hess, A. J. (2018, May 25). *Teen who grew up in homeless shelters earns full ride to Harvard University.* CNBC. https://www.cnbc.com/2018/05/25/teen-who-grew-up-in-homeless-shelters-earns-full-ride-to-harvard.html

Homeless, houseless, unhoused, or unsheltered: Which term is right?—Invisible People. (2022, August 25). https://invisiblepeople.tv/homeless-houseless-unhoused-or-unsheltered-which-term-is-right/

Homelessness in the United States: A state-by-state comparative analysis. (n.d.). Myelisting.Com. Retrieved May 31, 2023, from https://myelisting.com/commercial-real-estate-news/1444/homelessness-united-states-state-by-state-analysis/

Houghtaling, L. M., Simon, K., Gower, A. L., McCurdy, A., Rider, G. NH., Russell, S. T., & Eisenberg, M. E. (2024). Unaccompanied unstable housing among racially, ethnically, sexually, and gender diverse youth: Intersecting identities bearing the greatest burden. *American Journal of Orthopsychiatry*. Advance online publication. https://doi.org/10.1037/ort0000725

Humphry, J. (2019). "'Digital first'": Homelessness and data use in an online service environment. *Communication Research and Practice*, 5(2), 172–187. https://doi.org/10.1080/22041451.2019.1601418

Koblinsky, S. A., Gordon, A. L., & Anderson, E. A. (2000). Changes in the social skills and behavior problems of homeless and housed children during the preschool year. *Early Education and Development*, 11(3), 321-338.

Kosciw, J. G., & Cullen, M. K. (2002). The GLSEN 2001 national school climate survey: The school-related experiences of our nation's lesbian, gay, bisexual and transgender youth. https://www.glsen.org/sites/default/files/2020-11/2001%20National%20School%20Climate%20Survey%20Full%20Report.pdf

Kushel, M. (2022). Violence against people who are homeless: The hidden epidemic. Benioff Homelessness and Housing Initiative. https://homelessness.ucsf.edu/blog/violence-against-people-homeless-hidden-epidemic

Legal Information Institute. (n.d.). *42 U.S. Code § 11302—General definition of homeless individual.* Cornell Law School. https://www.law.cornell.edu/uscode/text/42/11302

Marler, W. (2021). "'You can't talk at the library'": The leisure divide and public internet access for people experiencing homelessness. *Information, Communication & Society*, 26(7), 1303–1321. https://doi.org/10.1080/1369118X.2021.2006742

Maslow, A. H. (1987). *Motivation and personality* (3rd ed.). Delhi, India: Pearson Education.

Masten, A. S., Miliotis, D., Graham-Bermann, S. A., Ramirez, M., & Neemann, J. (1993). Children in homeless families: Rrisks to mental health and development. *Journal of Consulting and Clinical Psychology*, 61(2), 335.

McGeough, C., Walsh, A., & Clyne, B. (2020). Barriers and facilitators perceived by women while homeless and pregnant in accessing antenatal and or postnatal healthcare: A qualitative evidence synthesis. *Health & Social Care in the Community*, 28(5), 1380–1393.

Milburn, N. G., Ayala, G., Rice, E., Batterham, P., & Rotheram-Borus, M. J. (2006). Discrimination and exiting homelessness among homeless adolescents. *Cultural Diversity and Ethnic Minority Psychology*, 12(4), 658.

National Alliance to End Homelessness. (n.d.). *State of homelessness: 2023 edition*. https://endhomelessness.org/homelessness-in-america/homelessness-statistics/state-of-homelessness/

National Center for Homeless Education. (2013). *Early care and education for young children experiencing homelessness*. https://files.eric.ed.gov/fulltext/ED574623.pdf

National Coalition for Homeless Veterans (n.d.) *Homeless veterans fact sheet*. https://nchv.org/images/uploads/Homeless-Veterans_factsheet.pdf

National Coalition for the Homeless. (2008, June). *A dream denied: The criminalization of homelessness in U.S. cities*. [Report]. https://www.issuelab.org/resources/1221/1221.pdf

National Homelessness Law Center National Homelessness Law Center. (2022, May 13). *Racial injustice in housing and homelessness in the United States*. https://homelesslaw.org/wp-content/uploads/2022/05/CERD-List-of-Themes-Housing-Homelessness-5-20221.pdf

Orenstein GA, Lewis L. Erikson's stages of psychosocial development. [Updated 2022, Nov 7]. https://www-ncbi-nlm-nih-gov.ezproxy4.library.arizona.edu/books/NBK556096/

Rahman, M. A., Turner, J. F., and Elbedour, S. (2015). The U.S. homeless student population: Homeless youth education, review of research classifications and typologies, and the U.S. federal legislative response. *Child & Youth Care Forum*, 44(5), 687–709.

Ray, N. (2006). Lesbian, gay, bisexual and transgender youth: An epidemic of homelessness. New York: National Gay and Lesbian Task Force Policy Institute and the National Coalition for the Homeless.

Rhoades, H., Wenzel, S. L., Rice, E., Winetrobe, H., & Henwood, B. (2017). No digital divide? Technology use among homeless adults. *Journal of Social Distress and the Homeless*, 26(1), 73-77.

Robbins, K. (2022, August 25). *Homeless, houseless, unhoused, or unsheltered: Which term is right?* Invisible People. https://invisiblepeople.tv/homeless-houseless-unhoused-or-unsheltered-which-term-is-right/

Romero, A. P., Goldberg, S. K., & Vasquez, L.A. (2020, April). *LGBT people and housing affordability, discrimination, and homelessness*. UCLA School of Law Williams Institute. https://williamsinstitute.law.ucla.edu/publications/lgbt-housing-instability/

Sample, K., & Ferguson, K. M. (2020). It shouldn't be this hard: Systemic, situational, and intrapersonal barriers to exiting homelessness among homeless young adults. *Qualitative Social Work*, 19(4), 580–598. http://dx.doi.org/10.1177/1473325019836280

Single Mother Statistics. (2023, May 17, October 26). *Single mother guide*. https://singlemotherguide.com/single-mother-statistics).

Smith, A. C., & Smith, D. I. (2001). *Emergency and transitional shelter population: 2000*. Census 2000 Special Reports. U.S. Census 2000 Special Reports. . http://www.census.gov/prod/2001pubs/censr01-2.pdf.

Smollar, J. (2001). Homeless youth in the United States. *The Prevention Researcher*,

State of Homelessness: 2023 Edition. (n.d.). National Alliance to End Homelessness. Retrieved May 17, 2023, from https://endhomelessness.org/homelessness-in-america/homelessness-statistics/state-of-homelessness/

Strawser, S., Markos, P. A., Yamaguchi, B. J., & Higgins, K. (2000). A new challenge for school counselors: Children who are homeless. *Professional School Counseling*, 3(3), 162–171.

Substance Abuse and Mental Health Services Administration. (n.d.). *Definitions of homelessness*. https://soarworks.samhsa.gov/article/definitions-of-homelessness

Thakarar, k., Morgan, J.R., Gaeta, j. M., Hohl, C., & Drainoni, M (2016). Homelessness, HIV, and incomplete viral suppression. *Journal of Health Care for the Poor and Underserved.* 145–156. doi: 10.1353/hpu.2016.0020

Thurman, W., Semwal, M., Moczygemba, L. R., & Hilbelink, M. (2021, September 29). Smartphone technology to empower people experiencing homelessness: Secondary analysis. *Journal of Medical Internet Research*, 23(9), e277871-12. https://doi.org/10.2196/27787

U.S. Department of Education. (2017). Education for homeless children and youths program non-regulatory guidance: Title VII-B of the McKinney-Vento Homeless Assistance Act, as amended by The Every Student Succeeds Act. https://www2.ed.gov/policy/elsec/leg/essa/160240ehcyguidance072716updated0317.pdf

U.S. Department of Housing and Urban Development.(2022, December). *The 2022 Annual Homelessness Assessment Report (AHAR to Congress) Part 1: Point-In-Time Estimates of Homelessness, December 2022.* (n.d.). https://www.huduser.gov/portal/sites/default/files/pdf/2022-ahar-part-1.pdf

Waguespack, D., & Ryan, B. (2019). *State index on youth homelessness.* True Colors United and the National Law Center on Homelessness and Poverty. https://homelesslaw.org/wp-content/uploads/2020/02/2019-State-Index.pdf

Walsh, M. E., & Buckley, M. A. (1994). Children's experiences of homelessness: Implications for school counselors. *Elementary School Guidance & Counseling*, 29(1), 4–15.

Weinreb, L., Goldberg, R., Bassuk, E., & Perloff, J. (1998). Determinants of health and service use patterns in homeless and low-income housed children. *Pediatrics*, 102(3), 554–562.

Williams, L. (2023, March 24). *Homelessness in the United States: A state-by-state comparative analysis.* MyeListing. https://myelisting.com/commercial-real-estate-news/1444/homelessness-united-states-state-by-state-analysis/

Youth.gov.(n.d.) *Child welfare system.* https://youth.gov/youth-topics/runaway-and-homeless-youth/child-welfare-system

Zerger, S., Bacon, S., Corneau, S., Skosriireva, A., McKenzie, K., Gapka, S., O'Campo, P., Sarang, A., & Stergiopoulos, V. (2014, December 14). Differential experiences of discrimination among ethnoracially diverse persons experiencing mental illness and homelessness. *BMC Psychiatry*, 14(1), 1-11353. https://doi-org.ezproxy4.library.arizona.edu/10.1186/s12888-014-0353-1https://doi.org/10.1186/s12888-014-0353-1

Chapter 5: Grief and Bereavement

Alvord, L. A. & Van Pelt, E. C. (1999). *The scalpel and the silver bear.* Bantam Books.

American Foundation for Suicide Prevention. (2023). *Suicide statistics.* https://afsp.org/suicide-statistics/

American Pet Products Association. (n.d.). *Home page.* https://www.americanpetproducts.org/

American Psychiatric Association. (2013). *Diagnostic and statistical manual of mental disorders* (5th ed.).

Asakawa, G. (2016). Funerals in the Japanese American community. *Discover Nikkei.* https://discovernikkei.org/en/journal/2016/6/2/funerals

Balk, D. (1983). How teenagers cope with sibling death: Some implications for school counselors. *The School Counselor*, 31, 150–158.

Ball, S. (2022, March 4). Waiting to be a widow: What every woman should know. *AARP.* https://www.aarp.org/caregiving/basics/info-2022/preparing-to-be-a-widow.html

Barrett, R. K. (1998). Sociocultural considerations for working with Blacks experiencing loss and grief. In K. J. Doka & J. D. Davidson (Eds.), *Living with grief: Who we are; how we grieve* (pp. 47–56). Hospice Foundation of America.

Boelen, P. A., & Smid, G. E. (2017). The traumatic grief inventory self-report version (TGI-SR): Introduction and preliminary psychometric evaluation. *Journal of Loss and Trauma*, 22(3), 196–212.

Bologna, C. (2020, November 5). *25 children's books that explain death and grief to kids.* HuffPost Life. https://www.huffpost.com/entry/childrens-books-death-grief_l_5fa38deec5b660630aee43fdhttps://www.huffpost.com/entry/childrens-books-death-grief_l_5fa38deec5b660630aee43fd

Bowlby, J. (1969). *Attachment. Attachment and loss: Vol. 1. Loss.* New York: Basic Books.

Carroll, B. (1998). Cultural aspects of peer support: An examination of one program's experience. In B. Carroll (Ed.), *Living with grief* (pp. 207–218). Routledge.

Center for Loss & Life Transition. (n.d.). *Grief and mourning basics.* https://www.centerforloss.com/grief/grief-mourning-basics/

Centers for Disease Control and Prevention. (2023, July 25). *Child health.* https://www.cdc.gov/nchs/fastats/child-health.htm

Clements, P. T., Focht-New, G., & Faulkner, M. J. (2004). Grief in the shadows: Exploring loss and bereavement in people with developmental disabilities. *Issues in Mental Health Nursing, 25,* 799–808.

Coriell, E. (2022, February 11). Chinese funerals: What to expect, customs, and traditions. *Cake.* https://www.joincake.com/blog/chinese-funerals-what-to-expect/

Costa, L., & Holliday, D. (1994). Helping children cope with the death of a parent. *Elementary School Guidance & Counseling, 28,* 206–213.

Dershimer, R. A. (1990). *Counseling the bereaved.* Pergamon.

Dowling, S., Hubert, J., White, S., & Hollins, S. (2006). Bereaved adults with intellectual disabilities: A combined randomized controlled trial and qualitative study of two community-based interventions. *Journal of Intellectual Disability Research, 50,* 277–287.

Fast, J. D. (2003). After Columbine: How people mourn sudden death. *Social Work, 48,* 484–491.

Gardy, A. (2005, September 20). Lost baby, and the pain of endless reminders in the mail. *The New York Times,* D5.

Gray, R. E. (1988). The role of school counselors with bereaved teenagers: With and without peer support groups. *School Counselors, 35,* 185–193.

Grollman, E. (1998). What you always wanted to know about your Jewish clients' perspectives concerning death and dying—but were afraid to ask. In K. J. Doka & J. D. Davidson (Eds.), *Living with grief: Who we are; how we grieve* (pp. 47–56). Hospice Foundation of America.

Hollins, S. (1995). Managing grief better: People with developmental disabilities. *The Habilitative Mental Healthcare Newsletter, 14(3),* 50–52.

Huber, B. R. (2021, September 28). *Life expectancy gap between black and white Americans closes nearly 50% in 30 years.* Princeton School of Public and International Affairs. https://spia.princeton.edu/news/life-expectancy-gap-between-black-and-white-americans-closes-nearly-50-30-years

Iglewicz, A., Shear, M. K., Reynolds III, C. F., Simon, N., Lebowitz, B., & Zisook, S. (2020). Complicated grief therapy for clinicians: An evidence-based protocol for mental health practice. *Depression and Anxiety, 37(1),* 90–98.

Jordan, J. R. (2001). Is suicide bereavement different? A reassessment of the literature. *Suicide and Life-Threatening Behavior, 31,* 91–101.

Judi's House. (n.d.). *Childhood bereavement estimation model.* https://judishouse.org/research-tools/cbem/

Lavin, C. (1998). Helping individuals with developmental disabilities. In K. J. Doka & J. D. Davidson (Eds.), *Living with grief: Who we are; how we grieve* (pp. 161–180). Hospice Foundation of America.

Lewis, M. M., & Trzinski, A. L. (2006). Counseling older adults with dementia who are dealing with death: Innovative interventions for practitioners. *Death Studies, 30(8),* 777–787.

Lindstrøm, T. C. (2002). "It ain't necessarily so" ... challenging mainstream thinking about bereavement. *Family and Community Health, 25(1),* 11–21.

Martin, T. L., & Doka, K. J. (2000). *Men don't cry—women do: Transcending gender stereotypes of grief.* Taylor & Francis.

Moore, J. W. (1976). *Mexican Americans.* Prentice-Hall.

Neimeyer, R. A. (2000). Searching for the meaning of meaning: Grief therapy and the process of reconstruction. *Death Studies, 24(9),* 541–558.

Ogrodniczuk, J. S., Piper, W. E., Joyce, A. S., Weidman, R., McCallum, M., Zaim, H. F., & Rosie, J. S. (2003). Differentiating symptoms of complicated grief and depression among psychiatric outpatients. *Canadian Journal of Psychiatry, 48(2),* 87–93.

Olaisen, R. H. (2020). QuickStats: Percentage of deaths, by place of death. National Vital Statistics System. https://www.cdc.gov/mmwr/volumes/69/wr/mm6919a4.htm

Parkes, C. M. (1998). Bereavement in adult life. *British Medical Journal, 316,* 856–860.

Prigerson, H. G., Maciejewski, P. K., Reynolds, C. F., III, Bierhals, A. J., Newsom, J. T., Fasiczka, A., Frank, E., Doman, J., & Miller, M. (1995). Inventory of complicated grief: A scale to measure maladaptive symptoms of loss. *Psychiatry Research, 59,* 65–79.

Raad, S. A. (1998). Grief: A Muslim perspective. In K. J. Doka & J. D. Davidson (Eds.), *Living with grief: Who we are; how we grieve* (pp. 47–56). Hospice Foundation of America.

Rosenzweig, A., Prigerson, H., Miller, M., & Reynolds C. F., III. (1997). Bereavement and late-life depression: Grief and its complications in the elderly. *Annual Review of Medicine*, *48*, 421–428.

Salvador, R. J. (2003).What do Mexicans celebrate on the Day of the Dead? In J. D. Morgan & P. Laungani (Eds.), *Death and bereavement in the Americas. Death, value and meaning series* (Vol. II, pp. 75–76). Amityville, NY: Baywood.

Samide, L. L., & Stockton, R. (2002). Letting go of grief: Bereavement groups for children in the school setting. *Journal for Specialists in Group Work*, *27*, 192–204.

Schut, H., Stroebe, M. S., Van den Bout, J., & Terheggen, M. (2001). The efficacy of bereavement interventions. In M. S. Stroebe, R. O. Hansson, W. Stroebe, & H. Schut (Eds.), *Handbook of bereavement research: Consequences, coping, and care* (pp. 705–737). American Psychological Association.

Servaty-Seib, H. L., Peterson, J., & Spang, D. (2003). Notifying individual students of a death loss: Practical recommendations for schools and school counselors. *Death Studies*, *27*(2), 167–186.

Shear, K., Frank, E., Houk, P. R., & Reynolds, C. F., III. (2005). Treatment of complicated grief: A randomized control trial. *JAMA*, *293*, 2601–2608.

Small, J. A., & Cochrane, D. (2020). Spaced retrieval and episodic memory training in Alzheimer's disease. *Clinical Interventions in Aging*, *15*, 519–536.

Spungen, D., & Piccicuto, A. (2002). *Working with children traumatized by homicide: A new paradigm*. Anti-Violence Partnership.

Stroebe, M., Gergem, M. M., Gergen, K. J., & Stroebe, W. (1992). Broken hearts or broken bonds: Love and death in historical perspective. *American Psychologist*, *47*(10), 1205–1212.

Stroebe, M., & Schut H. (1999). The dual process model of coping with bereavement: Rationale and description. *Death Studies*, *23*(3), 197–224.

Swihart, J., Silliman, B., & McNeil, J. (1992). Death of student: Implications for secondary school counselors. *School Counselor*, *40*(1), 55–60.

Van Dongen, C. J. (1990). Agonizing questions: Experiences of survivors of suicide victims. *Nursing Research*, *39*, 224–229.

Worden, J. W. (1991). *Grief counseling and grief therapy: A handbook for the mental health practitioner*. Springer.

Worden, J. W. (2004). *Grief counseling and grief therapy: A handbook for the mental health practitioner* (3rd ed.). Springer.

Worden, J. W. (2018). *Grief counseling and grief therapy: A handbook for the mental health practitioner* (5th ed.). Springer.

Xu, J. Q., Murphy, S. L., Kochanek, K. D., & Arias E. (2022). *Mortality in the United States, 2021*. National Center for Health Statistics Data Brief (no. 456). https://doi.org/10.15620/cdc:122516

Zieziula, F. (1998). The world of the Deaf community. In K. J. Doka & J. D. Davidson (Eds.), *Living with grief: Who we are; how we grieve* (pp. 181–198). Hospice Foundation of America.

Chapter 6: Trauma

Alisic, E., Zalta, A. K., Van Wesel, F., Larsen, S. E., Hafstad, G. S., Hassanpour, K., & Smid, G. E. (2014). Rates of post-traumatic stress disorder in trauma-exposed children and adolescents: Meta-analysis. *British Journal of Psychiatry*, *204*(5), 335–340. https://doi.org/10.1192/bjp.bp.113.131227

American Psychiatric Association. (1980). *Diagnostic and statistical manual of mental disorders* (Fifth edition). Author.

American Psychiatric Association. (2013). *Diagnostic and statistical manual of mental disorders* (Third Edition). Author.

American Psychological Association. (2017). *Clinical practice guidelines for the treatment of posttraumatic stress disorder (PTSD) in adults*. APA. https://www.apa.org/ptsd-guideline

American School Counselor Association. (n.d.). *Student-to-school-counselor ratio 2021-2022*. ASCA. https://www.schoolcounselor.org/getmedia/b9d453e7-7c45-4ef7-bf90-16f1f3cbab94/Ratios-21-22-Alpha.pdf

Andermann, L., Kanagaratnam, P., Wondimagegn, D., & Pain, C. (2021). PTSD in refuge and migrant mental health. In D. Bhugra (Ed.), *Oxford textbook of migrant psychiatry* (pp. 513–522). Oxford University Press. https://doi.org/10.1093/med/9780198833741.003.0060

Armenta, R. F., Rush, T., LeardMann, C. A., Millegan, J., Cooper, A., & Hoge, C. W. (2018). Factors associated with persistent posttraumatic stress disorder among U.S. military service members and veterans. *BMC Psychiatry, 18*(1), 1–11. https://doi.org/10.1186/s12888-018-1590-5

Arseneault, L. (2017). The long-term impact of bullying victimization on mental health. *World Psychiatry, 16*(1), 27–28. https://doi.org/10.1002/wps.20399

Arvay, M. (2001). Secondary traumatic stress among trauma counsellors: What does the research say? *International Journal for the Advancement of Counseling, 23,* 283–293.

Averill, P. A., & Beck, J. G. (2000). Post-traumatic stress disorder in older adults: A conceptual review. *Journal of Anxiety Disorders, 14,* 133–156.

Baggerly, J. N. (2005). Systematic trauma interventions for children: A 12 Step protocol. In J. Webber (Ed.), *Terrorism, trauma, and tragedies: A counselor's guide to preparing and responding* (pp. 93–96). American Counseling Association.

Bauman, S. (2008). *Essential topics for the helping professional.* Boston: A. B. Longman.

Bergmann, U. (2019). *Neurobiological foundations for EMDR practice.* Springer.

Birkeland, M. S., Skar, A.-M. S., & Jensen, T. K. (2022). Understanding the relationships between trauma type and individual posttraumatic stress symptoms: A cross-sectional study of a clinical sample of children and adolescents. *Journal of Child Psychology and Psychiatry, 63*(12), 1496–1504. https://doi.org/10.1111/jcpp.13602

Blais, R. K., Tirone, V., Orlowska, D., Lofgreen, A., Klassen, B., Held, P., Stevens, N., & Zalta, A. K. (2021). Self-reported PTSD symptoms and social support in U.S. military service members and veterans: A meta-analysis. *European Journal of Psychotraumatology, 12*(1), 1-17. https://doi.org/10.1080/20008198.2020.1851078

Blank, M. (2007). Posttraumatic stress disorder in infants, toddlers, and preschoolers. *BC Medical Journal 49(3),* 133–138.

Boscarino, J. A., Figley, C. R., & Adams, R. E. (2004). Compassion fatigue following the September 11 terrorist attacks: A study of secondary trauma among New York City social workers. *International Journal of Emergency Mental Health, 6*(2), 57-66.

Bosquet Enlow, M., Egeland, B., Blood, E. A., Wright, R. O., & Wright, R. J. (2012). Interpersonal trauma exposure and cognitive development in children to age 8 years: A longitudinal study. *Journal of Epidemiology and Community Health, 66*(11), 1005–1010. https://doi.org/10.1136/jech-2011-200727

Breiding, M.; Basile, K. C. Smith, S. G., Black, M. C., Mahendra, R. (2015). *Intimate partner violence surveillance uniform definitions and recommended data elements (version 2.0).* Center for Disease Control and Prevention. https://stacks.cdc.gov/view/cdc/31292

Bremner, J. D. (2006). Traumatic stress: Effects on the brain. *Dialogues in Clinical Neuroscience, 8*(4), 445–461. https://doi.org/10.31887/DCNS.2006.8.4/jbremner

Brom, D., Stokar, Y., Lawi, C., Nuriel-Porat, V., Ziv, Y., Lerner, K., & Ross, G. (2017). Somatic experiencing for post-traumatic stress disorder: A randomized controlled outcome study. *Journal of Traumatic Stress, 30*(3), 304-312. doi: 10.1002/jts.22189

Brown, A. (2011, July 7). *Lockerbie was hell on earth; It's crazy ... all that death and I am lying awake wondering how the wind can remove a man's belt.* Daily Record. https://www.dailyrecord.co.uk/news/real-life/lockerbie-was-hell-on-earth-its-crazy-1107378

Bryant, R. A. (2019). Post-traumatic stress disorder: A state-of-the-art review of evidence and challenges. *World Psychiatry, 18*(3), 259–269. https://doi.org/10.1002/wps.20656

Bryant-Davis, T. (2019). The cultural context of trauma recovery: Considering the posttraumatic stress disorder practice guideline and intersectionality. *Psychotherapy, 56*(3), 400–408. https://doi.org/10.1037/pst0000241

Busuttil, W. (2004). Presentations and management of post traumatic stress disorder and the elderly: A need for investigation. *International Journal of Geriatric Psychiatry, 19,* 429–439.

Cameron, L. (2022, November 1). Ex-soldier who helped at Lockerbie fronts new campaign for veterans. *Independent.* https://www.independent.co.uk/news/uk/lockerbie-ptsd-pan-am-new-york-london-b2214774.html

Carlson, E.B. (1997). *Trauma assessments: A clinician's guide.* Guilford

Carmona, M. (2023, August 31). *PTSD statistics and facts.* The Recovery Village. https://www.therecoveryvillage.com/mental-health/ptsd/ptsd-statistics/https://www.therecoveryvillage.com/mental-health/ptsd/ptsd-statistics/

Centers for Disease Control and Prevention (CDC). (2015). Intimate partner violence surveillance: Uniform definitions and recommended data elements, version 2.0. https://www.cdc.gov/violenceprevention/pdf/ipv/intimatepartnerviolence.pdf

Charlton, M., Kliethermes, M., Tallant, B., Taverne, A., & Tishelman, A. (2004). National Child Traumatic Stress Network Adapted Trauma Treatment Standards Work Group Subgroup on Developmental Disability. https://training.mhw-idd.uthscsa.edu/resources/nctsm-resource.pdf

Chatters, S., & Liu, P. (2020). Are counselors prepared? : Integrating trauma education into counselor education programs. *The Journal of Counselor Preparation and Supervision*, 13(1). http://dx.doi.org/http://doi.org/10.7729/131.1305

Cimolai, V., Schmitz, J., & Sood, A. B. (2021). Effects of mass shootings on the mental health of children and adolescents. *Current Psychiatry Reports*, 23(3), 1-10. https://doi.org/10.1007/s11920-021-01222-2

Clark, C., Classen, C. C., Fourt, A., & Shetty, M. (2015). *Treating the trauma survivor: An essential guide to trauma informed care*. Routledge.

Condino, V., Tanzilli, A., Speranza, A. M., & Lingiardi, V. (2016). Therapeutic interventions in intimate partner violence: An overview. *Research in Psychotherapy: Psychopathology, Process and Outcome*, 19(2), 79–88. https://doi.org/10.4081/ripppo.2016.241

Cook, J. M., Areán, P. A., Schnurr, P. P., & Sheikh, J. I. (2001). Symptoms differences between older depressed primary care patients with and without history of trauma. *International Journal of Psychiatry in Medidcine*, 31(4), 401–414.

Cook, J. M. & O'Donnell, C. (2005). Assessment and psychological treatment of posttraumatic stress in older adults. *Journal of Geriatric Psychiatry and Neurology*, 18, 61–71.

Cook, J. M., Newman, E., & Simiola, V. (2019). Trauma training: Competencies, initiatives, and resources. *Psychotherapy*, 56(3), 409–421. https://doi.org/10.1037/pst0000233

Cook, J. M., Newman, E., & The New Haven Trauma Competency Group. (2014). A consensus statement on trauma mental health: The New Haven ompetency Conference process and major findings. *Psychological Trauma: Theory, Research, Practice, and Policy*, 6(4), 300–307. https://doi.org/10.1037/a0036747

Copeland, L. A., Finley, E. P., Rubin, M. L., Perkins, D. F., & Vogt, D. S. (2023). Emergence of probable PTSD among US veterans over the military-to-civilian transition. *Psychological Trauma: Theory, Research, Practice, and Policy*, 15(4), 697–704. https://doi.org/10.1037/tra0001329.supp

Copeland, W. E., Wolke, D., Angold, A., & Costello, E. J. (2013). Adult psychiatric outcomes of bullying and being bullied by peers in childhood and adolescence. *JAMA Psychiatry*, 70(4), 419–426. https://doi.org/10.1001/jamapsychiatry.2013.504

Cronin, D. L., (2005). Building partnerships for the protection of persons with disabilities. *Critical Response*, 2(4),

Curic, A. (2022, August 6). *What is the ICD-11?* Very Well Mind. https://www.verywellmind.com/overview-of-the-icd-11-4589392

Danese, A., McLaughlin, K. A., Samara, M., & Stover, C. S. (2020). Psychopathology in children exposed to trauma: Detection and intervention needed to reduce downstream burden. *The BMJ*, 371, 1-4. https://doi.org/10.1136/bmj.m3073

DeRosa, R. R. & Rathus, J. H. (2013). Dialectical behavior therapy with adolescents. In J. D. Ford &and C. A. Courtois (Eds.), *Treating complex traumatic stress disorders in children and adolescents* (pp. 225–243). Guilford.

Dinnen, S., Simiola, V., & Cook, J. M. (2015). Post-traumatic stress disorder in older adults: A systematic review of the psychotherapy treatment literature. *Aging & Mental Health*, 19(2), 144–150.

Disabled Women's Network of Canada. (n.d.) *About us*. https://www.dawncanada.net/about/about/

Dogan-Ates, A (2010). Developmental differences in children's and adolescents' post-disaster Reactions. *Issues in Mental Health Counseling*, 31(7), 470–476. https://doi.org/10.3109/01612840903582528

Dokkedahl, S. B., Kirubakaran, R., Bech-Hansen, D., Kristensen, T. R., & Elklit, A. (2022). The psychological subtype of intimate partner violence and its effect on mental health: A systematic review with meta-analyses. *Systematic Reviews*, 11(1), 163-16. https://doi.org/10.1186/s13643-022-02025-z

Durity, R., Garry, A., Mallah, K., Nicolaisen, J., Oxman, A., Sterritt, M., & Stewart, A. (2004). *Facts on trauma and deaf children*. Louisiana Child Traumatic Stress Network. https://www.nctsn.org/sites/default/files/resources/facts_on_trauma_deaf_children.pdf

Dutton, M. A. (1992). *Empowering and healing the battered woman: A model for assessment and intervention*. Springer.

Erikson, E. (1982).*The life cycle completed*. W. W. Norton.

Eshuis, L. V., van Gelderen, M. J., van Zuiden, M., Nijdam, M. J., Vermetten, E., Olff, M., & Bakker, A. (2021). Efficacy of immersive PTSD treatments: A systematic review of virtual and augmented reality exposure therapy and a meta-analysis of virtual reality exposure therapy. *Journal of Psychiatric Research*, 143, 516–527. https://doi.org/10.1016/j.jpsychires.2020.11.030

European Institute for Gender Equality. (2023). *Understanding psychological violence against women*. EIGE. https://eige. europa.eu/sites/default/files/documents/EIGE_Factsheet_PsychologicalViolence.pdf

Fernández-Fillol, C., Pitsiakou, C., Perez-Garcia, M., Teva, I., & Hidalgo-Ruzzante, N. (2021). Complex PTSD in survivors of intimate partner violence: Risk factors related to symptoms and diagnoses. *European Journal of Psychotraumatology, 12*(1), 1–12. https://doi.org/10.1080/20008198.2021.2003616

Finkelhor, D., Turner, H. A., Shattuck, A., & Hamby, S. L. (2015). Prevalence of childhood exposure to violence, crime, and abuse: Results from the national survey of children's exposure to violence. *JAMA Pediatrics, 169*(8), 746–754.

Forman, H. M., Whisman, M. A., & Beach, S. R.H. (2015). Intimate partner relationship distress in the DSM-V. *Family Process, 54*(1), 48-63. doi: 10.1111/famp.12122

Forman-Hoffman, V., Middleton, J. C., Feltner, C., Gaynes, B. N., Weber, R. P., Bann, C., Viswanathan, M., Lohr, K. N., Baker, C., & Green, J. (2018a). *Psychological and pharmacological treatments for adults with posttraumatic stress disorder: A Systematic review update*. Agency for Healthcare Research and Quality (US). http://www.ncbi.nlm.nih.gov/books/NBK525132/

Forman-Hoffman, V. L., & Viswanathan, M. (2018b). Screening for depression in pediatric primary care. *Current Psychiatry Reports, 20*, 1-10. doi: https://doi.org/10.1007/s11920-018-0926-7

Gilbar, O., Charak, R., Trujillo, O., Cantu, J. I., Cavazos, V., & Lavi, I. (2023). Meta-analysis of cyber intimate partner violence perpetration and victimization: Different types and their associations with face-to-face IPV among men and women. *Trauma, Violence, & Abuse, 24*(3), 1948–1965. https://doi.org/10.1177/15248380221082087

Goldmann, E., & Galea, S. (2014). Mental health consequences of natural disasters. *Annual Review of Public Health, 35*, 169–183.

Grossman, A.B., Levin, B. E., Katzen, H. L., & Lechner, S. (2004). PTSD symptoms and onset of neurologic disease in elderly trauma survivors. *Journal of Clinical and Experimental Neuropsychology, 26*, 698-705.

Guérin-Marion, C., Sezlik, S., & Bureau, J. F. (2020). Developmental and attachment-based perspectives on dissociation: Beyond the effects of maltreatment. *European Journal of Psychotraumatology, 11*(1), 1-10. https://doi.org/10.1080/20008198 .2020.1802908

Gurwitch R. H. Silovsky, J. E., Shultz, S., Kees, M., & Burlingame, S. (2002). Reactions and guidelines for children following trauma/disaster. *Communication Disorders Quarterly, 23*(2), 93-99.

Gutermann, J., Schreiber, F., Matulis, S., Schwartzkopff, L., Deppe, J., & Steil, R. (2016). Psychological treatments for symptoms of posttraumatic stress disorder in children, adolescents, and young adults: A meta-analysis. *Clinical Child and Family Psychology Review, 19*(2), 77–93. https://doi.org/10.1007/s10567-016-0202-5

Hamblen, J., & Barnett, E. (n.d.) *PTSD in children and adolescents*. PTSD: National Center for PTSD, U.S. Department of Veterans Affairs.

Haselschwerdt, M. L. (2014). Theorizing children's exposure to intimate partner violence using Johnson's typology. *Journal of Family Theory & Review, 6*(3), 199–221. https://doi.org/10.1111/jftr.12040https://doi.org/10.1111/jftr.12040

HealthMatch Staff (2022). *What are the new treatments available for PTSD?* https://healthmatch.io/ptsd/new-treatments-for-ptsd

Herbert, A., Heron, J., Barter, C., Szilassy, E., Barnes, M., Howe, L. D., Feder, G., & Fraser, A. (2021). Risk factors for intimate partner violence and abuse among adolescents and young adults: Findings from a UK population-based cohort. *Wellcome Open Research, 5*, 176. https://doi.org/10.12688/wellcomeopenres.16106.3

Herman, J. (1997). *Trauma and recovery: The aftermath of violence from domestic abuse to political terror*. Basic Books.

Hughes, M. J., & Jones, L. (2000). Women, domestic violence, and posttraumatic stress disorder (PTSD). *Family Therapy 27*(3), 125-139.

Janoff-Bulman, R. (1992). *Shattered assumptions: Towards a new psychology of trauma*. The Free Press.

Jimenez, R. R., Andersen, S., Song, H., & Townsend, C. (2021). Vicarious trauma in mental health care providers. *Journal of Interprofessional Education & Practice, 24*, 1-5. https://doi.org/10.1016/j.xjep.2021.100451

Johnson, D. M., Zlotnick, C., & Perez, S. (2011). Cognitive behavioral treatment of PTSD in residents of battered women's shelters: results of a randomized clinical trial. *Journal of Consulting and Clinical Psychology, 79*(4), 542-551. doi: 10.1037/a0023822

Jou, Y. C., & Pace-Schott, E. F. (2022). Call to action: Addressing sleep disturbances, a hallmark symptom of PTSD, for refugees, asylum seekers, and internally displaced persons. *Sleep Health, 8*(6), 593–600. https://doi.org/10.1016/j. sleh.2022.09.003

Kaiser, A.P., Wachen, J.S., Potter, C., Moye, J., & Davison, E. (2022). *Posttraumatic stress symptoms among older adults: A review.* U.S. Department of Veterans Affairs. https://www.ptsd.va.gov/professional/treat/specific/symptoms_older_adults.asp

Kar, A., Das, N., Broadway-Horner, M., & Kumar, P. (2023). Intimate partner violence in same-sex relationships: Are we aware of the implications? *Journal of Psychosexual Health*, 5(1), 13–19. https://doi.org/10.1177/26318318221134268

Keeshin, B., Forkey, H. C., Fouras, G., MacMillan, H. L., Flaherty, E. G., Sirotnak, A. P., Budzak, A. E., Gavril, A. R., Haney, S. B., Idzerda, S. M., Laskey, A., Legano, L. A., Messner, S. A., Moles, R. L., Palusci, V. J., Springer, S. H., Vaden Greiner, M. B., Harmon, D. A., ... &... Valles, F. (2020). Children exposed to maltreatment: Assessment and the role of psychotropic medication. *Pediatrics*, 145(2), 1-15. https://doi.org/10.1542/peds.2019 3751

Kliethermes, M. Nanney, R. W., Cohen, J. A., & Mannarino, A. (2013). Trauma-focused cognitive behavioral therapy. In J. D. Ford and C. A. Courtois (Eds.), *Treating complex traumatic stress disorders in children and adolescents* (pp. 184–202). Guilford Publications.

Klostermann, K. (2015). PTSD and intimate partner violence: Clinical considerations and treatment options. *Journal of Addiction Medicine and Therapeutic Science*, 0013(1), 1–6. https://doi.org/10.17352/2455-3484.000018

Koo, K. H., Hebenstreit, C. L., Madden, E., & Maguen, S. (2016). PTSD detection and symptom presentation: Racial/ethnic differences by gender among veterans with PTSD returning from Iraq and Afghanistan. *Journal of Affective Disorders*, 189, 10–16. https://doi.org/10.1016/j.jad.2015.08.038

Kubany, E. S., Hill, E. E., Owens, J. A., Iannce-Spencer, C., McCaig, M. A., Tremayne, K. J., & Williams, P. L. (2004). Cognitive trauma therapy for battered women with PTSD (CTT-BW). *Journal of Consulting and Clinical Psychology*, 72(1), 3–18. https://doi.org/10.1037/0022-006X.72.1.3

Kubany, E. S., Hill, E. E., & Owens, J. O. (2003). Cognitive traumatherapy for battered women with PTSD (CTT-BW): Preliminary findings. *Journal of Traumatic Stress*, 16, 81–91.

Levin, A. P., Kleinman, S. B., & Adler, J. S. (2014). DSM-5 and posttraumatic stress disorder. *Journal of the American Academy of Psychiatry and the Law Online*, 42(2), 146–158. https://jaapl.org/content/42/2/146

Li, X., Curran, M. A., Butler, E., Mills-Koonce, W. R., & Cao, H. (2022). Sexual minority stressors and intimate partner violence among same-sex couples: Commitment as a resource. *Archives of Sexual Behavior*, 51(4), 2317–2335. https://doi.org/10.1007/s10508-021-02261-9https://doi.org/10.1007/s10508-021-02261-9

Livanou, M. (2001). Psychological treatments for post-traumatic stress disorder: an overview. *International Review of Psychiatry*, 13(3). 181–188.

Livingston, H. M., Livingston, M. G., & Fell, S. (1994). The Lockerbie disaster: A 3-year follow-up of elderly victims. *International Journal of Geriatric Psychiatry*, 9, 989–994.

Livingston, H. M., Livingston, M. G., Brooks, D. N., & McKinlay, W. W. (1992). Elderly survivors of the Lockerbie air disaster. *International Journal of Geriatric Psychiatry*, 7(10), 725–729.

Lystad, M. H. (1984). Children's responses to disaster: Family implications. *International Journal of Family Psychiatry*, 5(1), 41–60.

Makadia, R., Sabin-Farrell, R., & Turpin, G. (2017). Indirect exposure to client trauma and the impact on trainee clinical psychologists: Secondary traumatic stress or vicarious traumatization? *Clinical Psychology & Psychotherapy*, 24(5), 1059-1068.

March, J. S., Silva, S., Petrycki, S., Curry, J., Wells, K., Fairbank, J., Burns, B., Domino, M., McNulty, S., Vitiello, B., and Severe, J. (2014). Fluoxetine, cognitive-behavioral therapy, and their combination for adolescents with depression: Treatment for Adolescents With Depression Study (TADS) randomized controlled trial. *JAMA*, 292(7), 807–20.

McDougall, P., & Vaillancourt, T. (2015). Long-term adult outcomes of peer victimization in childhood and adolescence: Pathways to adjustment and maladjustment. *American Psychologist*, 70(4), 300–310. https://doi.org/10.1037/a0039174

McFarlane, A. C. (2014). PTSD and DSM-5: Unintended consequences of change. *The Lancet Psychiatry*, 1(4), 246–247. https://doi.org/10.1016/S2215-0366(14)70321-9

McLaughlin, K. (2022). *Posttraumatic stress disorder in children and adolescents: Epidemiology, pathogenesis, clinical manifestations, course, assessment, and diagnosis.* UpToDate. https://www.uptodate.com/contents/posttraumatic-stress-disorder-in-children-and-adolescents-epidemiology-clinical-features-assessment-and-diagnosis

McLaughlin, K., & Kar, J. A. (2019). Aftermath of the Parkland shooting: A case report of post-traumatic stress disorder in an adolescent survivor. *Cureus*, 11(11), 1–5. https://doi.org/10.7759/cureus.6146

Miller, T. W., Kraus, T. W., Tatevosyan, A., & Kamenchenko, P. (1993a). Post-traumatic stress disorder in children and adolescents of the Armenian earthquake. *Child Psychiatry and Human Development*, 24(2), 115–123.

Misca, G., & Forgey, M. A. (2017). The role of PTSD in bi-directional intimate partner violence in military and veteran populations: A research review. *Frontiers in Psychology, 8*, 1-8. https://www.frontiersin.org/articles/10.3389/fpsyg.2017.01394

Mitchell, J. M., Bogenschutz, M., Lilienstein, A., Harrison, C., Kleiman, S., Parker-Guilbert, K., Ot'alora G., M., Garas, W., Paleos, C., Gorman, I., Nicholas, C., Mithoefer, M., Carlin, S., Poulter, B., Mithoefer, A., Quevedo, S., Wells, G., Klaire, S. S., Van Der Kolk, B., & Doblin, R. (2021). MDMA-assisted therapy for severe PTSD: A randomized, double-blind, placebo-controlled phase 3 study. *Nature Medicine, 27*(6), 1025–1033. https://doi.org/10.1038/s41591-021-01336-3

Monahon, C. (1993). *Children and trauma: A guide for parents and professionals.* Lexington.

Murray, J. S. (2006). Addressing the psychosocial needs of children following disasters. *Journal for Specialists in Pediatric Nursing, 11*(2), 133–137.

NASP School Safety and Crisis Response Committee. (2015). Supporting students experiencing childhood trauma—tips for parents and educators. National Association of School Psychologists. https://www.nasponline.org/resources-and-publications/resources-and-podcasts/school-safety-and-crisis/mental-health-resources/trauma/supporting-students-experiencing-childhood-trauma-tips-for-parents-and-educators

Norris, F. H. (2002). Psychosocial consequences of disaster. *PTSD Quarterly, 13*(2), 1–3.

Norris, F. H., Friedman, M. J., Watson, P. J., Byrne, C. M., Diaz, E., & Kaniasty, K. (2002). 60,000 disaster victims speak: Part I. An empirical review of the empirical literature, 1981–2001. *Psychiatry, 65*(3), 207–239.

North, C. S., Surís, A. M., Clarke, D., Palka, J. M., Yousif, L., & Regier, D. A. (2022). A crosswalk study of DSM-IV and DSM-5 criteria for PTSD from the DSM-5 field trials. *Psychiatry, 85*(3), 228–245. https://doi.org/10.1080/00332747.2022.2034107

O'Donnell, M. L., & Forbes, D. (2016). Natural disaster, older adults, and mental health-a dangerous combination. *International Psychogeriatrics, 28*(1), 9–10. https://doi.org/10.1017/S1041610215001891

Olmsted, K. L. R., Bartoszek, M., Mulvaney, S., McLean, B., Turabi, A., Young, R., Kim, E., Vandermaas-Peeler, R., Morgan, J. K., Constantinescu, O., Kane, S., Nguyen, C., Hirsch, S., Munoz, B., Wallace, D., Croxford, J., Lynch, J. H., White, R., & Walters, B. B. (2020). Effect of stellate ganglion block treatment on posttraumatic stress disorder symptoms: A randomized clinical trial. *JAMA Psychiatry, 77*(2), 130–138. https://doi.org/10.1001/jamapsychiatry.2019.3474

Oram, S., Fisher, H. L., Minnis, H., Seedat, S., Walby, S., Hegarty, K., Rouf, K., Angénieux, C., Callard, F., Chandra, P. S., Fazel, S., Garcia-Moreno, C., Henderson, M., Howarth, E., MacMillan, H. L., Murray, L. K., Othman, S., Robotham, D., Rondon, M. B., … &… Howard, L. M. (2022). The Lancet Psychiatry Commission on intimate partner violence and mental health: Advancing mental health services, research, and policy. *The Lancet Psychiatry, 9*(6), 487–524. https://doi.org/10.1016/S2215-0366(22)00008-6

Parker, G., Lie, D., Siskind, D. J., Martin-Khan, M., Raphael, B., Crompton, D., & Kisely, S. (2016). Mental health implications for older adults after natural disasters—A systematic review and meta-analysis. *International Psychogeriatrics, 28*(1), 11–20. https://doi.org/10.1017/S1041610215001210

Peitzmeier, S. M., Malik, M., Kattari, S. K., Marrow, E., Stephenson, R., Agénor, M., & Reisner, S. L. (2020). Intimate partner violence in transgender populations: Systematic review and meta-analysis of prevalence and correlates. *American Journal of Public Health, 110*(9), e1–e14. https://doi.org/10.2105/AJPH.2020.305774

Perry, B. (2006). Applying principles of neurodevelopment to clinical work with maltreated and traumatized children. In N. B. Webb (Ed.), *Working with traumatized youth in child welfare* (pp. 27–52). Guilford Press.

Perry, B. D., Pollard, R. A., Blakley, T. L., Baker, W. L., & Vigilante, D. (1995). Childhood trauma, the neurobiology of adaptation, and "use-dependent" development of the brain: How "states" become "traits." *Infant Mental Health Journal, 16*(4), 271–291.

Petersilia, J. R. (2001). Crime victims with developmental disabilities: A review essay. *Criminal Justice and Behavior, 28*(6) 655-694.

Peterson, S. (2018, January 30). *Effects.* The National Child Traumatic Stress Network. https://www.nctsn.org/what-is-child-trauma/trauma-types/complex-trauma/effects

Pico-Alfonso, M. A. (2005). Psychological intimate partner violence: The major predictor of posttraumatic stress disorder in abused women. *Neuroscience & Biobehavioral Reviews, 29*(1), 181–193. https://doi.org/10.1016/j.neubiorev.2004.08.010

Pine, D. S., & Cohen, J. A. (2002). Trauma in children and adolescents: Risk and treatment of psychiatric sequelae. *Biological Psychiatry, 51*(7), 519–531.

Powney, D., & Graham-Kevan, N. (2019). Male victims of intimate partner violence: A challenge to the gendered paradigm. In J. A. Barry, R. Kingerlee, M. Seager, & L. Sullivan (Eds.), *The Palgrave handbook of male psychology and mental health* (pp. 123–143). Springer International Publishing. https://doi.org/10.1007/978-3-030-04384-1_7, https://doi.org/10.1007/978-3-030-04384-1_7

Prochaska, J. O., & Norcross, J. C. (2001). Stages of change. *Psychotherapy: Theory, Research, Practice, Training, 38*(4), 443–448.

Prosman, G.-J., Lo Fo Wong, S. H., & Lagro-Janssen, A. L. M. (2014). Why abused women do not seek professional help: A qualitative study. *Scandinavian Journal of Caring Sciences, 28*(1), 3–11. https://doi.org/10.1111/scs.12025

Putnam, F. W. (2006). The impact of trauma on child development. *Juvenile and Family Court Journal, 57*(1), 1–11. https://doi.org/10.1111/j.1755-6988.2006.tb00110.x

Pynoos, R. S., & Nader, K. (1993). Issues in the treatment of posttraumatic stress in children and adolescents. In *International handbook of traumatic stress syndromes* (pp. 535–549). Springer US.

Rauvola, R. S., Vega, D. M., & Lavigne, K. N. (2019). Compassion fatigue, secondary traumatic stress, and vicarious traumatization: A qualitative review and research agenda. *Occupational Health Science, 3*(3), 297–336. https://doi.org/10.1007/s41542-019-00045-1https://doi.org/10.1007/s41542-019-00045-1

Riggs, D. S., Cahill, S. P., Foa, E. B., Follette, V. M., & Ruzek, J. I. (2006). Prolonged exposure treatment of posttraumatic stress disorder. *Cognitive-Bbehavioral Therapies for Trauma, 2*, 65–95.

Rodgers, D. S. & Norman, S. B. (2004). Considering PTSD in the treatment of female victims of intimate partner violence. *Psychiatric Times, 21*(4), *https://www.psychiatrictimes.com/view/considering-ptsd-treatment-female-victims-intimate-partner-violence*

Rollè, L., Giardina, G., Caldarera, A. M., Gerino, E., & Brustia, P. (2018). When intimate partner violence meets same sex couples: A review of same sex intimate partner violence. *Frontiers in Psychology, 9.* https://www.frontiersin.org/articles/10.3389/fpsyg.2018.01506

Ruglass, L. M., Morgan-López, A. A., Saavedra, L. M., Hien, D. A., Fitzpatrick, S., Killeen, T. K., Back, S. E., & López-Castro, T. (2020). Measurement nonequivalence of the clinician-administered PTSD Scale by race/ethnicity: Implications for quantifying posttraumatic stress disorder severity. *Psychological Assessment, 32*(11), 1015–1027. https://doi.org/10.1037/pas0000943

Rumsey, A. D., & Milsom, A. (2018). Supporting school engagement and high school completion through trauma-informed school counseling. *Professional School Counseling, 22*(1), 2156759X19867254. https://doi.org/10.1177/2156759X19867254

Schore, A. N. (2002). Dysregulation of the right brain: A fundamental mechanism of traumatic attachment and the psychopathogenesis of posttraumatic stress disorder. *Australian & New Zealand Journal of Psychiatry, 36*(1), 9–30. https://doi.org/10.1046/j.1440-1614.2002.00996.x

Shapiro, E. (2018, February 14). *Parkland 3 years later: How survivors, parents are channeling trauma into change.* ABC News. https://abcnews.go.com/US/parkland-years-survivors-parents-channeling-trauma-change/story?id=75684600

Shipherd, J. C., Street, A. E., & Resick, P. A. (2006). Cognitive therapy for post-traumatic stress disorder. In V. C. Follette & J. I., Ruzek (Eds). *Cognitive behavioral therapies for trauma* (2nd ed.). (pp. 96–116). Guilford.

Shultz, J. M., Thoresen, S., Flynn, B. W., Muschert, G. W., Shaw, J. A., Espinel, Z., Walter, F. G., Gaither, J. B., Garcia-Barcena, Y., O'Keefe, K., & Cohen, A. M. (2014). Multiple vantage points on the mental health effects of mass shootings. *Current Psychiatry Reports, 16*(9), 469. https://doi.org/10.1007/s11920-014-0469-5

Silva, T. P. E., Cunha, O., & Caridade, S. (2022). Motivational interview techniques and the effectiveness of intervention programs with perpetrators of intimate partner violence: A systematic review. *Trauma, Violence, & Abuse, 24*(4), 2691-2710. https://doi.org/10.1177/15248380221111472

Silver, K. E., & Levant, R. F. (2019). An appraisal of the American Psychological Association's clinical practice guideline for the treatment of posttraumatic stress disorder. *Psychotherapy, 56*(3), 347–358. https://doi.org/10.1037/pst0000230

Simpson, G. K., & Tate. R. L. (2007). Preventing suicide after traumatic brain injury: Implications for general practice. *The Medical Journal of Australia, 187*(4), 229–232. https://doi.org/10.5694/j.1326-5377.2007.tb01206.x

SingleCare Team. (2023, January 20). PTSD statistics. *The Check-Up.* https://www.singlecare.com/blog/news/ptsd-statistics/

Solomon, D. T., Combs, E. M., Allen, K., Roles, S., DiCarlo, S., Reed, O., & Klaver, S. J. (2021). The impact of minority stress and gender identity on PTSD outcomes in sexual minority survivors of interpersonal trauma. *Psychology & Sexuality, 12*(1–2), 64–78. https://doi.org/10.1080/19419899.2019.1690033

Solomon, E. P., & Heide, K. M. (1999). Type III trauma: Toward a more effective conceptualization of psychological trauma. *International Journal of Offender Therapy and Comparative Criminology, 43*(2), 202–210. https://doi.org/10.1177/0306624X99432007

Spencer, T. (2023, February 14). *5 years after Parkland, families cope through good works.* NBC Miami. https://www.nbcmiami.com/news/local/5-years-after-parkland-families-cope-through-good-works/2972448/

Stevens, J. S., van Rooij, S.J.H., & Jovanovic, T. (2018). Developmental contributions to trauma response: The importance of sensitive periods, early environment, and sex differences. In E. Vermetten, D. G. Baker, & V. B. Risbrough (Eds.), *Behavioral neurobiology of PTSD* (pp. 1–22). Springer.

Stough, L. M., & Kelman, I. (2018). People with disabilities and disasters. In H. Rodríguez, W. Donner, & J. E. Trainor (Eds.), *Handbook of disaster research* (pp. 225–242). Springer International Publishing. https://doi.org/10.1007/978-3-319-63254-4_12

Substance Abuse and Mental Health Services Administration (SAMHSA). (2014). Samhsa's concept of trauma and guidance for a trauma-informed approach. HHS Publication No. (SMA) 14-4884. Rockville, MD: Substance Abuse and Mental Health Services Administration.

Substance Abuse and Mental Health Services Administration. (2023a). *Understanding child trauma.* https://www.samhsa.gov/child-trauma/understanding-child-trauma

Substance Abuse and Mental Health Services Administration (2023b). *Practical guide for implementing a trauma-informed approach.* SAMHSA Publication No. PEP23-06-05-005. Substance Abuse and Mental Health ServicesAdministration. https://store.samhsa.gov/sites/default/files/pep23-06-05-005.pdf

Sugar, M. (1999). Severe physical trauma in adolescence. In M. Sugar (Ed.). *Trauma and adolescence,* 183–201. International University Press.

Švecová, J., Furstova, J., Kaščáková, N., Hašto, J., & Tavel, P. (2023). The effect of childhood trauma and resilience on psychopathology in adulthood: Does bullying moderate the associations? *BMC Psychology,* 11(1), 1–12. https://doi.org/10.1186/s40359-023-01270-8

Swedo, E. A. (2023). Prevalence of adverse childhood experiences among U.S. adults—behavioral risk factor surveillance system, 2011–2020. *MMWR. Morbidity and Mortality Weekly Report,* 72(26), 707-715. https://doi.org/10.15585/mmwr.mm7226a2https://doi.org/10.15585/mmwr.mm7226a2

The Recovery Village. (2023, August 31). *PTSD statistics and facts.* https://www.therecoveryvillage.com/mental-health/ptsd/ptsd-statistics/

Thomason, M. E., & Marusak, H. A. (2017). Toward understanding the impact of trauma on the early developing human brain. *Neuroscience,* 342, 55–67.

Turnbull, G. J. (1998). A review of post-traumatic stress disorder. Part I: Historical development and classification. *Injury,* 29(2), 87-91.

U.S. Department of Veterans Affairs. (n.d.a.). *PTSD and DSM-5.* https://www.ptsd.va.gov/professional/treat/essentials/dsm5_ptsd.asp#one

U.S. Department of Veterans Affairs. (n.d.b.). *PTSD: National Center for PTSD.* https://www.ptsd.va.gov/professional/treat/specific/symptoms_older_adults.asphttps://www.ptsd.va.gov/professional/treat/specific/symptoms_older_adults.asp

van der Kolk, B. (2000). Posttraumatic stress disorder and the nature of trauma. *Dialogues in Clinical Neuroscience,* 2(1), 7–22. https://doi.org/10.31887/DCNS.2000.2.1/bvdkolk

Voth Schrag, R. J., Ravi, K., Robinson, S., Schroeder, E., & Padilla-Medina, D. (2021). Experiences with help seeking among non–service-engaged survivors of IPV: Survivors' recommendations for service providers. *Violence Against Women,* 27(12–13), 2313–2334. https://doi.org/10.1177/1077801220963861

Vukčević Marković, M., Bobić, A., & Živanović, M. (2023). The effects of traumatic experiences during transit and pushback on the mental health of refugees, asylum seekers, and migrants. *European Journal of Psychotraumatology,* 14(1), 2163064. https://doi.org/10.1080/20008066.2022.2163064

Walker, L. A. (1980). *Battered woman.* William Morrow Paperbacks.

Walker, L. A. (1984). Battered women, psychology, and public policy. *American Psychologist,* 39(10), 1178–1182. https://doi.org/10.1037/0003-066X.39.10.1178

Wesselman, D., & Shapiro, F. (2013). Eye movement desensitization and reprocessing. In J. D. Ford &and C. A. Courtois (Eds.), *Treating complex traumatic stress disorders in children and adolescents* (pp. 203–224). Guilford Publications.

What is the ICD-11? (n.d.). Verywell Mind. Retrieved August 19, 2023, from https://www.verywellmind.com/overview-of-the-icd-11-4589392

Whiteside, S. P. H., Deacon, B. J., Benito, K., & Stewart, E. (2016). Factors associated with practitioners' use of exposure therapy for childhood anxiety disorders. *Journal of Anxiety Disorders*, 40, 29–36. https://doi.org/10.1016/j.janxdis.2016.04.001

Wigham, S., & Emerson, E. (2015). Trauma and life events in adults with intellectual disability. *Current Developmental Disorders Reports*, 2(2), 93–99. https://doi.org/10.1007/s40474-015-0041-y

Winston, F. K., Kassam-Adams, N., Garcia-España, F., Ittenbach, R., & Cnaan, A. (2003). Screening for risk of persistent posttraumatic stress in injured children and their parents. *JAMA*, 290, 643–649.

Woods, S. J. (2005). Intimate partner violence and post-traumatic stress disorder symptoms in women: What we know and need to know. *Journal of Interpersonal Violence*, 20(4), 394–402. https://doi.org/10.1177/0886260504267882

World Health Organization. (2012). *Understanding and addressing violence among women: Intimate partner violence.* https://www.who.int/publications/i/item/WHO-RHR-12.43

World Health Organization. (2024). *International statistical classification of diseases and related health problems (ICD).* https://www.who.int/standards/classifications/classification-of-diseases

Zaleski, K. L., Johnson, D. K., & Klein, J. T. (2016). Grounding Judith Herman's trauma theory within interpersonal neuroscience and evidence-based practice modalities for trauma treatment. *Smith College Studies in Social Work*, 86(4), 377–393. https://doi.org/10.1080/00377317.2016.1222110

Zimering, R., & Gulliver, S. B. (2003, April 1). Secondary traumatization in mental health care providers. *Psychiatric Times*, 20(4). https://www.psychiatrictimes.com/view/secondary-traumatization-mental-health-care-providers

Zubenko, W. N. (2002). Developmental issues in stress and crisis. In W.N. Zubenko & J. Capozzoli (Eds.) *Children and disasters: A practical guide to healing and recovery* (pp. 85–100). Oxford University Press. https://doi.org/10.15585/mmwr.mm7226a2

Chapter 7: Suicide

American Academy of Pediatrics. (n.d.). *Suicide: Blueprint for youth suicide prevention.* https://www.aap.org/en/patient-care/blueprint-for-youth-suicide-prevention/

American Psychiatric Asssociation. (2019). *Suicide prevention: Native American youth.* https://www.psychiatry.org/news-room/apa-blogs/suicide-prevention-native-american-youth

American Psychiatric Association & American Academy of Child and Adolescent Psychiatry. (2018). The use of medication in treating childhood and adolescent depression: Information for parents and families. https://www.aacap.org/App_Themes/AACAP/docs/resource_centers/resources/med_guides/parentsmedguide_2010_depression.pdf

Bauman, S. (2008). Essential topics for the helping professional. A. B. Longman.

Becnel, A. T., Range, L., & Remley Jr, T. P., Jr. (2021). School counselors' exposure to student suicide, suicide assessment self-efficacy, and workplace anxiety: Implications for training, practice, and research. *Professional Counselor*, 11(3), 327–339.

Borge, O., Cosgrove, V., Grossman, S., Perkins, S., & Van Meter, A. (2021). How search engines handle suicide queries. *Journal of Online Trust and Safety*, 1(1), 1-19. doi:10.54501/jots.v1i1.16

Bridge, J. A., Ruch, D. A., Sheftall, A. H., Hahm, H. C., O'Keefe, V. M., Fontanella, C. A., Brock, G., Campo, J.V., &. Horowitz, L. M. (2023). Youth suicide during the first year of the COVID-19 pandemic. *Pediatrics*, 151(3), 1-22. doi:10.1542/peds.2022-058375

Canady, V. A. (2021, September 20). TikTok launches MH guide on social media impact on teens. *Mental Health Weekly*, 31(36), 5-6.

Canino, G., & Roberts, R. E. (2001). Suicidal behavior among Latin youth. *Suicide and Life Threatening Behavior*, 31, 122–131.

Centers for Disease Control and Prevention. (2023a). *Preventing suicide requires a comprehensive approach.* https://www.cdc.gov/suicide/pdf/2023_CDC_SuicidePrevention_Infographic.pdf

Centers for Disease Control and Prevention. (2023b, August 10). *Suicide data and statistics.* Centers for Disease Control and Prevention. https://www.cdc.gov/suicide/suicide-data-statistics.html

Centers for Disease Control and Prevention. (2023c). *Disparities in suicide*. https://www.cdc.gov/suicide/facts/disparities-in-suicide.html

Charlifue, S. W., & Gerhart, K. A. (1991). Behavioral and demographic predictors of suicide after traumatic spinal cord injury. *Archives of Physical and Medical Rehabilitation, 72*, 488–492.

Chung, R. C-Y. (2002). Combatting racism: Speaking up and speaking out. In J. Kottler (Ed.), *Finding your way as a counselor* (2nd ed.), pp. 105–108). American Counseling Association.

Cohen, R., & Biddle, L. (2022). The influence of suicidal media on suicidal behaviour among students. In M. Mallon & J. Smith (Eds.). *Preventing and responding to student suicide: A practical guide for FE and SE settings* (94-107). UK: Jessica Kingsley Publishers.

Cohen, R., Rifkin-Zybutz, R., Moran, P., & Biddle, L. (2022). Web-based support services to help prevent suicide in young people and students: A mixed-methods, user-informed review of characteristics and effective elements. *Health & Social Care in the Community, 30*(6), 2404–2413.

Cohen-Almagor, R., & Lehman-Wilzig, S. (2022). Digital promotion of suicide: a platform-level ethical analysis. *Journal of Media Eethics, 37*(2), 108–127.

Conforti, A. (2022, July 13). *More than a hotline: 988 meant to ease access to mental health services*. Cronkite News. Retrieved from https://cronkitenews.azpbs.org/2022/07/13/988-mental-health-hotline-launch-july-crisis-ease/

Conwell, Y. (1997). Management of suicidal behaviors in the elderly. *Psychiatric Clinics of North America, 20*, 667–683.

Curry, J. (2001). Specific psychotherapies for childhood and adolescent depression. *Biological Psychiatry, 49*, 1091–1100.

Davis, T. (2004). Counseling suicidal children. In D. Capuzzi (Ed.) *Suicide across the life span: Implications for counselors* (pp. 211–234). American Counseling Association.

De Leo, D., Hickey, P. A., Meneghel, G., & Cantol, M. B., (1999). Blindness, fear of sight loss, and suicide. *Psychosomatics, 40*, 339–344.

Dhingra, K., Klonsky, E. D., & Tapola, V. (2019). An empirical test of the three-step theory of suicide in UK university students. *Suicide and Life-Threatening Behavior, 49*(2), 478–487.

Dubicka, C., & Goodyer, I. (2005). Should we prescribe antidepressants to children? *Psychiatry Bulletin, 29*, 164–167.

Durante, J. C., & Lau, M. (2022). Adolescents, suicide, and the COVID-19 pandemic. *Pediatric Annals, 51*(4), e144–e149. https://doi.org/10.3928/19382359-20220317-02

Edinoff, A. N., Akuly, H. A., Hanna, T. A., Ochoa, C. O., Patti, S. J., Ghaffar, Y. A., Kaye, A. D., Viswanath, O., Uris, I., Boyer, A. G., Cornett, E. M., & Kaye, A. M. (2021). Selective serotonin reuptake inhibitors and adverse effects: Aa narrative review. *Neurology International, 13*(3), 387–401.

Emslie, G. J., & Mayes, T. L. (2001). Mood disorders in children and adolescents: Psychopharmacological treatment. *Biological Psychiatry, 49*, 1082–1090.

Erikson, E. (1982). *The life cycle completed*. W. W. Norton & Company.

Fahey, R. A., Matsubayashi, T., & Ueda, M. (2018). Tracking the Werther effect on social media: Emotional responses to prominent suicide deaths on twitter and subsequent increases in suicide. *Social Science & Medicine, 219*, 19–29.

Feinstein, A. (2002). An examination of suicidal intent in patients with multiple sclerosis. *Neurology, 59*(5), 674-678.

Fieldstadt, E. (2020, January 23). *Michelle Carter, convicted in texting suicide case, released from jail*. NBC News. Retrieved from https://www.nbcnews.com/news/us-news/michelle-carter-convicted-texting-suicide-case-released-jail-n1120411

Foster, C. A., & McAdams III, C. R., III. (1999). The impact of client suicide in counseling training: Implications for counseling education and supervision. *Counselor Education & Supervision, 39*, 22–34.

Frangou, S. (2020, July 16) *Suicidality is found to affect 8 in 100 U.S. children before puberty in new study*. Brain & Behavior Research Foundation. (2020, July 16). https://www.bbrfoundation.org/content/suicidality-found-affect-8-100-us-children-puberty-new-study

From science to practice: Managing chronic illness to protect against ... (n.d.). https://www.mentalhealth.va.gov/suicide_prevention/docs/FSTP-Chronic-Illness.pdf

Garlow, S. J., Purcelle, D., & Heninger, M. (2005). Ethnic differences in patterns of suicide across the life cycle. *American Journal of Psychiatry, 162*, 319–323.

Gary, F. A., Baker, M., & Grandbois, D. M. (2005, March 28). Perspective on suicide prevention among American Indians and Alaska native children and adolescents: A call for help. *Online Journal of Issues in Nursing, 10*(2), 6. https://doi.org/10.3912/OJIN.Vol19No02HirshPsy01

Ghasemi, P.arvin, Abdolreza Shaghaghi, P., &and Hamid Allahverdipour, H. (2015). Measurement scales of suicidal ideation and attitudes: Aa systematic review article. *Health Promotion Perspectives, 5*(3), 156–168.

Giles, C. (1997). *Structured clinical interview for suicide risk.* [unpublished scale]. Lubbock, Texas: John Monfort Unit, Texas Department of Criminal Justice.

Goldman, S., & Beardslee, W. R. (1999). Suicide in children and adolescents. In D. G. Jacobs (Ed.), *The Harvard Medical School guide to assessment and intervention* (pp. 417–442). Jossey-Bass.

Goldston, D. B. (2003). *Measuring suicidal behavior and risk in children and adolescents.* Washington, DC: American Psychological Association.

Haley, M. (2004). Risk and protective factors. In D. Capuzzi (Ed.), *Suicide across the life span: Implications for counselors* (pp. 95–138). American Counseling Association.

Hanna, F. J., & Green, A. G. (2004). Hope and suicide: Establishing the will to live. In D. Capuzzi, (Ed.), *Suicide across the life span* (pp. 63–92). American Counseling Association.

Harrington, R., Whittaker, J., & Shoebridge, P. (1998). Psychological treatment of depression in children and adolescents: A review of treatment research. *British Journal of Psychiatry, 173,* 291–298.

Hartkopp, A., Bronnum-Hansen, H., Seidenschnur, A., & Biering-Sorensen, F. (1998). Suicide in spinal cord injured populations: In relation to functional status. *Archives of Physical and Medical Rehabilitation, 79,* 1356–1361.

Henderson, D. (2006, September 20). Half of deaf people have felt suicidal, survey finds. *The Herald.* https://infoweb-newsbank-com.ezproxy2.library.arizona.edu/apps/news/openurl?ctx_ver=z39.88-2004&rft_id=info%3Asid/infoweb.newsbank.com&svc_dat=AWNB&req_dat=0E5B363304A57755&rft_val_format=info%3Aofi/fmt%3Akev%3Amtx%3Actx&rft_dat=document_id%3Anews%252F1144C67CF1BB7200

Hollon, S. D., Thase, M. E., & Markowitz, J. C. (2002) Treatment and prevention of depression. *Psychological Science in the Public Interest, 3,* 39–71.

Howard, J. (2022, September 9). *Calls to suicide prevention lifeline rose 45% after changeover to 988 number.* CNN. https://www.cnn.com/2022/09/09/health/988-suicide-prevention-calls-hhs-wellness/index.html

Hurlbut, S. C., & Sher, K. J. (1992). Assessing alcohol problems in college students. *College Health, 41,* 49–58.

Jacobs, D. G. (Ed.). (1999). *The Harvard Medical School guide to suicide assessment and intervention.* San Jossey-Bass.

Joe, S., Baser, R. E., Breeden, G., Neighbors, H. W., & Jackson, J. S. (2006). Prevalence and risk factors for lifetime suicide attempts among Blacks in the United States. *JAMA, 296,* 2112–2123.

Joiner, T. (2005). *Why people die by suicide.* Harvard University Press.

Juhnke, G. A. (1996). The Adapted-Sad Persons: A suicide assessment scale designed for use with children. *Elementary School Guidance & Counseling, 30,* 252–259.

Kaldenberg, J. (2005, December 11). *Vision-related issues facing baby boomers and the elderly population* [Paper presentation]. Presentation at the White House Conference on Aging Solutions. Washington, D.C. http://www.whcoa.gov

Kalichman S. C., Heckman, T., Kochman, A., Sikkema, K., & Bergholte, J. (2000). Depression and thoughts of suicide among middle-aged and older persons living with HIV-AIDS. *Psychiatric Service, 51,* 903–907.

Kaufman, A. (2017). "'13 Reasons Why'" is affecting America's classrooms. Teachers tell us their stories. *Los Angeles Times.* https://www.latimes.com/entertainment/tv/la-et-st-13-reasons-why-schools-teachers-20170510-htmlstory.html

Kirk, W. G. (1993). *Adolescent suicide: A school-based approach to assessment and intervention.* Research Press.

Klonsky, E. D., & May, A. M. (2015). The three-step theory (3ST): A new theory of suicide rooted in the "ideation-to-action" framework. *International Journal of Cognitive Therapy, 8*(2), 114–129.

Kposowa, A. J. (2000). Marital status and suicide in the National Longitudinal Mortality Study. *Journal of Epidemiology & Community Health, 54*(4), 254–261.

Léon-Carrión, J., Sedio-Arias, M. L., Cabezas, F. M., Roldan, J. M. D., Dominguez-Morales, R., Barroso y Martin, J. M., & Sanchez, M. A. M. (2001). Neurobehavioral and cognitive profile of traumatic brain injury patients at risk for depression and suicide. *Brain Injury, 15,* 175–181.

Ma, J., Batterham, P. J., Calear, A. L., & Han, J. (2016). A systematic review of the predictions of the Interpersonal-Psychological Theory of suicidal behavior. *Clinical Psychology Review, 46,* 34–45. https://doi.org/10.1016/j.cpr.2016.04.008

Mackelprang, J. L., Karle, J., Reihl, K. M., & Cash, R. E. (2014). Suicide intervention skills: Graduate training and exposure to suicide among psychology trainees. *Training and Education in Professional Psychology, 8*(2), 136.

Madireddy, S., & Madireddy, S. (2022). Supportive model for the improvement of mental health and prevention of suicide among LGBTQ+ youth. *International Journal of Adolescence and Youth*, 27(1), 85–101.

Mann, J. J. (2002). A current perspective of suicide and attempted suicide. *Annual of Internal Medicine*, 136, 302–311.

March, J., Silva, S., Petrycki, S., Curry, J., Wells, K., Fairbank, J., Burns, B., Domino, M.,McNulty, S. & Severe, J. (2004). Floxetine, cognitive-behavioral therapy, and their combination for adolescents with depression: Treatment for adolescents for adolescents with depression study (TADS) randomized controlled trial. *JAMA*, 292(7), 807-820. doi: 10.1001/jama.292.7.80

Marchant, A., Hawton, K., Stewart, A., Montgomery, P., Singaravelu, V., Lloyd, K., … & John, A. (2017). A systematic review of the relationship between internet use, self-harm and suicidal behaviour in young people: The good, the bad and the unknown. *PloS Oone*, 12(8), e0181722.

Matthews, S., & Paxton, R. (2001). *Suicide risk: A guide for primary care and mental health staff*. Northumberland, UK: Newcastle, North Tyneside and Northumberland Mental Health NHS Trust.

McGlothlin, J., Page, B., & Jager, K. (2016). Validation of the SIMPLE STEPS model of suicide assessment. *Journal of Mental Health Counseling*, 38(4), 298–307.

Metha, A., & Webb, L. D. (1996). Suicide among American Indian youth: The role of the schools in prevention. *Journal of American Indian Education*, 36(1), 22-32.

Moezzi, M. (2021, January 7). Suicide prevention shouldn't be optional. *Inside Higher Ed.* https://www.insidehighered.com/views/2021/06/08/colleges-failure-mandate-suicide-prevention-training-ignorant-and-reckless-opinion

Motto, J. A. (1999). Critical points in the assessment and management of suicide risk. In D.G. Jacobs (Ed.), The *Harvard Medical School guide to suicide assessment and intervention* (pp. 224–238). San Francisco: Jossey-Bass.

Mufson, L., Weissman, M. M., Donna Moreau, D., & Garfinkel, R. (1999). Efficacy of interpersonal psychotherapy for depressed adolescents. *Archives of General Psychiatry*, 56, 573–579.

National Institute of Mental Health. (2021a). *Information sheet*. https://www.nimh.nih.gov/sites/default/files/documents/research/research-conducted-at-nimh/asq-toolkit-materials/asq-tool/information_sheet_asq_nimh_toolkit.pdf

National Institute of Mental Health (2021b). *Ask suicide-screening questions (ASQ) toolkit*. https://www.nimh.nih.gov/research/research-conducted-at-nimh/asq-toolkit-materials

National Institute of Mental Health (NIMH). (2023, May). *Suicide*. National Institute of Mental Health. https://www.nimh.nih.gov/health/statistics/suicide

Nowack, W. J. (2006, August, 29). *Psychiatric disorders associated with epilepsy.*https://infoweb-newsbank-com.ezproxy2.library.arizona.edu/apps/news/openurl?ctx_ver=z39.88-2004&rft_id=info%3Asid/infoweb.newsbank.com&svc_dat=AWNB&req_dat=0E5B363304A57755&rft_val_format=info%3Aofi/fmt%3Akev%3Amtx%3Actx&rft_dat=document_id%3Anews%252F1144C67CF1BB7200

O'Connor, R. C., & Nock, M. K. (2014). The psychology of suicidal behaviour. *The Lancet Psychiatry*, 1(1), 73–85. https://doi.org/10.1016/S2215-0366(14)70222-6

Osgood N. J., & Thielman, S. (1990). Geriatric suicidal behaviors: Assessment and treatment. In S. J. Blumenthal & D. J. Kupfer (Eds.), *Suicide over the life cycle: Risk factors, assessment, and treatment of suicidal patients* (pp. 341–380). American Psychiatric Press.

Park, A. (2023, April 13). Suicide rates rose in 2021 after a pandemic-era drop. *Time.* https://time.com/6271257/suicide-rates-increased-2021/

Patterson, W. M., Dohn, H. H., Bird, J., & Patterson, G. (1983). Evaluation of suicidal patients: The SAD PERSONS Scale. *Psychosomatics*, 24, 343–349.

Potter, L. B., Kresnow, M., Powerrl, K. E., Simon, T. R., Mercy, J. A., Lee, R. K., Frankowski, R. F., Swann, A. C., Bayer, T., & O'Carroll, P. W. (2001). The influence of geographic mobility on nearly lethal suicide attempts. *Suicide and Life Threatening Behavior*, 32, (Supplement), 42–48.

Remley, T. P. (2004) Suicide and the law. In D. Capuzzi, (Ed.), *Suicide across the life span* (pp. 185–208). Alexandria, VA: American Counseling Association.

Rossello, J., & Bernal, G. (1999). The efficacy of cognitive-behavioral and interpersonal treatments for depression in Puerto Rican adolescents. *Journal of Consulting and Clinical Psychology*, 67, 734–745.

Runeson, B., Odeberg, J., Pettersson, A., Edbom, T., Jildevik Adamsson, I., & Waern, M. (2017). Instruments for the assessment of suicide risk: A systematic review evaluating the certainty of the evidence. *PLoS One*, 12(7), e0180292. https://doi.org/10.1371/journal.pone.0180292

Russell, S. T. (2003). Sexual minority youth and suicide risk. *American Behavioral Scientist*, 46, 1241–1257.

Sander, J. W., & Bell, G. S. (2004). Reducing mortality: An important aim of epilepsy management. *Journal or Neurology, Neurosurgery and Psychiatry*, 75, 349–351.

Schwartz, A. J., & Whittaker, L. C. (1990). Suicide among college students: Assessment, treatment, and intervention. In S. J. Blumenthal & D. J. Kupfer (Eds.), *Suicide over the life cycle: Risk factors, assessment, and treatment of suicidal patients* (pp. 303–340). Washington, DC: American Psychiatric Press.

Screening patients for suicide risk in medical settings—NIMH. (n.d.-b). https://www.nimh.nih.gov/sites/default/files/documents/research/research-conducted-at-nimh/asq-toolkit-materials/asq-tool/information_sheet_asq_nimh_toolkit.pdf

Shapiro, J. (2005, June 22). Reformers seek to reinvent nursing homes. *Morning Edition*. NPR. https://www.npr.org/2005/06/22/4713566/reformers-seek-to-reinvent-nursing-homes

Simon, S. R. S. (2004). Counseling suicidal adults: Rebuilding connections. In D. Capuzzi (Ed.), *Suicide across the life span: Implications for counselors* (pp. 271–304). American Counseling Association.

Simpson, G. K., & Tate. R. L. (2007). Preventing suicide after traumatic brain injury: Implications for general practice. *The Medical Journal of Australia*, 187(4), 229-232. https://doi.org/10.5694/j.1326-5377.2007.tb01206.x

Spirito, A., Boergers, J., & Donaldson, D. (2000). Adolescent suicide attempters: Post-attempt couse and implications for treatment. *Child Psychology & Psychotherapy*, 7, 161–173.

Stefanowski-Harding, S. (1990). Child suicide: A review of the literature and implications for school counselors. *School Counselor*, 37, 328–340.

Stillion, J. M., & McDowell, E. E. (1996). *Suicide across the lifespan: Premature exits* (2nd ed.). Washington, DC: Taylor & Francis.

Substance Abuse and Mental Health Services Administration. (2020). *Treatment for suicidal ideation, self-harm, and suicide attempts among youth.* https://store.samhsa.gov/sites/default/files/pep20-06-01-002.pdf *SAMHSA Publication No. PEP20-06-01-002* National Mental Health and Substance Use Policy Laboratory. Substance Abuse and Mental Health Services Administration.

Tian, N., Cui, W., Zack, M., Kobau, R., Fowler, K. A., & Hesdorffer, D. C. (2016). Suicide among people with epilepsy: A population-based analysis of data from the U.S. National Violent Death Reporting System, 17 states, 2003-2011. *Epilepsy Behavior*, 61, 210-217. https://doi.org/10.1016%2Fj.yebeh.2016.05.028

U.S. Department of Veteran Affairs. (n.d.). *From science to practice: Managing chronic illness to protect against suicide risk.* https://www.mentalhealth.va.gov/suicide_prevention/docs/FSTP-Chronic-Illness.pdf

Waern, M., Rubenowitz, E., Runeson, B., Skoog, I., Wilhemson, K., & Allebeck, P. (2002). Burden of illness and suicide in elderly people: Case-control study. *British Medical Journal*, 324, 1355–1358.

Webb, L. D., & Metha, A. (1996). Suicide in American Indian youth: The role of the schools in prevention. *Journal of American Indian Education*, 36, 22–32.

Welding, L. (2023). *Suicide at colleges: Rates, research, and statistics.* https://www.bestcolleges.com/research/suicide-in-colleges-rates-research-statistics/

Williams, A. J., Jones, C., Arcelus, J., Townsend, E., Lazaridou, A., & Michail, M. (2021, January 22). A systematic review and meta-analysis of victimisation and mental health prevalence among LGBTQ+ young people with experiences of self-harm and suicide. *PLoS One*, 16(1), e0245268. https://doi.org/10.1371/journal.pone.0245268

Yorkey, B. (Creator). *13 reasons why.* (2017). [Netflix TV series]. Netflix.

Chapter 8: Eating Disorders

Abou-Saleh, M. T., Younis, Y., & Karim, L. (1998). Anorexia nervosa in an Arab culture. *International Journal of Eating Disorders*, 23, 207–212.

Albaladejo, L., Périnet-Marquet, P., Buis, C., Lablanche, S., Iceta, S., Arnol, N., Logerot, S., Borel, J.-C., & Bétry, C. (2023). High prevalence with no gender difference of likely eating disorders in type 1 mellitus diabetes on insulin pump. *Diabetes Research and Clinical Practice, 199.* https://doi.org/10.1016/j.diabres.2023.110630

American Psychiatric Association. (n.d.). *What are eating disorders?ed*https://www.psychiatry.org:443/patients-families/eating-disorders/what-are-eating-disorders

Anorexia Nervosa and Related Eating Disorders, Inc. (n.d.a.). *Statistics: How many people have eating disorders?* https://www.anred.com/stats.html

Anorexia Nervosa and Related Eating Disorders, Inc. (n.d.b.). *Diabetes and eating disorders.* https://www.anred.com/diab.html

Auger, N., Potter, B. J., Ukah, U. V., Low, N., Israël, M., Steiger, H., Healy-Profitós, J., & Paradis, G. (2021). Anorexia nervosa and the long-term risk of mortality in women. *World Psychiatry, 20*(3), 448–449. https://doi.org/10.1002/wps.20904

Bardick, A., Bernes, K., McCulloch, A., Witko, K., Spriddle, J., & Roset, A. (2004). Eating disorder intervention, prevention, and treatment: Recommendations for school counselors. *Professional School Counseling, 8,* 168–174.

Becker, A. E., Burwell, R. A., Gilman, S. E., Herzog, D. B., Hamburg, P. (2002). Eating behaviours and attitudes following prolonged exposure to television among ethnic Fijian adolescent girls. *The British Journal of Psychology, 180,* 509–14.

Bloomgarden, A. (2000). Therapist's self-disclosure and genuine caring: Where do they belong in the therapeutic relationship? *Eating Disorders: The Journal of Treatment and Prevention, 8,* 347–352.

Buckland, D. (2022, December 4). Alarm at "epidemic" of eating disorders: Exclusive *The Express on Sunday,* 15.

Bulik, C. M., Blake, L., & Austin, J. (2019). Genetics of eating disordered: What the clinician needs to know. *Psychiatric Clinics, 42*(1), 59–73. https://doi.org/10.1016/j.psc.2018.10.007

Bulik, C. M., Sullivan, P. F., & Kendler, K. S. (2003). Genetic and environmental contributions to obesity and binge-eating. *International Journal of Eating Disorders, 33*(3), 293–298.

Burke, N. L., Hazzard, V. M., Schaefer, L. M., Simone, M., O'Flynn, J. L., Rodgers, R. F. (2023). Socioeconomic status and eating disorder prevalence: At the intersections of gender identity, sexual orientation, and race/ethnicity. *Psychological Medicine, 53*(9), 4255–4265. https://doi.org/10.1017/S0033291722001015

Chapa, D. A. N., Johnson, S. N., Richson, B. N., Bjorlie, K., Won, Y. Q., Nelson, S. V., Ayres, J., Jun, D., Forbush, K. T., Christensen, K. A., & Perko, V. L. (2022). Eating-disorder psychopathology in female athletes and non-athletes: A meta-analysis. *International Journal of Eating Disorders, 55*(7), 861–885. https://doi.org/10.1002/eat.23748

Claude-Pierre, P. (1977). *The secret language of eating disorders: The revolutionary new approach to understanding and curing anorexia and bulimia.* Random House.

Conviser, J. H., Tierney, A. S., & Nickols, R. (2018). Essentials for best practice: Treatment approachesa for athletes with eating disorders. *Journal of Clinical Sport Psychology, 12*(4), 495–507. https://doi.org/10.1123/jcsp.2018-0013

Cooper, P. (2021). *Overcoming bulimia nervosa and binge-eating: A self-help guide using cognitive behavioral techniques* (3rd ed.). Robinson.

Costin, C. (1999). *The eating disorder sourcebook* (2nd ed.). Lowell House.

Couturier, J., Isserlin, L., Norris, M., Spettigue, W., Brouwers, M., Kimber, M., McVey, G., Webb, C., Findlay, S., Bhatnagar, N., Snelgrove, N., Ritsma, A., Preskow, W., Miller, C., Coelho, J., Boachie, A., Steinegger, C., Loewen, R., Loewen, T., … && Pilon, D. (2020). Canadian practice guidelines for the treatment of children and adolescents with eating disorders. *Journal of Eating Disorders, 8*(1), 4. https://doi.org/10.1186/s40337-020-0277-8

Croll, J., Neumark-Sztainer, D., Story, M., & Ireland, M. (2002). Prevalence and risk and protective factors related to disordered eating behaviors among adolescents: Relationship to gender and ethnicity. *Journal of Adolescent Health, 31,* 166–175.

Crowther, J. H., & Sherwood, N. E. (1997). Assessment. In D. M. Garner & P. E. Garfinkel (Eds.), *Handbook of treatment for eating disorders* (2nd ed., pp. 34–49). Guilford.

Dare, C., & Eisler, I. (1997). Family therapy for anorexia nervosa. In D. M. Garner & P. E. Garfinkel (Eds.), *Handbook of treatment for eating disorders* (2nd ed., pp. 307–326). Guilford.

Davis, H., & Attia, E. (2017). Pharmacotherapy of eating disorders. *Current Opinion in Psychiatry, 30*(6), 452–457. https://doi.org/10.1097/YCO.0000000000000358

de Valle, M. K., & Wade, T. D. (2022). Targeting the link between social media and eating disorder risk: A randomized controlled pilot study. *International Journal of Eating Disorders, 55*(8), 1066–1078. https://doi.org/10.1002/eat.23756

Eddy, K. T., Tabri, N., Thomas, J. J., Murray, H. B., Keshaviah, A., Hastings, E., Edkins, K., Krishna, M., Herzog, D. B., Keel, P. K., & Franko, D. L. (2017). Recovery from anorexia nervosa and bulimia nervosa at 22-year follow-up. *The Journal of Clinical Psychiatry*, 78(2), 184–189. https://doi.org/10.4088/JCP.15m10393

Egbert, A. H., Hunt, R. A., Williams, K. L., Burke, N. L., & Mathis, K. J. (2022). Reporting racial and ethnic diversity in eating disorder research over the past 20 years. *International Journal of Eating Disorders*, 55(4), 455–462. https://doi.org/10.1002/eat.23666

Ellen, B. (2018, November 11). Like women, men are now suffering in their pursuit of the "perfect" body; The obsessive quest to achieve a physical ideal is taking a needless toll on male health. *The Observer*. https://www.theguardian.com/commentisfree/2018/nov/11/men-suffer-as-much-as-women-in-their-pursuit-of-the-perfect-body

Emerson, E. (2003). Prevalence of psychiatric disorders in children and adolescents with and without intellectual disability. *Journal of Intellectual Disability Research*, 47, 51–58.

Erriu, M., Cimino, S., & Cerniglia, L. (2020). The role of family relationships in eating disorders in adolescents: A narrative review. *Behavioral Sciences*, 10(4). https://doi.org/10.3390/bs10040071

Fairburn, C. (1995). *Overcoming binge eating*. Guilford.

Fairburn, C. G., Bailey-Straebler, S., Basden, S., Doll, H. A., Jones, R., Murphy, R., O'Connor, M. E., & Cooper, Z. (2015). A transdiagnostic comparison of enhanced cognitive behaviour therapy (CBT-E) and interpersonal psychotherapy in the treatment of eating disorders. *Behaviour Research and Therapy*, 70, 64–71. https://doi.org/10.1016/j.brat.2015.04.010

Fairburn, C. G., Cooper, Z., O'Connor, M. (2008). Eating disorder examination, edition 16.0D. In Fairburn, C. G., editor. *Cognitive behavior therapy and eating disorders*. Guilford Press, New York: 2008.

Fairburn, C. G. (1997). Eating disorders. In D. M. Clark & C. G. Fairburn (Eds.), *Science and practice of cognitive behaviour therapy* (pp. 209–241). Oxford University Press.

Fardouly, J., & Vartanian, L. R. (2016). Social media and body image concerns: Current research and future directions. *Current Opinion in Psychology*, 9, 1–5. https://doi.org/10.1016/j.copsyc.2015.09.005

Farrell, E. (2000). *Lost for words: The psychoanalysis of anorexia and bulimia*. Process Press.

Fogelkvist, M., Parling, T., Kjellin, L., & Gustafsson, S. A. (2021). Live with your body—participants' reflections on an acceptance and commitment therapy group intervention for patients with residual eating disorder symptoms. *Journal of Contextual Behavioral Science*, 20, 184–193. https://doi.org/10.1016/j.jcbs.2021.04.006

Galmiche, M., Dechelotte, P., Lambert, G., & Tavolacci, M. P. (2019). Prevalence of eating disorders over the 2000-2018 period: A systematic review of the literature. *American Journal of Clinical Nutrition*, 109, 1402–1413.

Garfinkel, P. E., & Walsh, B. T. (1997). Drug therapies. In D. M. Garner & P. E. Garfinkel (Eds.), *Handbook of treatment for eating disorders* (2nd ed., pp. 372–382). Guilford.

Garner, D. M. (1997). Psychoeducational principles in treatment. In D. M. Garner & P. E. Garfinkel (Eds.), *Handbook of treatment for eating disorders* (2nd ed., pp. 145–177). Guilford.

Garner, D. M., & Needleman, L. D. (1997). Sequencing and integration of treatments. In D. M. Garner & P. E. Garfinkel (Eds.), *Handbook of treatment for eating disorders* (2nd ed., pp. 50–63). Guilford.

Gerrard, Y. (2020, March 9). TikTok has a pro-anorexia problem. *Wired*. https://www.wired.com/story/opinion-tiktok-has-a-pro-anorexia-problem/

Gravestock, S. (2003). Diagnosis and classification of eating disorders in adults with intellectual disability: The "diagnostic criteria for psychiatric disorders for use with adults with learning disabilities/mental retardation (DC-LD)" approach. *Journal of Intellectual Disability Research*, 47, 72–83.

Grilo, C. M., Gueorguieva, R., & Pittman, B. (2021). Examining depression scores as predictors and moderators of treatment outcomes in patients with binge-eating disorder. *International Journal of Eating Disorders*, 54(8), 1555–1559. https://doi.org/10.1002/eat.23569

Haas, H. L., & Clopton, J. R. (2003). Comparing clinical and research treatments for eating disorders. *International Journal of Eating Disorders*, 33, 412–420.

Hanlan, M. E., Griffith, J., Patel, N., & Jaser, S. S. (2013). Eating disorders and disordered eating in type 1 diabetes: Prevalence, screenings, and treatment options.to *Current Diabetes Reports*, 13(6), 909–916. https://doi.org/10.1007/s11892-013-0418-4

Harriger, J. A., Evans, J. A., Thompson, J. K., & Tylka, T. L. (2022). The dangers of the rabbit hole: Reflections on social media as a portal into a distorted world of edited bodies and eating disorder risk and the role of algorithms. *Body Image*, 41, 292–297. https://doi.org/10.1016/j.bodyim.2022.03.007

Hay, P. (2020). Current approach to eating disorders: A clinical update. *Internal Medicine Journal, 50*(1), 24–29. https://doi.org/10.1111/imj.14691

Hayes, S. C., Strosahl, K. D., & Wilson, K. G. (2011). *Acceptance and commitment therapy: The process and practice of mindful change* (2nd ed.). Guilford.

Jantz, G. L., & McMurray, A. (2010). *Hope, help, and healing for eating disorders: A whole-person approach to treatment of anorexia, bulimia, and disordered eating.* Waterbrook.

Keys, A., Brožek, J., Henschel, A., Mickelsen,O., Taylor, H. L. (1950). *The biology of human starvation.* (2 Vols). University of Minnesota Press.

Kinnaird, E., Norton, C., Pimblett, C., Stewart, C., & Tchanturia, K. (2019). "There's nothing there for guys": Do men with eating disorders want treatment adaptations? A qualitative study. *Eating and Weight Disorders, 24*(5), 845–852. https://doi.org/10.1007/s40519-019-00770-0

Klump, K. L., McGue, M., & Iacono, W. G. (2003). Differential heritability of eating attitudes and behaviors in prepubertal versus pubertal twins. *International Journal of Eating Disorders, 33,* 287–292.

Krentz, A., & Arthur, N. (2001). Counseling culturally diverse students with eating disorders. *Journal of College Student Psychotherapy, 15*(4), 7–21.

Lipson, S., & Sonneville, K. (2017). Eating disorder symptoms among undergraduate and graduate students at 12 U.S. colleges and universities. *Eating Behaviors, 24,* 81–88. https://doi.org/10.1016/j.eatbeh.2016.12.003

Littleton, H. L., & Ollendick, T. (2003). Negative body image and disordered eating behavior in children and adolescents: What places youth at risk and how can these problems be prevented? *Clinical Child and Family Psychology Review, 6,* 51–66.

Marcus, M. D. (1997). Adapting treatment for patients with binge-eating disorder. In D. M. Garner & P. E. Garfinkel (Eds.), *Handbook of treatment for eating disorders* (2nd ed., pp. 284–293). Guilford.

Marks, R. J., De Foe, A., & Collett, J. (2020). The pursuit of wellness: Social media, body image and eating disorders. *Children and Youth Services Review, 119.* https://doi.org/10.1016/j.childyouth.2020.105659

McFarland, B. (1995). *Brief therapy and eating disorders: A practical guide to solution-focused work with clients.* Jossey-Bass.

Mitchell, J. E., Pomeroy, C., & Adson, D. E. (1997). Managing medical complications. In D. M. Garner & P. E. Garfinkel (Eds.), *Handbook of treatment for eating disorders* (2nd ed., pp. 383–393). Guilford.

Monteleone, A. M., Pellegrino, F., Croatto, G., Carfagno, M., Hilbert, A., Treasure, J., Wade, T., Bulik, C. M., Zipfel, S., Hay, P., Schmidt, U., Castellini, G., Favaro, A., Fernandez-Aranda, F., Il Shin, J., Voderholzer, U., Ricca, V., Moretti, D., Busatta, D., … & Solmi, M. (2022). Treatment of eating disorders: A systematic meta-review of meta-analyses and network meta-analyses. *Neuroscience & Biobehavioral Reviews, 142.* https://doi.org/10.1016/j.neubiorev.2022.104857

Murphy, R., Straebler, S., Basden, S., Cooper, Z. and Fairburn, C. G. (2012). Interpersonal psychotherapy for eating disorders. *Clinical Psychology & Psychotherapy 19,* 150–158. https://doi.org/10.1002/cpp.1780

Nagata, J. M., Ganson, K. T., & Austin, S. B. (2020). Emerging trends in eating disorders among sexuals and gender minorities.gm *Current Opinion in Psychiatry, 33*(6), 562–567. https://doi.org/10.1097/YCO.0000000000000645

National Eating Disorder Association. (2017a, February 25). *Eating disorder in men & boys.*https://www.nationaleatingdisorders.org/learn/general-information/research-on-males

National Eating Disorders Association. (2017b, February 26). *Orthorexia.* https://www.nationaleatingdisorders.org/learn/by-eating-disorder/other/orthorexia

Norton, K. I., Olds, S., & Dank, S. (1996). Ken and Barbie at life size. *Sex Roles, 34,* 287–294.

Omizo, S., & Omizo, M. (1992). Eating disorders: The school counselor's role. *School Counselor, 39,* 217–224.

Onnink, C. M., Konstantinidou, Y., Moskovich, A. A., Karekla, M. K., & Merwin, R. M. (2022). Acceptance and commitment therapy (ACT) for eating disorders: A systematic review of intervention studies and call to action. *Journal of Contextual Behavioral Science, 26,* 11–28. https://doi.org/10.1016/j.jcbs.2022.08.005

Ralph-Nearman, C., Achee, M., Lapidus, R., Stewart, J. L., & Filik, R. (2019). A systematic and methodological review of attentional biases in eating disorders: Food, body, and perfectionism. *Brain and Behavior, 9*(12), e01458. https://doi.org/10.1002/brb3.1458

Rintala, M., & Mustajoki, P. (2002). Could mannequins menstruate? *British Medical Journal, 305,* 1575–1576.

Rodgers, R. F., Berry, R., & Franko, D. L. (2018). Eating disordersin ethnic minoritiese: An update. *Current Psychiatry Reports, 20*(10), 90. https://doi.org/10.1007/s11920-018-0938-3

Saiphoo, A. N., & Vahedi, Z. (2019). A meta-analytic review of the relationship between social media use and body image disturbance. *Computers in Human Behavior, 101,* 259–275. https://doi.org/10.1016/j.chb.2019.07.028

Schaefer, L. M., Crosby, R. D., Machado, P. P. (2021). A systematic review of instruments for the assessment of eating disorders among adults. *Current Opinion in Psychiatry, 34*(6), 543–562.

Scheuing, N., Bartus, B., Berger, G., Haberland, H., Icks, A., Knauth, B., Nellen-Hellmuth, N., Rosenbauer, J., Teufel, M., Holl, R. W., on behalf of the DPV Initiative, & the German BMBF Competence Network Diabetes Mellitus. (2014). Clinical characteristics and outcome of 467 patients with a clinically recognized eating disorder identified among 52,215 patients with type 1 multicenter German/Austrian study. *Diabetes Care, 37*(6), 1581–1589 https://doi.org/10.2337/dc13-2156

Schiele, B., Weist, M. D., Martinez, S., Smith-Millman, M., Sander, M., & Lever, N. (2020). Improving school mental health services for students with eating disorders. *School Mental Health, 12*(4), 771–785. https://doi.org/10.1007/s12310-020-09387-6

Shafir, H. (2023, Novemebr 18). *Best eating disorder apps.* Choosing Therapy. https://www.choosingtherapy.com/best-eating-disorder-recovery-apps/

Shapiro, S., Newcomb, M., Loeb, T. B. (1997). Fear of fat, disregulated-restrained eating, and bodyesteem: Prevalence and gender differences among eight to ten year old children. *Journal of Clinical Child Psychology 26,* 358–365.

Silén, Y., Keski-Rahkonen, A. (2022). Worldwide prevalence of DSM-5 eating disorders among young people. *Current Opinion in Psychiatry 35*(6), 362–371.

Sivyer, K., Allen, E., Cooper, Z., Bailey-Straebler, S., O'Connor, M. E., Fairburn, C. G., & Murphy, R. (2020). Mediators of change in cognitive behavior therapy and interpersonal psychotherapy for eating disorders: A secondary analysis of a transdiagnostic randomized controlled trial. *International Journal of Eating Disorders, 53*(12), 1928–1940. https://doi.org/10.1002/eat.23390

Solmi, M., Radua, J., Stubbs, B., Ricca, V., Moretti, D., Busatta, D., Carvalho, A. F., Dragioti, E., Favaro, A., Monteleone, A. M., Shin, J. I., Fusar-Poli, P., & Castellini, G. (2020). Risk factors for eating disorders: An umbrella review of published meta-analyses. *Brazilian Journal of Psychiatry, 43*(3), 314–323. https://doi.org/10.1590/1516-4446-2020-1099

Striegel-Moore, R. H. & Cachelin, F. M. (1999). Body image concerns and disordered eating in adolescent girls: Risk and protective factors. In N. G. Johnson, M. C. Roberts, J. Worell (Eds.), *Beyond appearance: A new look at adolescent girls* (pp. 85–108). Washington, DC: American Psychological Association.

Striegel-Moore, R. H., Garvin, V., Dohm, F., & Rosenheck, R. A. (1999). Psychiatric comorbidity of eating disorders in men: A national study of hospitalized veterans. *International Journal of Eating Disorders, 24,* 405–414.

Trace, S. E., Baker, J. H., Peñas-Lledó, E., & Bulik, C. M. (2013). The genetics of eating disorders. *Annual Review of Clinical Psychology, 9*(1), 589–620. https://doi.org/10.1146/annurev-clinpsy-050212-185546

Tyrka. A. R., Waldron, I., Graber, J. A., & Brooks-Gunn, J. (2002). Prospective predictors of the onset of anorexic and bulimic syndromes. *International Journal of Eating Disorders, 32,* 282–290.

van der Wege, A. J., & Vandereycken, W. (1995). The last word: Eating disorders and ""blindness" in clinicians. *Eating Disorders, 3,* 187–191.

Wasil, A., Venturo-Conerly, K., Shingleton, R., & Weisz, J. (2019). The motivating role of recovery self-disclosures from therapists and peers in eating disorder recovery: Perspectives of recovered women. *Psychotherapy, 56*(2), 170–180. https://doi.org/10.1037/pst0000214

Watson, T. L., Bowers, W. A., & Anderson, A. E. (2000). Involuntary treatment of eating disorders. *American Journal of Psychiatry, 157,* 1806–1810.

Within Health. (2022, October 22). *Harmful outcomes of the pro-ana movement.* https://withinhealth.com/learn/articles/harmful-outcomes-of-the-pro-ana-movement

Wonderlich, S. A., Crosby, R. D., Mitchell, J. E., Roberts, J. A., Haseltine, B., DeMuth, G. R., & Thompson, K. M. (2000). Relationship of childhood sexual abuse and eating disturbances in children. *Journal of the American Academy of Child & Adolescent Psychiatry, 39,* 1277–1283.

Yager, A., & O'Dea, J. (2005). The role of teachers and other educators in the prevention of eating disorders and child obesity; What are the issues? *Eating Disorders, 13,* 261–278.

Zagaria, A., Vacca, M., Cerolini, S., Ballesio, A., & Lombardo, C. (2022). Associations between orthorexia, disordered eating, and obsessive–compulsive symptoms: A systematic review and meta-analysis. *International Journal of Eating Disorders*, 55(3), 295–312. https://doi.org/10.1002/eat.23654

Chapter 9: Self-Harm

Alderman, T. (1997). *The scarred soul: Understanding and ending self-inflicted violence.* New Harbinger.

American Counseling Association. (2014). *2014 ACA code of ethics*.

American Psychiatric Association. (2022). *DSM-5-TR classification*.

Arendt, F., Scherr, S., & Romer, D. (2019). Effects of exposure to self-harm on social media: Evidence from a two-wave panel study among young adults. *New Media & Society*, 21(11–12), 2422–2442. https://doi.org/10.1177/1461444819850106

Australian Institute of Health and Welfare. (2023). Suicide & self-harm monitoring: Suicide & self-harm monitoring data. https://www.aihw.gov.au/suicide-self-harm-monitoring/data

Azalia Novoa, S. (2021). *Supervisor development: Clinical supervisors' lived experiences of supervising counselors who counsel clients who engage in NSSI* [Dissertation, UTSA]. https://www.proquest.com/openview/84cc3913c8c-21525705222c8a6ed05bf/1.pdf?pq-origsite=gscholar&cbl=18750&diss=y

Briere, J., & Gil, E. (1998). Self-mutilation in clinical and general population samples: Prevalence, correlates, and functions. *American Journal of Orthopsychiatry*, 68, 609–620.

Buelens, T., Luyckx, K., Kiekens, G., Gandhi, A., Muehlenkamp, J. J., & Claes, L. (2020). Investigating the DSM-5 criteria for non-suicidal self-injury disorder in a community sample of adolescents. *Journal of Affective Disorders*, 260, 314–322. https://doi.org/10.1016/j.jad.2019.09.009

Chakraborti, K., Arensman, E., & Leahy, D. (2021). The experience and meaning of repeated self-harm among patients presenting to Irish hospital emergency departments. *Issues in Mental Health Nursing*, 42(10), 942–950. https://doi.org/10.1080/01612840.2021.1913681

Chaney, S. (2019). *Psyche on the skin: A history of self-harm.* Reaktion Books.

Connors, R. E. (2000). *Self-injury: Psychotherapy with people who engage in self-inflicted violence.* Aronson.

Conterio, K., & Lader, W. (1998). *Bodily harm.* Hyperion.

Cowmeadow, P. (1994). Deliberate self-harm and cognitive analytic therapy. *International Journal of Short-Term Psychotherapy*, 9, 135–150.

Daukantaitė, D., Lantto, R., Liljedahl, S. I., Helleman, M., & Westling, S. (2020). One-year consistencyyc in lifetime frequency estimates and functions of non-suicidal self-injury in a clinical sample. *Frontiers in Psychiatry*, 11. https://www.frontier-sin.org/articles/10.3389/fpsyt.2020.00538

DeAngelis, T. (2015, August). Who self-injures? *APA Monitor*, 46(7), 60.

Evans, K., Tyrer, P., Catalan, J., Schmidt, U., Davison, K., Dent, J., Tata, P., Thornton, S., Barber, J., & Thompson, S. (1999). *Psychological Medicine*, 29, 19–25.

Faradiba, A. T., Paramita, A. D., & Dewi, R. P. (2022). Emotion dysregulation and deliberate self-harm in adolescents. *Konselor*, 11(1), 20–24. https://doi.org/10.24036/02021103113653-0-00

Favazza, A. R., (1996). *Bodies under siege: Self-mutilation and body modification in culture and psychiatry* (2nd ed.). Johns Hopkins University Press.

Favazza, A. (2011). *Bodies Under Siege: Self-mutilation, Nonsuicidal Self-injury, and Body Modification in Culture and Psychiatry*, 3rd edition. The Johns Hopkins University Press.

Froeschle, J., & Moyer, M. (2004). Just cut it out: Legal and ethical challenges in counseling students who self-mutilate. *Professional School Counseling*, 7, 131–135.

Hodge, L., & Baker, A. (2021). Purification, punishment, and control: Eating disorders, self-harm, and child sexual abuse. *Qualitative Health Research*, 31(11), 1963–1975. https://doi.org/10.1177/10497323211017490

House, A. (2020). Social media, self-harm and suicide. *BJPsych Bulletin*, 44(4), 131–133. https://doi.org/10.1192/bjb.2019.94

Jung, K. Y., Kim, T., Hwang, S. Y., Lee, T. R., Yoon, H., Shin, T. G., Sim, M. S., Cha, W. C., & Jeon, H. J. (2018). Deliberate self-harm among young people begins to increase at the very early age: A nationwide study. *Journal of Korean Medical Science*, 33(30), e191. https://doi.org/10.3346/jkms.2018.33.e191

Kaess, M., Koenig, J., Bauer, S., Moessner, M., Fischer-Waldschmidt, G., Mattern, M., Herpertz, S. C., Resch, F., Brown, R., In-Albon, T., Koelch, M., Plener, P. L., Schmahl, C., Edinger, A., & the STAR Consortium. (2019). Self-injury: Treatment, Assessment, Recovery (STAR): OnlineO intervention for adolescent non-suicidal self-injury—study protocol for a randomized controlled trial. *Trials*, 20(1), 425. https://doi.org/10.1186/s13063-019-3501-6

Khasawneh, A., Chalil Madathil, K., Dixon, E., Wiśniewski, P., Zinzow, H., & Roth, R. (2020). Examining the self-harm and suicide contagion effects of the blue whale challenge on YouTube and Twitter: Qualitative study. *JMIR Mental Health*, 7(6), e15973. https://doi.org/10.2196/15973

Kotsopoulou, A., & Melis, A. (2015). Non suicidal self injury on adolescents: The ethical dilemmased for psychologists. *European Psychiatry*, 30, 1404. https://doi.org/10.1016/S0924-9338(15)31087-7

Kress, V. E. W. (2003). Self-injurious behaviors: Assessment and diagnosis. *Journal of Counseling and Development*, 81, 490–496.

Kress, V. E. W., Drouhard, N., & Costin, A. (2006). Students who self-injure: School counselor ethical and legal considerations. *Professional School Counseling*, 10(2), 203–209. http://www.jstor.org/stable/24029165

Lamb, W. (1998). *I know this much is true*. Regan Books.

Lavis, A., McNeil, S., Bould, H., Winston, A., Reid, K., Easter, C. L., Pendrous, R., & Michail, M. (2022). Self-Harm in eating disorders (SHINE): A mixed-methods exploratory study. *BMJ Open*, 12(7), e065065. https://doi.org/10.1136/bmjopen-2022-065065

Lieberman, R., & Poland, S. (2006). Self-mutilation. In G. G. Bear & K. M. Minke (Eds.), *Children's needs III: Development, prevention, and intervention* (pp. 965–976). National Association of School Psychologists.

Lin, H.-C., Li, M., Stevens, C., Pinder-Amaker, S., Chen, J. A., & Liu, C. H. (2021). Self-harm and suicidality in US college students: Associations with emotional exhaustion versus multiple psychiatric symptoms. *Journal of Affective Disorders*, 280, 345–353. https://doi.org/10.1016/j.jad.2020.11.014

Linehan, M. M., Wilks, C. R. (2015). The course and evolution of dialectical behavior therapy. *American Journal of Psychotherapy*, 69(2), 97–110.

Martin, P., & Guth, C. (2005). Unusual devastating self-injurious behavior in a patient with a severe learning disability: Treatments with citalopram. *Psychiatric Bulletin*, 29, 108–110.

McClintock, K., Oliver, C. (2003). Risk markers associated with challenging behaviours in people with intellectual disabilities: A meta-analytic study. *Journal of Intellectual Disability Research*, 47, 405–416.

McManus, S., Gunnell, D., Cooper, C., Bebbington, P. E., Howard, L. M., Brugha, T., Jenkins, R., Hassiotis, A., Weich, S., & Appleby, L. (2019). Prevalence of non-suicidal self-harm and service contact in England, 2000–14: Repeated cross-sectional surveys of the general population. *The Lancet Psychiatry*, 6(7), 573–581. https://doi.org/10.1016/S2215-0366(19)30188-9

Mesirow T. R. (1999). Self-mutilation: Analysis of a psychiatric forensic population. *Dissertation Abstracts International: Section B*, 60, 2354.

Miller, D. (1996). Challenging self-harm through transformation of the trauma story. *Sexual Addiction and Compulsivity*, 3(3), 213–227.

Miller, M., Redley, M., & Wilkinson, P. O. (2021). A qualitative study of understanding reasons for self-harm in adolescent girls.ag *International Journal of Environmental Research and Public Health*, 18(7), 3361. https://doi.org/10.3390/ijerph18073361

Mughal, F., Chew-Graham, C. A., Babatunde, O. O., Saunders, B., Meki, A., & Dikomitis, L. (2023). The functions of self-harm in young people and their perspectives about future general practitioner-led care: A qualitative study. *Health Expectations*, 26(3), 1180–1188. https://doi.org/10.1111/hex.13733

Nock, M. K. (Ed.). (2014). *The Oxford handbook of suicides and self-injury*. Oxford University Press. https://doi.org/10.1093/oxfordhb/9780195388565.001.0001

Persano, H. L. (2022). Self-harm. *The International Journal of Psychoanalysis*, 103(6), 1089–1103. https://doi.org/10.1080/00207578.2022.2133093

Pirkis, J., Mok, K., & Robinson, J. (2017). Suicide and newer media: The good, the bad, and the googly. In Niederkrotenthaler, T. & Stack, S. (Eds.) *Media and suicide: International perspectives on research, theory, and policy* (pp. 87–98). Routledge.

Rahman, F., Webb, R. T., & Wittkowski, A. (2021). Risk factors for self-harm repetition in adolescents: A systematic review. *Clinical Psychology Review, 88*. https://doi.org/10.1016/j.cpr.2021.102048

Ross, S., & Heath, N. (2002). A study of the frequency of self-mutilation in a community sample of adolescents. *Journal of Youth and Adolescence, 31*(1), 67–77.

Rudd, M. D., Mandrusiak, M., and Joiner, T. E., Jr. (2006). The case against no-suicide contracts: the commitment to treatment statement as a practice alternative. *Journal of Clinical Psychology, 62*(2), 243–51.

Self-Injury Institute. (2014). Just say no: Why group therapy is contraindicated for self-harm. https://selfinjuryinstitute.com/just-say-no-why-group-therapy-is-contraindicated-for-self-harm/

Seong, E., Noh, G., Lee, K. H., Lee, J.-S., Kim, S., Seo, D. G., Yoo, J. H., Hwang, H., Choi, C.-H., Han, D. H., Hong, S.-B., & Kim, J.-W. (2021). Relationship of social and behavioral characteristics to suicidality in community adolescents with self-harm: Considering contagion and connection on social media.sm *Frontiers in Psychology, 12*. https://doi.org/10.3389/fpsyg.2021.691438

Sharp, C. (2022). Personality disorders. *The New England Journal of Medicine, 387*(10), 916–923. https://doi.org/10.1056/NEJMra2120164

Sheard, T., Evans, J., Cash, D., Hicks, J., King, A., Morgan, N., Nereli, B., Porter, I., Rees, H., Sandford, J., Slinn, R., Sunder, K., & Ryle, A. (2000). A CAT-derived one to three session intervention for deliberate self-harm: A description of the model and initial experience of trainee psychiatrists using it. *British Journal of Medical Psychology, 73*, 179–196.

Soloman, Y., & Farrand, J. (1996). "Why don't you do it properly?": Young women who self-injure. *Journal of Adolescence, 19*, 111–119.

Strong, M. (1998). *A bright red scream*. Penguin.

Talmon, A., & Ginzburg, K. (2021). The differential role of narcissism in the relations between childhood sexual abuse, dissociation, and self-harm. *Journal of Interpersonal Violence, 36*(9–10), NP5320–NP5339. https://doi.org/10.1177/0886260518799450

Tao, Y., Bi, X.-Y., & Deng, M. (2020). The impact of parent–child attachment on self-injury behaviors: Negative emotion and emotional coping style as serial mediators. *Frontiers in Psychology, 11*. https://www.frontiersin.org/articles/10.3389/fpsyg.2020.01477

Taylor, P. J., Jones, S., Huntley, C. D., & Seddon, C. (2017). What are the key elements of cognitive analytic therapy for psychosis? A Delphi study. *Psychology and Psychotherapy, 90*(4), 511–529. https://doi.org/10.1111/papt.12119

Te Maro, B., Cuthbert, S., Sofo, M., Tasker, K., Bowden, L., Donkin, L., & Hetrick, S. E. (2019). Understanding the experience and needs of school counsellors when working with young people who engage in self-harm. *International Journal of Environmental Research and Public Health, 16*(23), 4844. https://doi.org/10.3390/ijerph16234844

Townsend, M. L., Jain, A., Miller, C. E., & Grenyer, B. F. S. (2022). Prevalence, response and management of self-harm in school children under 13 years of age: A qualitative study. *School Mental Health, 14*(3), 685–694. https://doi.org/10.1007/s12310-021-09494-y

Turner, B. J., Austin, S. B., & Chapman, A. L. (2014). Treating nonsuicidal self-injury: A systematic reviewsr of psychological and pharmacological interventions. *Canadian Journal of Psychiatry // Revue Canadienne de Psychiatrie, 59*(11), 576–585.

Vesper, J. H. (1996). Ethical and legal considerations with self-mutilating and lethal clients. *American Journal of Forensic Psychology, 14*(4), 25–38.

Walsh, B., & Rosen, P. M. (1988). *Self-mutilation: Theory, research, and treatment*. Guilford.

Warne, N., Heron, J., Mars, B., Moran, P., Stewart, A., Munafò, M., Biddle, L., Skinner, A., Gunnell, D., & Bould, H. (2021). Comorbidity of self-harm and disordered eating in young people: Evidence from a UK population-based cohort. *Journal of Affective Disorders, 282*, 386–390. https://doi.org/10.1016/j.jad.2020.12.053

Weinz, F. V. (1977). Ecological variation in self-injury behavior. *Suicide & Life-Threatening Behavior, 7*, 92–99.

Whisenhunt, J., Stargell, N., & Perjessy, C. (2016, July 24). *Addressing ethical issues in treating client self-injury*. Counseling Today. https://ct.counseling.org/2016/07/addressing-ethical-issues-treating-client-self-injury/

Whitlock, J., Eckenrode, J., & Silverman, D. (2006a). Self-injurious behaviors in a college population. *Pediatrics, 117*, 1939–1948.

REFERENCES **285**

Whitlock, J. L., Powers, J. L., & Eckenrode, J. (2006b). The virtual cutting edge: The internet and adolescent self-injury. *Developmental Psychology, 42*, 407–417.

Whotton, E. (2002). What to do when an adolescent self-harms. *Emergency Nurse, 10*(5), 12–17.

Wilson, E., & Ougrin, D. (2021). Commentary: Defining self-harm: how inconsistencies in language persist—a commentary/reflection on Ward and Curran (2021). *Child and Adolescent Mental Health, 26*(4), 372–374. https://doi.org/10.1111/camh.12502

Yip, K. (2006). A strengths perspective in working with an adolescent with self-cutting behaviors. *Child and Adolescent Social Work Journal, 23*, 134–146.

Zila L. M., & Kiselica, M. S. (2001). Understanding and counseling self-mutilation in female adolescents and young adults. *Journal of Counseling and Development, 79*, 46–52.

Chapter 10: Reflections

American Counseling Association. (2014). *2014 ACA code of ethics*.

Lattie, E. G., Stiles-Shields, C., & Graham, A.K. (2022)., An overview of and recommendations for more accessible digital mental health services. *National Review of Psychology, 1*, 87–100. https://doi.org/10.1038/s44159-021-00003-1

Maldonado, D. A. P., Eusebio, J. R., Amezcua, L., Vasileiou, E. S., Mowry, E. M., Hemond, C. C., ... & Fitzgerald, K. C. (2022). The impact of socioeconomic status on mental health and health-seeking behavior across race and ethnicity in a large multiple sclerosis cohort. *Multiple Sclerosis and Related Disorders, 58*, 103451.

McNamara, A. (2020, January 23). *Michelle Carter, who urges her boyfriend to kill himself in texts, is released early from jail*. CBS News. https://www.cbsnews.com/news/michelle-carter-suicide-text-case-boyfriend-conrad-roy-released-from-jail-today-2020-01-23/

National Board for Certified Counselors. (n.d.). *Portability proposal*. https://www.nbcc.org/portability

Tambling, R.R., D'Aniello, C. & Russell, B. S. (2023). Mental health literacy: A critical target for narrowing racial disparities in behavioral health. *International Journal of Mental Health Addiction, 21*, 1867–1881. https://doi.org/10.1007/s11469-021-00694-w

Toporek, R., & Daniels, J. (2018). *ACA competency domains*. https://www.counseling.org/docs/default-source/competencies/aca-advocacy-competencies-updated-may-2020.pdf

Index

9 781793 588821